The precession method
in x-ray crystallography

Also by M. J. Buerger

Elementary crystallography
  an introduction to the fundamental geometrical features of crystals

X-ray crystallography

Vector space
  and its application in crystal-structure investigation

Crystal-structure analysis

The precession method

in x-ray crystallography

Martin J. Buerger

Professor of Mineralogy and Crystallography
Massachusetts Institute of Technology

John Wiley and Sons, Inc.   New York   ·   London   ·   Sydney

To

Lila

Preface

The precession method was devised in my laboratory in the 1930's as a variation of the oscillating-crystal method which preserved symmetry. When de Jong and Bouman showed how to record reflections for the rotating-crystal method in such a way that the reflections mapped out an undistorted level of the reciprocal lattice, I immediately extended their theory to the precession method, and the result was the precession instrument essentially as it is known today. The theory and practice of the precession method were discussed in detail in a monograph entitled "The photography of the reciprocal lattice" published by the American Society for X-Ray and Electric Diffraction in April 1944. Because the new method provided a simple and direct way of establishing the space group and unit cell of a crystal, and because the precession instrument became commercially available a year or two later, the method came into general use in many laboratories. The apparatus was manufactured commercially in the United States, Germany, Japan, the Netherlands, and Switzerland, and in 1962 one of the American manufacturers estimated he had produced some 700 instruments.

As the precession method gained popularity, books treating x-ray diffraction methods began to include short discussions of the theory and practice of the method, but none treated it very fully. Meanwhile, from time to time advances were made in both theory and technique so that the original monograph became outdated and a need arose for a new one.

An opportunity for filling this need occurred when, on the invitation of Professor Nahum Joel, I spent a sabbatical term teaching in the Instituto de Física y Matimáticas of the University of Chile, Santiago. There the congenial atmosphere permitted writing a manuscript and improving it through several revised typescripts. A number of further revisions followed, and I am indebted to Lucia Fuentes, Magdalena de Gabler, Shirley Veale, Gay Lorraine, and Erica Moore for their patient help in typing numerous improved versions of the text. Many students and colleagues read the text and improved it by pointing out errors and difficult parts and by suggesting better approaches. I am especially indebted to Dr. Bernhardt Wuensch and Mr. Wayne Dollase in this respect. Dr. Wuensch, Mr. Dollase, and Dr. Charles T. Prewitt read the page proof.

I am grateful to a number of people for contributions to the tables and illustrations of the book. Dr. Charles T. Prewitt kindly wrote a program for computing the Lorentz-polarization correction, and with its aid computed the values in Table 1 of Chapter 11; Dr. Hajo Onken computed Tables 5 and 6 of Chapter 8. Mr. Wayne Dollase computed a number of the shorter tables. Mr. Charles Supper supplied photographs of the latest-model precession instrument and integrating device. Dr. F. Hanic contributed the photograph of the Czechoslovakian precession instrument. Originals of published figures were kindly provided by Professor D. Jerome Fisher, Professor L. V. Azároff, Dr. Bernhardt Wuensch, and Dr. R. D. Burbank. Most of the line drawings, however, were prepared especially for this book by Mr. Wayne Dollase. He also made the 60-odd precession and cone-axis photographs, which represent a selection from some ten times as many trials.

This book contains a list of all relevant literature known to me. An attempt has been made to incorporate information from this literature either in its original or in an improved form, in the book. In addition there is some unpublished new material, including the theory of orientation photographs, cone-axis photographs, recordable range, and equi-inclination precession photographs.

I will be grateful if important omissions of literature, as well as errors in the text, are called to my attention.

MARTIN J. BUERGER

Massachusetts Institute of Technology
August 1964

Contents

List of tables xv

Chapter 1.   Historical introduction 1

Background 1
Shortcomings of the oscillating-crystal method 3
The Mark I precession apparatus 6
The de Jong-Bouman principle 7
The de Jong-Bouman apparatus 7
Generalization of the de Jong-Bouman principle 8
Application to the precession method 9

Chapter 2.   Invariant Laue cones 10

Cone-axis photographs 10
Laue-cone discussion of precession photographs 13

Chapter 3.   Theory of reciprocal-lattice photography 15

General principles 15
The geometry of upper-level recording 17
Limits of the record 18
Theoretical limits 18
Mechanical limits 25
Isolating the level 25
The determination of ζ 28

Chapter 4.   The Mark II precession instrument 30

Requirements 30
First version 30
Second version 34
Conventional design 34
Other variations 41

Chapter 5.   The use of the precession apparatus 44

Appropriate x-ray tube and table 44
Aligning the instrument 44
Mounting the crystal 46

Adjusting the crystal 48
 Centering 48
 Study preliminary to orienting 49
 Calibration of dial readings 50
 Use of the autocollimator 51
 Crystallographic adjustment with the autocollimator 52
   Orthorhombic crystal, one pinacoidal surface 52
   Orthorhombic crystal, two pinacoidal surfaces 54
   Orthorhombic crystal, two prismatic surfaces 55
   Monoclinic crystal, two pinacoidal surfaces parallel to unique axis . . 55
   Monoclinic crystal, two surfaces parallel to unique axis 56
 Correction of orientation errors 56
Cone-axis photographs 57
Planning the precession photographs required 58
 Purpose of photographs 58
 Requirements for geometrical determination 58
 Space group 58
 Unit cell 59
Making precession photographs 61
 Zero-level photographs 61
 Upper-level photographs 61
 Widths of slits in layer-line screens 67

Chapter 6.   The geometrical interpretation of precession photographs   69

Space group 69
 Viewpoint 69
 Diffraction symbols 70
   Friedel symmetry 71
   Lattice type 72
   Glide planes and screw axes 73
 Determination of the space group 76
Unit cell 76
 Measurable geometrical features 76
 Measuring device for precession photographs 76
Measurement of angles 80
 Angles in the plane of the photograph 80
 Angles between the planes of two photographs 81
Measurement of distances 82
 Measurement of translations in the reciprocal lattice 82
 Measurement of row spacings 82
Determination of the cell of the direct lattice 83
 Determination from one setting of the crystal 83
 Orthogonal systems 83
 Hexagonal and monoclinic crystals 84
 Triclinic crystals 84
Accuracy of the results 88
 General appraisal 88
 Precautions 89
   Knowledge of M 89
   Crystal size and shape 89

Crystal centering 90
Orientation errors 90
Film shrinkage 90
Error analysis 91

Chapter 7.   Errors in satisfying the generalized de Jong-Bouman
condition 92

Errors in setting $M\zeta$ 92
General features 92
Quantitative discussion 96
Determination of the setting error 97
Use of general-radiation streaks 100
Use of β spots 101
Angular errors. 102
Bulging of the film 104
Elimination of doubling by non-recording. 104

Chapter 8.   Orientation errors. 106

Orientation photographs. 106
Technique 106
General-radiation streaks. 107
Quantitative relations. 107
Appearance of photographs 114
Determination of the error 116
Correction of orientation errors. 120
Routine procedure. 120
Laves' method 126
Orientation photographs for large errors 127
Technique 127
Appearance of photographs 127
Theory of the common chord. 133
Theory of the shape of the shaded area. 136
The curvature of the boundary of the recorded region . . . 142
Application to oblique crystals 145
Application to unoriented crystal fragments 145

Chapter 9.   Cone-axis photographs 150

Determination of the translation 150
Relevant relations. 150
Techniques 151
Calibration of s 152
Calculation of ζ 153
Indexing cone-axis photographs. 154
Alternative indexing procedure. 160
Record produced by a single reciprocal-lattice point. 161
Symmetry of cone-axis photographs 162
Relation between symmetries of level and ring 162
Symmetry of the zero-level ring 163

General-radiation streaks 163
Orientation errors. 169
Fractional-cycle cone-axis photographs 172

Chapter 10.   Intensity determination 176

Planning the photographs required. 176
  Data for two-dimensional investigations 177
  Data for three-dimensional investigations 177
  Some reciprocity relations 178
Precautions 180
  Background. 180
  General radiation 180
  Harmonics 182
  Doublets 182
The plateau method 182
  Plateau from natural convergence 184
  Plateau from a focusing monochromator 184
  Plateau from an integrating cassette 186
Density measurement 186

Chapter 11.   The Lorentz factor 191

Lorentz factor for motion of pure precession 191
  Velocity of a point through the sphere 192
  Geometrical evaluation 193
  Alternative evaluation 195
  Trigonometric evaluation. 196
  Evaluation of η. 197
  Practical application 197
Lorentz factor for the Mark II suspension 198
  Coordinate systems 198
  Behavior of angles with time. 200
  Motion of the sphere of reflection 201
  Practical application 217
The Mark III suspension 219

Chapter 12.   Absorption 221

Basic absorption theory 221
Intensity distribution in the direct beam 223
Correction for absorption by hand calculation 224
  Correction for absorption by a spherical specimen. . . 224
  Correction for absorption by a plate parallel to the reciprocal-lattice plane 224
  Correction for absorption by a cylinder perpendicular to the reciprocal-lattice plane 226
Correction for absorption in more complicated cases. . . 228
  Nature of the problem 228
  The LpT correction 228
  Angular variables 229

Contents

Evaluation of diffraction angles 230
Practical applications 233
Surface-reflection fields 233
Fields for a single plane 233
Fields for crystal habits 237
Application to absorption. 237
Background patterns 237
The Wells effect 241

Literature 243

Appendix.   Heating and cooling techniques 247

Heating devices 247
Crystal-growing and heating device. 247
Furnaces for the range 0–300°C 248
Furnaces for temperature up to about 1300°C 248
Heating devices for the range 1000°C to 2000°C 256
Low-temperature techniques 257
Literature 260

Index. 261

List of tables

Chapter 3

Table 1.   Limits of front-reflection precession photographs   25

Chapter 5

Table 1A.   Data for the zero-level record   59
Table 1B.   Values of the zero-level screen setting s for various screen radii, r,
and precession angles, $\bar{\mu}$ 59
Table 2.   Value of the screen setting, $s = r \cot \cos^{-1} (\cos \bar{\mu} - \zeta)$, as a function of ζ, for some discrete values of $\bar{\mu}$ and r   62
Table 3.   Example of computation of settings for upper-level precession
photographs   67
Table 4.   Limiting values of the translation period for non-recording of
additional levels   68

Chapter 6

Table 1.   The Friedel symmetries and their distribution among the point
groups   70
Table 2.   The 10 point groups in a plane.   72
Table 3.   Determination of the reciprocal-lattice type from precession
photographs   75
Table 4.   Types of symmetry planes with translation components, indicated
by various patterns of missing reciprocal-lattice points on the zero level   77
Table 5.   Types of symmetry axes with translation components, indicated by
various patterns of missing reciprocal-lattice points on the zero level . .   78
Table 6.   Comparison of cell dimensions obtained by the precession method
and back-reflection Weissenberg method   88

Chapter 8

Table 1.   Allowable orientation error, ϵ, as a function of screen setting s for
screens with circular openings   117
Table 2A.   Displacement ($\times 2$, in reciprocal-lattice units) of the center of the
shaded area in orientation photographs, as a function of the orientation
error, ϵ   119
Table 2B.   Displacement ($\times 2$, in distance on the film, $M = 6$ cm.) of the
center of the shaded area in orientation photographs, as a function of the
orientation error, ϵ   119
Table 3.   Common chord of zero-level shaded areas in orientation photographs   133

Table 4. Radii, in direction of orientation error, of recorded region of reciprocal-lattice plane for various orientation errors   139
Table 5. Radius, ξ, of the edge of the recorded region in orientation photographs
($\bar{\mu} = 5°$), as a function of its angle τ from the direction of maximum error, for
various error angles ϵ   146
Table 6. Radius, ξ, of the edge of the recorded region in orientation photographs
($\bar{\mu} = 10°$), as a function of its angle τ from the direction of maximum error, for
various error angles ϵ   148

Chapter 9

Table 1. Values of the translation t for which the first negative-order Laue
cone just appears on cone-axis photographs   151
Table 2. Example of computation of d^* from cone-axis data   154

Chapter 10

Table 1. Some simple directions in the direct lattice and related features in
the reciprocal lattice   180

Chapter 11

Table 1. Lorentz-polarization corrections $1/Lp$ for the precession method,
as a function of the cylindrical reciprocal-lattice coordinates ξ, ζ and
ϕ ($\bar{\mu} = 30°$).   206

The precession method
in x-ray crystallography

1

Historical introduction

Background

One of the triumphs of science during the last half-century was the determination of the arrangements of atoms in thousands of different kinds of crystals. This advance in the detailed knowledge of the nature of solid matter has renovated those sciences in which crystals are important, particularly chemistry, mineralogy, and physics, as well as metallurgy and ceramics. The technique that yielded these results, known as crystal-structure analysis, may be expected to be an important tool in many fields of science and technology for some time to come.

The systematic procedure of determining the arrangement of atoms in a crystal, which is followed whenever possible, begins with finding out how the possible arrangements of atoms are restricted by the symmetry and by the translational periodicity of the crystal. This calls for determining the space group and unit cell of the crystal. In addition to its use in crystal-structure analysis, the determination of these geometrical properties of a crystal may be useful for other purposes. For even if the structure is not determined, these data may permit assigning a crystal to a family, or set of isotypes.[†] They are also useful in systematic tabulations prepared for identification purposes.[§]

In earlier days the determination of the space group and cell was limited by technical difficulties, and unambiguous conclusions were not always possible. The difficulties were due to the fact that the early methods of recording x-ray reflections attempted to map the three reflection indices h, k, and l on the two dimensions of a photographic film, and

---

[†] For example, J. D. H. Donnay and Gabrielle Donnay. *Crystal data, determinative tables.* (Am. Crystallographic Soc., Washington, D. C., 2nd Ed., 1963).

[§] For example, Hugo Strunz. *Mineralogische Tabellen, eine Klassifizierung der Mineralien auf kristallchemischer Grundlage.* (Akademische Verlag, Leipzig, 1957).

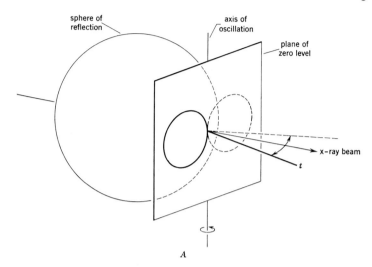

A

Fig. 1*A*.

A zero-level plane of the reciprocal lattice whose normal t is oscillating to equal limits to each side of the x-ray beam.

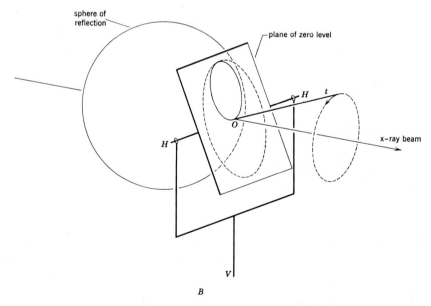

B

Fig. 1*B*.

A zero-level plane of the reciprocal lattice whose normal t is precessing about the direct x-ray beam.

this led to ambiguities in indexing. The problem disappeared with the invention of moving-film methods of recording the x-ray diffraction. The solution was based upon isolating (with the aid of a layer-line screen), a set of reflections having one index constant and then moving the film in such a way as to spread the remaining two indices over the two dimensions of the film. It was comparatively easy to find the transformation from film coordinates to reflection indices.

The first such method was the Weissenberg method, which is still much used. But performing the transformation between film coordinates and reflection indices for Weissenberg photographs constituted a minor annoyance. When the de Jong-Bouman and precession methods were devised this transformation was no longer necessary. In these methods the symmetry is so obvious that it can be determined by inspection, and the unit cell can be computed rather precisely by measurements which are easily and quickly made.

The convenience of interpreting precession photographs and some of the incidental advantages of having a precession apparatus, such as the readiness with which crystals can be oriented, have caused the precession method to be used in almost every laboratory doing single-crystal investigation. This book is devoted to a discussion of that method. It is not intended as the first book in x-ray diffraction for the beginner since the background common to all x-ray diffraction methods is treated in a number of books already available. It is assumed that the reader has this background, specifically that he has some understanding of elementary crystallography,[†] elementary x-ray diffraction theory (especially the use of the reciprocal lattice), and that he is acquainted with the application of this theory to single-crystal x-ray diffraction techniques.[§]

Shortcomings of the oscillating-crystal method

Annoyance with the limitation of the oscillating-crystal method in providing direct symmetry information about a crystal was the cause of devising the precession method. The limitation is caused by the comparatively low symmetry of the geometry of oscillation, which is $2mm$. The symmetry of the diffraction effect is a combination of the Friedel symmetry[¶] of the crystal and the symmetry of the motion which brings

---

[†] This can be supplied, for example, by F. C. Phillips, *An introduction to crystallography* (Longman Green and Co. London, 1956); and M. J. Buerger, *Elementary crystallography*. (John Wiley and Sons, New York, revised printing, 1963).

[§] As discussed, for example, by M. J. Buerger, *X-ray crystallography*. (John Wiley and Sons, New York, 1942).

[¶] See Chapter 6.

Fig. 2.
The Mark I precession instrument.

the crystal to the various reflection positions. For the oscillating-crystal method the motion symmetry is *2mm*, so that the greatest symmetry that can be displayed by an oscillating-crystal photograph is *2mm*. Obviously such photographs can only have symmetries which are sub-groups of *2mm*, namely *2mm*, 2, *m*, and 1, and they cannot have symmetries 3, *3m*, 4, *4mm*, 6, or *6mm*. The only symmetry information about a crystal which the oscillating-crystal method can give is therefore that the symmetry of a section or projection of the crystal contains a sub-group of *2mm*. Even when such a symmetry is indicated, it cannot be inferred that this reveals the symmetry of the crystal, but only that the crystal symmetry contains the indicated symmetry.

It was this situation which inspired the invention of a new method of recording x-ray diffraction. The limitation of the oscillating-crystal method in regard to symmetry detection is due entirely to the restricting symmetry of its motion. The nature of the remedy was obvious. A motion was needed which had radial symmetry so that the symmetry of the crystal would not be degraded by the symmetry of the recording motion.

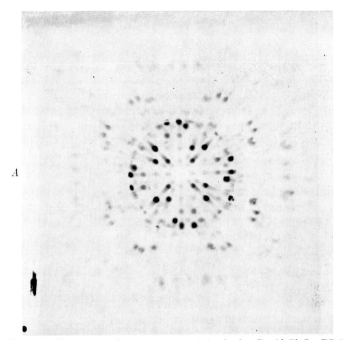

A

Fig. 3A. Displaying plane symmetry 4 (meionite $Ca_4Al_6Si_6O_{24}CO_3$).

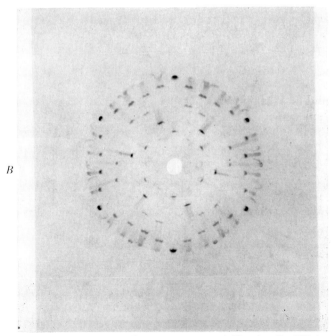

B

Fig. 3 B. Displaying plane symmetry 6 (willemite, Zn_2SiO_4).
Examples of precession photographs taken with the Mark I precession instrument.

The Mark I precession apparatus

The oscillating-crystal motion is epitomized in Fig. 1*A*. The maximum symmetry information concerning the direction *t* is obtained if this direction is set initially parallel to the x-ray beam, and then caused to oscillate to equal limits on both sides of the beam. The area of the zero-level reciprocal-lattice plane normal to *t* which can give rise to diffraction is then contained within two equal circles tangent to the axis of oscillation at the origin. The area of the diffraction record obviously has symmetry *2mm*. To give it radial symmetry, the reciprocal-lattice plane must be permitted to rotate not only about a vertical axis but also about a horizontal one as well. One way of accomplishing this is suggested in Fig. 1*B*. Here the reciprocal-lattice plane is suspended on a fork similar in function to the gimbal upon which a nautical compass is mounted. The plane can be rotated about a vertical axis *V* and a horizontal axis *H* but cannot be rotated about the axis *t*, which is normal to itself. To assure that the area of the reciprocal-lattice plane which is permitted to reflect has radial symmetry, the circle of intersection should remain constant in size while it rotates about *O*. This can be accomplished by causing *t* to precess about the direction of the x-ray beam. This characteristic motion of *t* gives rise to the name *precession method*. The first instrument[1] constructed to use this motion is shown in Fig. 2. To distinguish it from later instruments incorporating other features, this one may be called the *Mark I* precession instrument. Photographs of crystals with 4-fold and 6-fold symmetry taken with this instrument are shown in Figs. 3*A* and 3*B*.

Photographs made by the Mark I instrument not only reveal the symmetry of the reciprocal-lattice plane giving rise to the diffraction, but the locations of the diffraction spots are such that the photograph is an only slightly distorted map of the points in the reciprocal-lattice plane. The reason for this is evident on examining Fig. 4, which shows a section of the sphere of reflection containing the incident and diffracted x-ray beams. Reciprocal-lattice point *P*, at a distance ξ from the origin, gives rise to a diffracted beam which is recorded on the film at a distance *R* from its center. These values are seen to be related to θ by

$$\sin \theta = \frac{\xi}{2}, \tag{1}$$

and
$$\tan 2\theta = \frac{R}{M}. \tag{2}$$

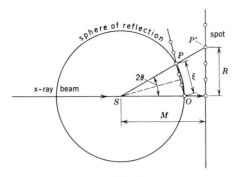

Fig. 4.

If these are combined, the relation to R to ξ is found to be

$$R = M \tan 2 \sin^{-1} \frac{\xi}{2}. \tag{3}$$

For small values of ξ, an approximation is

$$R \approx M\xi, \tag{4}$$

so that each recorded diffraction spot is approximately equal to ξ on a scale M, a constant for the instrument. This assures that the photograph is an only slightly distorted map of the reciprocal-lattice plane.

Photographs made with the Mark I instrument suffer from a perceptible doubling of some of the diffraction spots. The doubling is caused by the fact that, in general, a point of the reciprocal lattice enters and leaves the sphere of reflection at different places, thus producing two records on the film.

With the publication of the de Jong-Bouman principle of photography of the reciprocal lattice it became possible to correct these two aberrations of the precession method. The application of this principle is discussed next.

The de Jong-Bouman principle

The de Jong-Bouman apparatus. In a series of papers,[†][§][¶][‡] de Jong and Bouman showed how it was possible to make distortionless photographs of the reciprocal lattice with a new kind of apparatus which was

† W. F. de Jong and J. Bouman. *Das Photographieren von reziproken Kristallnetzen mittels Röntgenstrahlen.* Z. Krist. (A) **98** (1938), 456–459.

§ W. F. de Jong, J. Bouman, and J. J. de Lange. *X-ray photography of zero-order reciprocal net planes of a crystal.* Physica **5** (1938) 188–192.

¶ W. F. de Jong and J. Bouman. *Das Photographieren von reziproken Netzebenen eines Kristalles mittels Röntgenstrahlen.* Physica **5** (1938) 220–224.

‡ W. F. de Jong. *Axinit. Das reziproke und das Bravaissche Gitter.* Z. Krist. (A) **99** (1938) 326–335.

based upon the rotating-crystal method.   As in the Weissenberg method,
the level to be photographed is rotated about an axis normal to itself
(Fig. 5); the diffraction is recorded on a flat photographic film parallel to
the level; the film is also rotated about its own normal.   The key feature
is that a line drawn from the center of the sphere of reflection to the level
origin, when continued, meets the film at the point of intersection with its
rotation axis.

Generalization of the de Jong-Bouman principle.   The de Jong-
Bouman idea can be readily generalized.   Any level of the reciprocal
lattice can be recorded on a flat film without distortion, and any motion of
the reciprocal lattice whatever can be utilized to bring the various points
into reflecting condition, provided only that a corresponding motion is
given to the photographic film.   For example, the oscillating-crystal
apparatus[1] can be slightly modified[2], so that it too can record the reciprocal-lattice points on a flat film without distortion of the relative locations

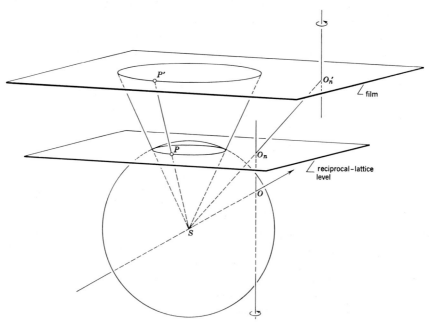

Fig. 5.
The de Jong-Bouman principle of photographing the reciprocal lattice of a rotating
crystal.

of the points. All that is required is that the plane of the film be arranged to oscillate about an axis parallel to the crystal-oscillation axis, and coupled to oscillate in synchronism with that axis.

Application to the precession method. The application of the generalization of the de Jong-Bouman principle to the precession method is illustrated in Fig. 6. The plane of the reciprocal lattice is seen supported in a fork. Normal to any rational plane in the reciprocal lattice

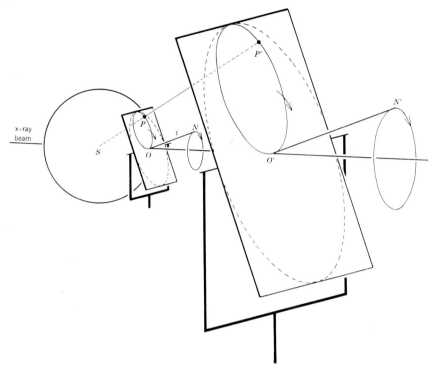

Fig. 6.
Generalization of the de Jong-Bouman principle applied to precession motion.

is a rational direction, t, in the direct lattice. A point somewhere on t is caused to perform a circular motion about the x-ray beam, and this causes the rational direction t to undergo a precessing motion. In Fig. 6 a flat film is added to what is seen in Fig. 1B in such a way that the suspension of the crystal is duplicated by a parallel suspension of the film, and the direct beam travels through the invariant centers of each suspension. The motion of the reciprocal-lattice plane and the film are so coupled that every motion of one is duplicated by a motion of the other. Instruments based upon this arrangement are called *Mark II* precession instruments.

2

Invariant Laue cones

Cone-axis photographs

In Fig. 1*A* a crystal is diagrammatically shown mounted in the ordinary precession suspension. Some rational direction, *t*, of the crystal (ordinarily a crystallographic axis) is selected for consideration; Fig. 1 emphasizes this by representing the crystal as elongated in that direction.

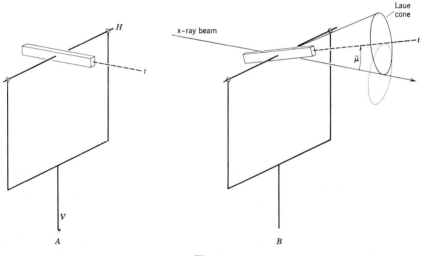

Fig. 1.

Suppose that the crystal is placed in an x-ray beam and set so that this direction makes some selected angle $\bar{\mu}$ with the x-ray beam, as shown in Fig. 1*B*. Now, the diffraction by a crystal is limited to the Laue cones coaxial with the possible rational directions of the crystal. Consider the

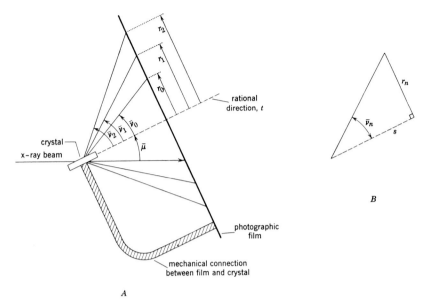

A

Fig. 2.

Diagrammatic section of a crystal and the Laue cones corresponding to its translation
t.   The crystal has been inclined to the x-ray beam by angle $\bar{\mu}$ while remaining rigidly
connected to the photographic film.

particular nest of cones coaxial with the selected direction, t.   These are
shown diagrammatically in Fig. 2A.

The zero-order cone is unique in that its half-opening angle is the same
as the inclination angle, i.e., $\bar{\nu}_0 = \bar{\mu}$, so that one of the generators of this
cone is the direct beam.   Now the angle $\bar{\mu}$ between the x-ray beam and
the rational direction t under consideration can be kept constant by
causing t to precess about the x-ray beam, as suggested by Fig. 1B.
When this is done, all the Laue cones coaxial with t remain invariant in
opening angle.   The diffraction is then entirely confined to the rays along
the generators of this nest of cones, and it can be recorded as a set of
concentric circles on a photographic film if the film is placed normal to
the axis of the cones and rigidly attached to the crystal, as suggested in
Fig. 2A.   Such photographs can be taken with the precession instrument
and are called *cone-axis photographs*.   Examples are shown in Chapter 9.

Cone-axis photographs are important auxiliaries to the regular precession photographs, which will be described later.   The cone-axis photograph has two valuable properties: It permits determination of the
identity period along t, and it permits the symmetry of the direction t
to be recognized by inspection.   It thus possesses the useful properties
of both a rotating-crystal photograph (with rotation about t) and a Laue

photograph (with the x-ray beam along the direction t) at the same time. These properties will now be briefly considered.

The relation between the half-opening angle of a Laue cone and the translation t is given[†] by

$$\frac{n\lambda}{t} = \cos \bar{\mu} - \cos \bar{\nu}_n, \tag{1}$$

where n is the order of the cone. Figure $2B$ shows that $\bar{\nu}_n$ is readily determined from

$$\tan \bar{\nu}_n = \frac{r_n}{s}, \tag{2}$$

so that

$$\frac{n\lambda}{t} = \cos \bar{\mu} - \cos \tan^{-1} \frac{r_n}{s}. \tag{3}$$

In (3), λ, $\bar{\mu}$, and s are experimental constants. Thus, if the radius r_n of the nth Laue cone is measured, the translation t is readily computed from

$$t = \frac{n\lambda}{\cos \bar{\mu} - \cos \tan^{-1} (r_n/s)}. \tag{4}$$

The symmetry properties of the cone-axis photograph are due to the fact that the photographic film is always held fixed with respect to the crystal and moves with the crystal. The symmetry of the diffraction effects about t is the same as the symmetry of the crystal about t (as modified by Friedel's law[§]). If all the directions in the Laue cone are treated equally, as they are in ideal precession motion, the film receives and records equivalent diffraction effects with the same distribution about the direction t as the properties are distributed about this direction in the crystal. The circular record of the Laue cone thus reveals the symmetry of t as modified by Friedel's law. More specifically, each upper-level circle has the symmetry of the direction t, but (because of Friedel's law) the zero-level circle has this symmetry augmented by an inversion center, if a center is not already present. It also has the further symmetry due to any other symmetry element in the zero level of the reciprocal lattice.

Thus, cone-axis photographs give both translation and symmetry information. Unlike the Laue photograph, in which the records of the diffraction from all levels are intermixed, in the cone-axis photograph the records are distinct, so by necessity the symmetry record of each level is presented separately. In this respect the symmetry record is more elegant than that of the Laue photograph. The separation is often valuable in revealing that specific levels show pseudo-symmetry.

[†] See M. J. Buerger. *X-ray crystallography.* (John Wiley and Sons, New York, 1942) 29–41.

[§] See Chapter 6 for a discussion of Friedel's law.

Some other aspects of cone-axis photographs are presented in Chapters 3, 5, and 9.

Laue-cone discussion of precession photographs

Before entering into a detailed study of the precession method with the aid of the relatively powerful reciprocal-lattice methods, it is instructive to consider the recording of a zero-level precession photograph by continuing to make use of the Laue cone and interpreting the results with

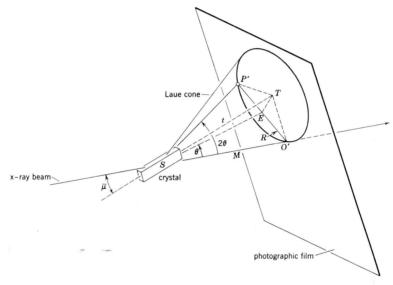

Fig. 3.

Geometry of diffraction along the zero-order Laue cone by a crystal whose translation t is inclined by angle $\bar{\mu}$ to an x-ray beam, and the record of the diffraction on a photographic film whose center is fixed at O' while its surface is maintained perpendicular to t.

the aid of the Bragg equation. In Fig. 3 the crystal is shown with its direction t making an angle $\bar{\mu}$ with the x-ray beam; t is also the axis of the zero-order Laue cone. The generalized de Jong-Bouman condition will presently be shown to be satisfied if a flat film is suspended in the same way as the crystal, with the center of the suspension O' in the path of the x-ray beam, provided that the surface of the film is always maintained normal to the direction t. The normality of the film and t are effected by some mechanism not shown. The distance between the suspensions of crystal and film is M, which will be shown to be a magnification factor.

With this geometry, all the rays from the crystal to the film along the surface of the cone have equal lengths. Now if the crystal diffracts x-rays in the zero order for the rational direction[†] t, it must do so along some generator of the zero-order Laue cone when the Bragg condition is satisfied. Let the direction of this reflection be SP' so that it records on the film as P'. Then the triangle $O'SP'$ is isosceles, with angle $O'SP' = 2\theta$. Thus

$$\sin \theta = \frac{R/2}{M}. \tag{5}$$

But Bragg's relation can be written

$$\sin \theta = \frac{\lambda}{2d_{hkl}}. \tag{6}$$

Comparison of (5) and (6) gives, for $l = 0$,

$$R = M \frac{\lambda}{d_{hk0}}. \tag{7}$$

Since the ray from the origin of the reciprocal lattice to the point $hk0$ has a length given by

$$\xi_{hk0} = \frac{\lambda}{d_{hk0}} \tag{8}$$

it is evident that the length of R is ξ scaled by the crystal-to-film distance, M.

To prove that R has also the direction of ξ it must be shown that R is perpendicular to the reflecting plane. This is evident from the following reasoning. The geometry of reflection requires the reflecting plane to be perpendicular to the plane of 2θ (and to bisect 2θ, so that the intersection is along SE, where $O'SE = ESP' = \theta$). By hypothesis the reflecting plane contains the axis t of the Laue cone, which in the precession method is always perpendicular to the film. Therefore the reflecting plane is also perpendicular to the film. Accordingly, the reflecting plane is perpendicular to the plane of the angle 2θ, and perpendicular to the film, therefore it must be perpendicular to their intersection, i.e., to $O'P' = R$. Thus R has the direction of ξ as well as its magnitude, scaled by M; accordingly R is the vector ξ scaled by M.

This demonstration of the distortionless photography of point locations of the reciprocal lattice is independent of the nature of the motion of the crystal. If the motion is an ideal precession motion, then the intensities of the spots also conform to the Friedel symmetry of the crystal, as discussed in the last section.

[†] For example, if t is the c axis, the zero-order diffraction indices must have the third index zero, i.e., they correspond to reflections $hk0$.

3

Theory of reciprocal-lattice photography

General principles

The basic features of the geometry of the generalized de Jong-Bouman principle are illustrated in Fig. 1. The x-ray beam is traveling from left to right. The zero-level plane is seen intersecting the sphere of reflection in the reflecting circle. The point P is in reflecting position on the reflecting circle and is responsible for the diffracted ray SPP'. Provided that the film is parallel with the reciprocal-lattice plane, then, from similar triangles,

$$\frac{O'P'}{OP} = \frac{SO'}{SO} = \frac{M}{1}, \tag{1}$$

from which

$$O'P' = M(OP). \tag{2}$$

Thus the recorded distance $O'P'$ of the diffraction record is proportional to the distance OP of the reciprocal-lattice point, each distance being measured from the direct x-ray beam in its own plane. This proportion is accurately maintained with the same proportionality constant M, provided that the crystal-to-film distance M is held constant, and provided that the film is maintained parallel with the reciprocal-lattice plane.

In order to bring other reciprocal-lattice points into reflecting position. it is necessary to give some motion to the reciprocal-lattice plane other than that of pure rotation about the direction SO of the x-ray beam. As pointed out in the last chapter, any motion whatever may be used. Two particular kinds of motion have the property of maintaining the nest of Laue cones invariant. The de Jong-Bouman method accomplishes

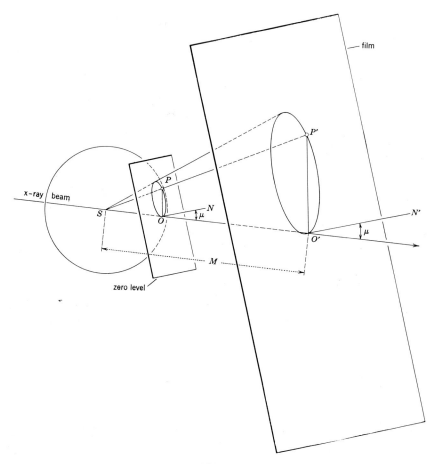

Fig. 1.
Diffraction by a point P in a zero-level plane of the reciprocal lattice.

this by fixing the position of the plane, but rotating it about its normal (Chapter 1, Fig. 5). Thus the position of the cones remains fixed. In the precession method, the axis of the nest of Laue cones is caused to precess about the x-ray beam. The scheme for accomplishing this was illustrated in Fig. 6 of Chapter 1. The normal to the reflecting plane is set at a selected angle $\bar{\mu}$ from the x-ray beam. This requires the plane to intersect the sphere of reflection in a small circle (shown solid in Fig. 6 of Chapter 1). Although the plane itself is prevented from rotating by its suspension, its normal ON is made to precess about the x-ray beam.

The precessing motion of the normal causes the circle of intersection to rotate about the point O. When the circumference of the circle passes through any reciprocal-lattice point P a reflection arises which is recorded at the corresponding point P' of the similar circle on the film shown at the right of the figure.

The geometry of upper-level recording

The discussion just given applies directly to the recording of any zero level of the reciprocal lattice. When upper levels are to be recorded, additional factors must be taken into account.

The geometry of upper-level recording is indicated in Figs. $2A$ and $2B$. The origin of the reciprocal lattice is, of course, the point where the x-ray beam leaves the sphere of reflection. Figure $2A$ shows an upper level at a distance ζ from the zero-level plane. In order that the film may record the photograph of this level without distortion, it is necessary that the film be displaced along the axis $N'O'$ by a distance proportional to the distance of the upper-level plane from the zero-level plane. This provides

$$\frac{\zeta'}{\zeta} = \frac{M}{1}. \tag{3}$$

Thus the film must be displaced by an amount

$$\zeta' = M\zeta. \tag{4}$$

The precession instrument (Fig. 3 of Chapter 4) is provided with a slide which permits setting the film forward by the amount ζ', which may be controlled accurately by a scale and vernier.

That the photograph recorded in this way is actually an undistorted replica of the reciprocal-lattice level and has the same proportionality factor as the zero-level recording can be appreciated with the aid of Fig. $2B$. In similar triangles SO_nP_n and $SO_n'P_n'$,

$$\frac{O_n'P_n'}{O_nP_n} = \frac{SO_n'}{SO_n}. \tag{5}$$

Also, in similar triangles SOO_n and $SO'O_n'$,

$$\frac{SO_n'}{SO_n} = \frac{SO'}{SO} = \frac{M}{1}. \tag{6}$$

Combining (5) and (6) gives

$$\frac{O_n'P_n'}{O_nP_n} = \frac{M}{1} \tag{7}$$

from which

$$O_n'P_n' = M(O_nP_n). \tag{8}$$

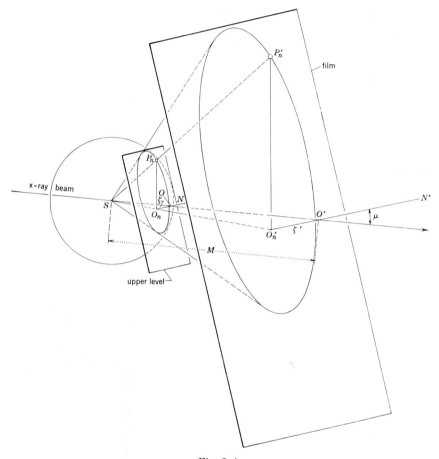

Fig. 2 *A*.

Diffraction by a point P_n in an upper-level plane of the reciprocal lattice.

Thus the distance of the diffraction record from the center of the film is proportional to the distance of the corresponding reciprocal-lattice point from the center of the reciprocal-lattice level, and the same proportionality constant M holds as in the case of the zero-level recording (2). Examples of precession photographs appear in Figs. 3 and 4.

Limits of the record

Theoretical limits. A characteristic of upper-level precession photographs (to be noted, for example, in Figs. 3*B* and 4*B*) is that the record is missing in the center. The cause of this can be found in Fig. 5, which shows the reciprocal-lattice planes at the upper extreme of the precession motion. The central region of radius O_nQ of the reciprocal-lattice

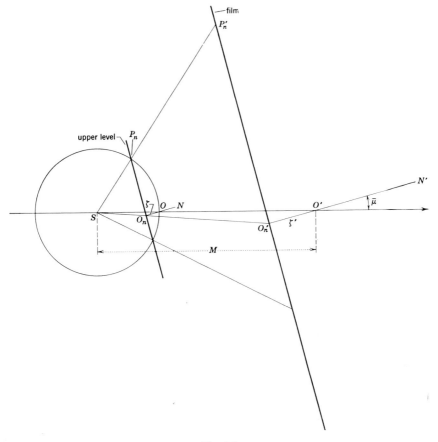

Fig. 2*B*.
Section in the plane SP_nO.

plane never passes through the sphere of reflection, and consequently never gives rise to a reflection. The radius of this *blind region* can be evaluated from Fig. 5, where it is evident that

$$O_nQ = T_nQ - TO \tag{9}$$

$$\therefore \; \xi_{min} = \sin \bar{\nu} - \sin \bar{\mu}. \tag{10}$$

It should also be observed that reciprocal-lattice points having a central distance ξ greater than O_nU also do not pass through the sphere. This limiting radius can be evaluated from Fig. 5:

$$O_nU = OT + T_nU \tag{11}$$

$$\xi_{max} = \sin \bar{\mu} + \sin \bar{\nu}. \tag{12}$$

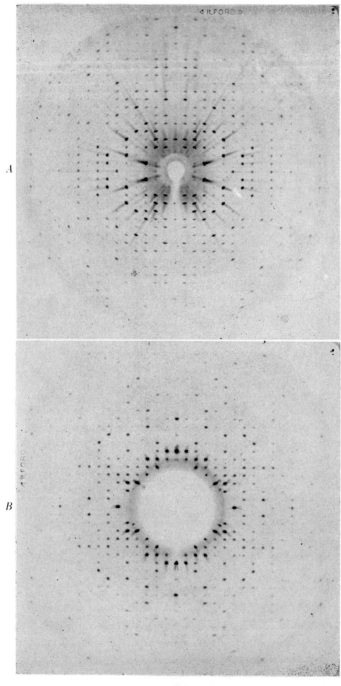

Fig. 3.

A: Example of a zero-level precession photograph. (Berthierite, FeSb$_2$S$_4$, $\bar{\mu} = 30°$, $M = 6$ cm; Mo$K\alpha$, 35kV, 12 mA, 18 hours.)

B: Example of an upper-level precession photograph. (Berthierite, FeSb$_2$S$_4$, $\bar{\mu} = 25°$, $M = 6$ cm; Mo$K\alpha$, 35 kV, $12\frac{1}{2}$ mA, 22 hours.)

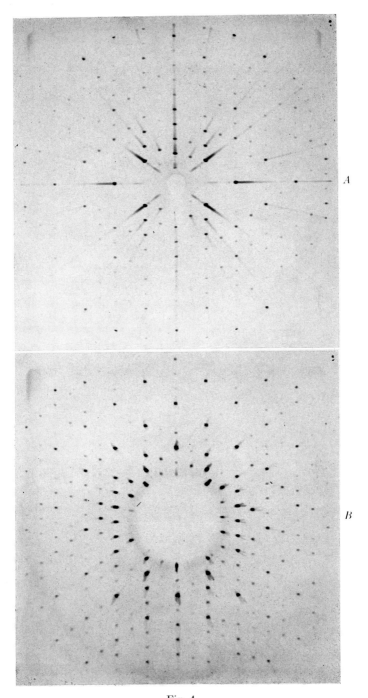

Fig. 4.

A: Example of a zero-level precession photograph. (Wollastonite,
CaSiO$_3$, $\bar{\mu} = 30°$, $M = 6$ cm; MoKα, 35 kV, 15 mA, 8 hours.)

B: Example of an upper-level precession photograph. (Wollastonite,
CaSiO$_3$, $\bar{\mu} = 25°$, $M = 6$ cm; MoKα, 35 kV, 15 mA, 16 hours.)

The recordable region of the reciprocal-lattice level thus lies within an annulus limited by radii given by (10) and (12). The width of this annulus is found by subtracting (10) from (12):

$$\xi_{max} - \xi_{min} = 2 \sin \bar{\mu}. \tag{13}$$

which is independent of $\bar{\nu}$. The center of the annulus is the average value of (12) and (10), namely

$$\frac{\xi_{max} + \xi_{min}}{2} = \sin \bar{\nu}, \tag{14}$$

which is independent of $\bar{\mu}$.

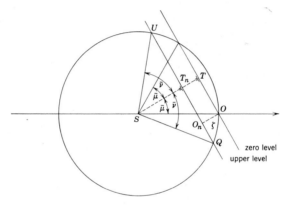

Fig. 5.

With the aid of these relationships it is possible to compute and plot the recordable region of the reciprocal lattice for any precession angle $\bar{\mu}$ and any Laue cone of half-opening angle $\bar{\nu}$. Figure 5 shows that ζ, $\bar{\mu}$, and $\bar{\nu}$ are also related by

$$OO_n = TS - T_nS$$

$$\zeta = \cos \bar{\mu} - \cos \bar{\nu} \tag{15}$$

so that, for any selected pair of values $\bar{\mu}$ and $\bar{\nu}$, the reciprocal-lattice coordinate ζ can be determined for the level being considered. This permits plotting the inner and outer radii ξ_{min} and ξ_{max} of the recordable range as a function of the reciprocal-lattice coordinate ζ of the plane being recorded. (Such a plot is shown in Fig. 9.)

Although relations (10), (12), and (15) are suitable for computing the exact size of the recorded region, they do not easily reveal the simple geometry involved. This can be demonstrated with the aid of Fig. 6. In Fig. 6A a set of planes of the reciprocal lattice is shown at the upper extreme of the precession motion; in Fig. 6B the same set is shown at the lower extreme. In both phases of the motion the outer limit and inner limit of recording are at opposite ends of the chord of the circle determined by the intersection of the sphere of reflection with the reciprocal-lattice plane in question. Now, if both sets of inner and outer limits are to be represented in the same reciprocal-lattice plane, the two different locations of the plane in Figs. 6A and 6B must be brought together.

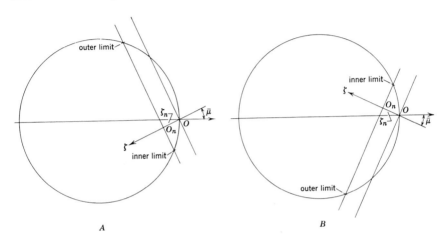

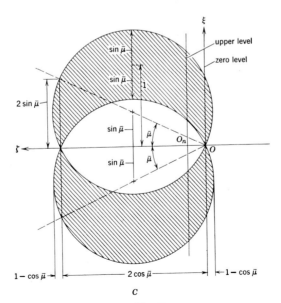

Fig. 6.

When this is done, the sphere of reflection is represented by two spheres separated by an angle $2\bar{\mu}$ as seen in Fig. 6C.

In Fig. 6C the portion of the reciprocal lattice recordable by the precession method is seen to occupy the exclusive parts of two intersecting spheres which are separated by angle $2\bar{\mu}$. In section, this recordable part comprises two lunes symmetrical in the ζ axis. Although the two lunes are formed by two equal circles which are separated by an angle $2\bar{\mu}$, the figure also has the symmetry of two equal circles separated by a translation in the direction of the ξ axis, which is seen to be $2 \sin \bar{\mu}$. This is therefore the width of the recorded region and is constant from $\zeta = 0$ to $\zeta = 2 \cos \bar{\mu}$.

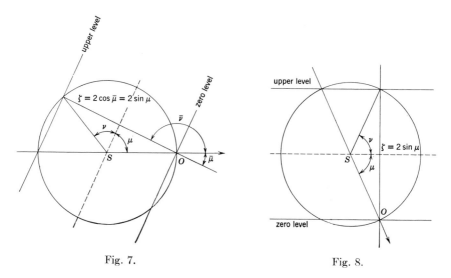

Fig. 7.   Fig. 8.

At $\zeta = \cos \bar{\mu}$, however, the central blind region reaches its maximum radius, namely $\xi = 1 - \sin \bar{\mu}$, while the outer limit of recording also attains its maximum radius, namely $\xi = 1 + \sin \bar{\mu}$. This information can also be obtained for (10) and (12) by setting $\sin \bar{\nu}$ at its maximum value of unity; this requires setting $\cos \bar{\nu} = 0$ in (15).

Figure 6C brings out two interesting possibilities of the precession method:

(a) It is possible to record levels of the reciprocal lattice having negative values of ζ down to the lower limit of $\zeta = \cos \bar{\mu} - 1$. Such photographs also have a central blind region.

(b) It is possible to take equi-inclination precession photographs. The key to this is suggested by Fig. 6C, which shows that if an upper level is set at $\zeta = 2 \cos \bar{\mu}$, then there is no central blind spot. If this situation is represented as in Fig. 6B, then Fig. 7 results. It is evident that, for an upper level having an origin distance ζ, if the precession angle is set so that $2 \cos \bar{\mu} = \zeta$, then the upper level can be recorded in the back-reflection region. To obtain such precession photographs requires an arrangement whereby the photographic film is set, and precessing, in the back-reflection position. That this condition is equi-inclination can be checked by rotating Fig. 7 clockwise by angle μ; its features then come to coincide with those of the equi-inclination condition of rotating-crystal methods shown in Fig. 8.

Mechanical limits. It can be appreciated from Fig. 10, for example, that for ordinary front-reflection precession photographs a mechanical upper limit for ζ is attained when, with increasing displacement of the photographic film away from its origin O', the film comes to coincide with the crystal at S. When this occurs, $QSU = 180°$ and $TSU = \bar{\nu} = 90°$. If this value is substituted into (15), it is seen that $\zeta_{lim} = \cos \bar{\mu}$.

A more conservative mechanical limitation occurs when the film cassette fouls the goniometer head, layer-line screen, or some other part of the precession apparatus. Some of these limits found in the instrument currently manufactured by the Charles Supper Company are suggested in Table 1.

Table 1
Limits of front-reflection precession photographs

$\bar{\mu}$	Theoretical $\zeta = \cos \bar{\mu}$ limit	Mechanical limit		
		Screen	ζ Limit	Limitation
15°	.966	40 mm (45 mm)	.465 (.50)	Cassette fouls screen at $M\zeta > 27.9$ mm
20°	.940	40 mm	.45	Cassette fouls yoke at $M\zeta > 27$ mm
25°	.906	40 mm (45 mm)	.41 (.44)	Layer-line screen fouls goniometer head at $M\zeta > 24.6$ mm
30°	.866	40 mm	.35	Cassette fouls dial support at $M\zeta > 21$ mm

Figure 9 is a detailed drawing corresponding to Fig. 6C, but for the front-reflection region only. The limits of the record for various precession angles are shown as required by theoretical considerations and by the mechanical construction of the Supper apparatus.

Isolating the level

The diffraction corresponding to a single level of the reciprocal lattice must be isolated for each precession photograph. Since the locus of dif-

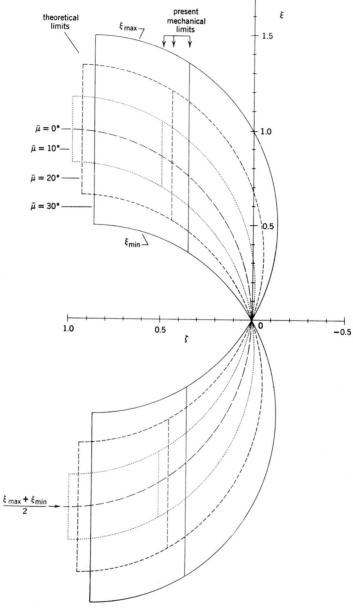

Fig. 9.
Theoretical and practical limits of recording with the precession method in the front
reflection region.

fraction directions for a single level is the surface of a circular cone, this locus can be isolated by permitting the cone to pass through an annular aperture in a flat screen (the *layer-line screen*) as shown in Fig. 10. For a particular constant precession angle $\bar{\mu}$ the cone angle is the same for the zero level of any set of reciprocal-lattice planes. But the cone angle varies from one upper level to another of the same set, so that the layer-line screen must be reset for each new upper-level photograph.

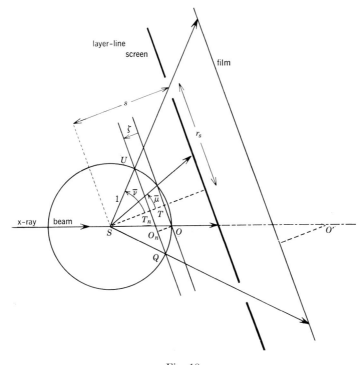

Fig. 10.

Figure 10 shows the geometry concerned with the setting of the layer-line screen. It is evident that

$$\frac{r_s}{s} = \tan \bar{\nu}.\tag{16}$$

Since the angle $\bar{\nu}$ is not measured or otherwise used as a setting value, it is desirable to express (16) in terms of other more usable quantities of the reciprocal lattice. Relation (15) shows that

$$\bar{\nu} = \cos^{-1}(\cos \bar{\mu} - \zeta).\tag{17}$$

When this is combined with (16) there results the following useful relation:

$$\frac{r_s}{s} = \tan \cos^{-1}(\cos \bar{\mu} - \zeta). \tag{18}$$

It is convenient to construct a layer-line screen with a definite and fixed annular aperture of mean radius r_s. In order to isolate a particular diffraction cone, therefore, the distance s of the screen from the crystal must be varied. The computation for this setting is made easy by rearranging (18) in the following form:

$$s = r_s \cot \cos^{-1}(\cos \bar{\mu} - \zeta). \tag{19}$$

Since a new value of s must be determined from (19) for every upper-level photograph, it is convenient to solve it graphically for commonly used values of the instrumental setting $\bar{\mu}$ and for a set of layer-line screen radii r_s. Such graphical solutions are given in Fig. 6, Chapter 5.

The determination of ζ

In order to make a photograph of any upper-level reciprocal-lattice plane, the value of ζ for that plane must be known, not only in order to set the layer-line screen, as just described, but also in order to set forward the film position by the amount $M\zeta$, as noted in (4). There are two general strategies for finding the required value of ζ.

It often happens that little is known about the crystal being examined, in any event in respect to the translation t of the direct lattice for the orientation being studied. This occurs, for example, when an examination is being begun on a crystal whose cell is, as yet, unknown, or when a crystal fragment has been oriented by one of the methods discussed later, so that a rational but unknown direction has been made parallel to the precessing axis. In these instances the data for further precession photographs must come from this particular setting of the crystal. In this event, a single cone-axis photograph supplies the necessary information for the settings of all upper-level photographs. In Chapter 2, cone-axis photographs were discussed briefly from the point of view of Laue cones. The highlights of the corresponding reciprocal-lattice interpretation are as follows.

In Fig. 11, an upper level at a distance ζ from the origin is shown. The diffraction for that level is limited to rays which extend from the center of the sphere S through the intersection of the level with the sphere. The rays from the upper-level cone meet the cone-axis film in a circle whose radius is r_n. The latter is determined by

$$\tan \bar{\nu} = \frac{r_n}{s},\tag{20}$$

where s is the crystal-to-film distance. It has already been seen in (15) that

(15): $\qquad\qquad \zeta = \cos \bar{\mu} - \cos \bar{\nu}.$

The value of $\bar{\nu}$ is given by (20), so that the computation involved is

$$\zeta = \cos \bar{\mu} - \cos \tan^{-1} \frac{r_n}{s}.\tag{21}$$

The values of $\bar{\mu}$ and s are chosen for the experiment. When r_n is measured, ζ for that particular level can be readily computed from (21).

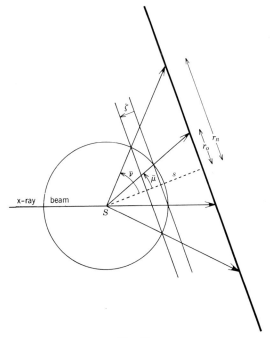

Fig. 11.

An alternative procedure is desirable if the translation t is known, or has been more carefully investigated from the cone-axis photograph as described later. In this event ζ can be computed with more accuracy from d^*_{uvw} or t_{uvw} by using the relation

$$\zeta_n = nd^* = n \frac{\lambda}{t}.\tag{22}$$

4

The Mark II precession instrument

Requirements

In the Mark II instrument, both crystal and film are suspended in gimbals so that the center of the crystal and the center of the zero-level position of the film remain unmoved and in line with the x-ray beam. The precession mechanism proper must perform two chief functions. It must cause the crystal to undergo precessing motion, and it must cause the photographic film to execute a duplicate motion. These last requirements have been accomplished in two somewhat differing manners in two different versions of the precession instrument.

First version

The first and somewhat older means of maintaining crystal and film parallel is illustrated in diagrammatic form in Fig. 1. The normal to the reciprocal-lattice plane is the line ON. This is represented mechanically by a steel shaft, of which the part nearest to the crystal is omitted to permit getting the shaft behind the film. Substituting for the missing part of the shaft is a hacksaw-like arm which is rigidly attached to the crystal. The plane normal ON is caused to take a precessing motion because one end of it is carried around the driveshaft by an arc-shaped arm AA. Any predetermined angle can be selected for the precession cone by setting the socket for the shaft ON at the proper angle $\bar{\mu}$ on the arc.

Meanwhile the film-normal shaft $O'N'$ is maintained parallel with the plane-normal shaft by means of a parallelogram linkwork. When either of the two following instrumental settings is changed, the linkwork slips parallel to the shafts but continues to maintain them parallel: (*a*) when the cone half-angle $\bar{\mu}$ is changed, and (*b*) when the film distance M is changed.

This version of the mechanism was adopted on the first model of the Mark II precession apparatus and on the early commercial copies. A photograph of the first model is shown in Fig. 2*A*. The crystal and the photographic film are each supported in gimbal suspensions like those illustrated diagrammatically in Fig. 6 of Chapter 1. The points of each suspension that remain unmoved are aligned along the path of the x-ray beam. Accordingly, the directions of the crystal axis and film normal can be varied without changing the positions of the center of the crystal or the center of the film.

While the suspension for holding the film is of simple fork-like design, the suspension for holding the crystal is somewhat more complicated to

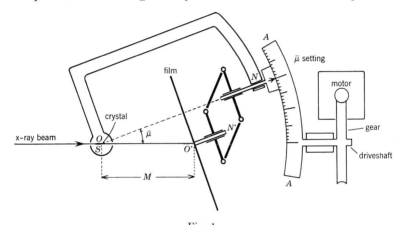

Fig. 1.
Diagram of first version of the Mark II precession instrument.

permit holding the crystal in a conventional goniometer head and to take care of making adjustments of the position and orientation of the crystal. To hold the crystal in the conventional goniometer head, one vertical arm of the fork is omitted, and the other alone supports the horizontal axis of the crystal. The horizontal axis is fitted with several of the customary devices for adjusting the orientation and position of the crystal with respect to the x-ray beam. When the goniometer head is set in position, the location of the crystal along the horizontal axis can be adjusted by turning the left-hand milled knob seen in Fig. 2*B*, and the orientation of the crystal with respect to rotation about this axis can be adjusted by turning the larger knob next to it. The angular coordinate of the orientation of the crystal can be read on the large dial attached to this rotation knob, the reading being made against a vernier graduated to 5 minutes; this axis is usually called the *dial axis*. When the crystal has been rotated to the desired position, the horizontal axis of this gimbal can be locked to the hacksaw-like arm by means of a short lever. This,

A

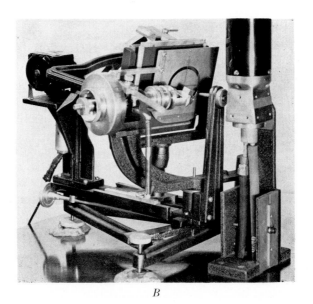

B

Fig. 2.
First version of the Mark II precession instrument.
A and *B*.   Instrument aligned with x-ray beam.

C

Fig. 2.
C. Instrument swung away from x-ray tube, and with autocollimator in place.

in effect, fixes the normal of the reciprocal-lattice plane coincident with the shaft *ON*, Fig. 1.

The magnification factor M can be easily and instantly varied by unlocking the base of the suspension holding the film and sliding it along a dovetailed track. The crystal-to-film distance M (which is also the magnification factor), is read by means of a millimeter scale and vernier.

For the purpose of making upper-level photographs, the film can be set forward from the suspension center. The film holder slides in a dovetail slide, seen near its top, and is fixed at any desired position by means of a clamp. The amount $M\xi$ by which the film is set forward is read accurately by means of a millimeter scale on the film slide and a vernier on the dovetail.

The layer-line screen is attached to the hacksaw-like arm and therefore is carried with the crystal and shares its precessing motion. The position of the screen is set by means of a slide and clamp near the crystal end of the hacksaw-like arm. The position s of the screen is read on a scale located near the clamp. Since the range of motion of the screen is restricted by the film in one direction and by the crystal and its adjusting holder in the other, several layer-line screens are necessary to cover the required range of reciprocal-lattice-level positions ζ. Each layer-line screen has a different radius of annular opening and covers a limited range of possible cone angles. It is necessary to have a set of such screens

whose annular openings have different radii. A desirable set has radii of
15, 20, 25, 30, 35, 40, and 45 mm, each with a 5 mm-wide annulus. For
isolating the adjacent levels of a crystal for which the distance d^* between
levels of the reciprocal lattice is unusually small,[†] it is desirable to have a
second set for which the widths of the annuli are only 2 or 3 mm, and in
which the sides of the annuli are beveled to eliminate the effect of thickness of the layer-line plate. The screen inserts are square brass plates
which slip accurately into place in slots in the layer-line screen carrier.
By this method the layer-line screens can be conveniently and quickly
changed. The annular opening in the insert is made by suspending a
brass disk in a circular holder of larger radius. The disk is suspended on
a sheet of thin, uniform plastic.

The entire precession instrument can be swung away from the x-ray
tube, pivoting on a point near its rear (i.e., away from the x-ray source)
as shown in Fig. 2C. This permits one to look through the pinhole system[§] at the crystal for the purpose of making adjustments. The technique of adjusting the crystal is discussed in the next chapter. The
precession apparatus can be locked in either position by means of the
large milled knob seen at the back of the apparatus. A stop assures that
it is always returned accurately to its original position.

Second version

Conventional design.   An alternative means of maintaining crystal
and film parallel has been widely used on instruments of recent commercial manufacture. This version was adopted because the three-
dimensional parallelogram which connects $O'N'$ to ON in Fig. 1 was
deemed difficult to manufacture, and because the possibility of varying
the crystal-to-film distance M was found to be unnecessary in ordinary
practice. In most instruments M is now fixed at 6.00 cm.

The alternative version is shown diagrammatically in Fig. 3. The
basic difference between the motions of Figs. 1 and 3 is that in Fig. 1
the crystal's orientation is directly controlled by the arc setting, the film
then being made parallel, while in Fig. 3 the reverse is true. Thus in
Fig. 1 the setting arc has a large radius ON, while in Fig. 3 it has a
smaller radius $O'N'$. As a consequence of the primary control of orientation of the film in Fig. 3, a different parallelizing device must be used.
This is illustrated in simplified form in Fig. 3. Actually the parallelizing
must be accomplished in three dimensions, so that Fig. 3 is too simple a
representation; the more complicated requirements in three dimensions

---

[†] See end of Chapter 5.
[§] Described in more detail on page 37.

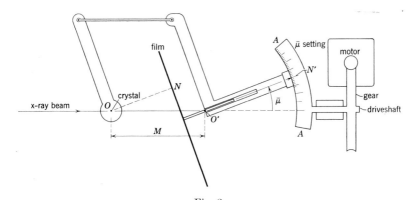

Fig. 3.
Simplified diagram of second version of Mark II precession instrument.

are shown in Fig. 4.   Here the gimbal suspensions for both crystal and
film are illustrated diagrammatically.   All features of both gimbals must
be kept parallel.   The instrument is constructed so that the distance VV'
between them is fixed; the angular motions of the two suspensions about
these two axes can be coupled very simply by a single connecting link of
length VV' attached by pins to the two suspensions.   The motions of the
horizontal axes H and H' must also be coupled regardless of the angular

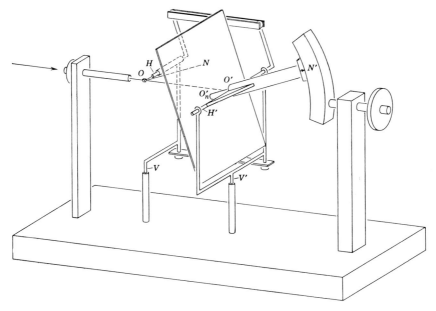

Fig. 4.
Diagram of the three-dimensional linkage used to maintain the photographic film
perpendicular to ON in the second version of the Mark II precession instrument.

A

B

Fig. 5.
The Mark II precession instrument.
A and B: Instrument aligned with x-ray beam.
(Courtesy of the Charles Supper Company).

C

Fig. 5.
C. Instrument swung away from x-ray tube, and with autocollimator in place.

position of the suspensions about their vertical axes. This is arranged, as shown in Fig. 4, by a second link; in this case the attachment of the link to the suspensions must be made by means of ball-and-socket joints, since the directions of the horizontal axes are not, in general, normal to the link.

The actual instrument is seen in Fig. 5. Some of its features are as follows.

(*a*) The instrument has a lower base which is fitted with three leveling screws. This base remains fixed with respect to the x-ray tube during adjustments of the precession mechanism, as noted below.

(*b*) The precession mechanism proper is mounted on an upper base. This base can be rotated about an axis in the fixed lower base. When this is done, the longitudinal axis of the precession mechanism can be swung out of the direction of the x-ray beam to a position where one can remove or change the pinhole system and can also comfortably look through the pinhole system at the crystal for the purpose of adjusting it. Along the longitudinal axis of this base are aligned four vertical posts which carry parts described in sequence below.

(*c*) The x-ray beam is defined by a removable collimator in the form of a pinhole system. This is essentially a tube within which are mounted two lead disks drilled with concentric holes of the required diameters;

beyond the second aperture there is the usual guard aperture to remove the radiation scattered from the second aperture. The pinhole tube is inserted in a round hole in a support attached to the upper base; its location and direction are controlled by a circular flange machined as an integral part of the tube.

For most uses, a pinhole system in which the two beam-defining apertures are each 0.8 mm in diameter is recommended. This rather large diameter permits all rays from the illuminated area of the target to reach the crystal. This assures maximum x-ray intensity at the crystal and consequently minimum exposure times. It also assures a large plateau of intensity in the cross-section of the direct beam, which is desirable when the reflection intensities are to be measured.[†] In addition to this pinhole system it is desirable to have available an alternative one with smaller apertures, say $\frac{1}{2}$-mm diameter. This produces smaller diffraction spots on the film due to the reduced divergence of the direct beam, and this characteristic is valuable when one wishes to make more precise measurements of the cell edges. The smaller apertures also reduce the amount of unused x-radiation if the crystal is small, and so give rise to less background on the film.

A third insert for the collimating system is also necessary. This is merely a tube with locating flange, having the same shape as the ordinary pinhole system, but without lead disks. It contains a clear axial hole of $\frac{3}{16}$-in (≈ 5 mm) diameter. This coarse collimating system is useful both in the preliminary alignment of the apparatus to the x-ray beam, and also to permit adjustment of the crystal by auto-collimation as described later. It should be provided with three accessories: One is a removable cylindrical plug having an axial hole $1\frac{1}{2}$ mm in diameter (see Fig. 2, Chapter 5). This is to be slipped into the outer end of the tube to reduce its diameter there. The second is a small disk of fluorescent screen at the end of a cap which fits over the other end of the tube. This is used in the preliminary alignment of the instrument. There should also be a long rod pointed at one end, which fits the tube well. When $\bar{\mu}$ is set at zero, this rod can be pushed into the tube till it reaches the layer-line screen; this permits checking and adjusting the center of the holder or any insert.

The support which carries the pinhole system also provides attachment for the direct-beam stop. In order to prevent the direct beam from reaching the film after passing the crystal, it is intercepted by a lead disk at the bottom of a small brass cup. The cup is fixed at the end of a tiny rod, and the whole unit can be quickly removed and replaced with another stop of different diameter. The unit is mounted on the main support through an eccentric axis which permits the stop to be swung out of

[†] See Chapter 12, especially Fig. 1.

the beam and away from the crystal. When this is done the film may be momentarily exposed to the direct beam, or the goniometer head may be removed without fouling the crystal on the beam stop. The assembly is designed so that the crystal-to-stop distance can be varied. The stop should be as far as possible from the film to reduce background. On the other hand, the closer the stop is to the crystal, the larger the blind spot it produces on the film. The blind spot must not be permitted to be so large that it covers an area in which the innermost reflections would otherwise be recorded.

(*d*) The gimbal nearest the collimating system carries the crystal as well as the layer-line screen. The crystal, mounted on a standard goniometer head, is attached to the horizontal axis of the gimbal in exactly the same way it is attached to the rotation axis of a Weissenberg apparatus. This axis is usually called the *dial axis* on the precession apparatus since the orientation of this axis is indicated on the dial of the instrument. A diagrammatic cross-section of the dial-axis assembly is shown in Fig. 6. A clamp, shown in about the middle of the upper drawing, when loosened, permits freeing the horizontal axis, with its rigidly attached crystal and dial, from the coupling link. In this way the orientation of the crystal about the dial axis can be varied, and its position can be read on the dial. This has a diameter of $3\frac{1}{2}$ in. and is graduated in degrees, and the vernier is divided into 5-min intervals.

The crystal can be adjusted to the center of the line of sight of the collimating system by means of three mutually orthogonal translations, two on the goniometer head and the third the dial axis already described.

(*e*) The layer-line screen holder is permanently attached to the linkage which causes the precessing axis of the crystal and the film normal to be always parallel. The layer-line screen, when inserted in the holder, is thus always in the correct position, i.e., normal to the precessing axis. The angular adjustments of the crystal, just described, and particularly the dial adjustment, permit orienting the selected translation of the crystal parallel to the axis of the nest of Laue cones defined by the center of the layer-line screen holder. The layer-line screen itself is a thin brass plate with an annular opening; it can be inserted in the screen holder by slipping it into slots. The holder slides in a track parallel to the cone axis, and its distance *s* from the crystal can be read by scale and vernier to the nearest 0.01 cm. The smallest distance (about 2.3 cm) is controlled by the effective diameter of the goniometer head, and the largest distance (about 4.5 cm) is controlled by the possibility of fouling the layer-line screen on the cassette.

The layer-line screen holder also serves the alternative function of holding the very thin cone-axis cassette whenever cone-axis photographs are desired. The cassette utilizes a film $3\frac{3}{4}$ in. square. The screen holder also accommodates a slide carrying a fluorescent screen which is used in aligning the apparatus to the x-ray beam.

(*f*) The gimbal farthest from the collimating system carries a removable cassette. The cassette is attached by means of a dovetail and clamp to a heavy cylindrical bar whose axis is normal to the film. The rod slides in a sleeve so that it can be displaced to provide any desired displacement of the film $M\zeta$, and clamped firmly in that position. The magnitude of the displacement is measured directly by a centimeter scale and vernier.

The cassette, and certain pieces of the apparatus attached or linked to it mechanically, constitute a system which is not in balance about the horizontal axis of the suspension of the cassette. This is compensated by a permanent weight which just counterbalances the system when the cassette is set at the zero-level position. When the cassette is displaced by $M\zeta$, a small trimming weight may be shifted to maintain balance.

The cassette holds a film $4\frac{15}{16}$ in. square. This curious size is based on the fact that the commercial 5 x 7-in.-film has actual dimensions of $4\frac{15}{16}$ x $6\frac{15}{16}$ in. The appropriate film for the precession camera is prepared by trimming the long side of this 5 x 7 film so that it equals the short side; the remaining strip, approximately 2 in. wide, is preserved for use in preliminary orientation trials. (It is important that the 7-in. length of film is trimmed to $4\frac{15}{16}$ in. If it is trimmed to 5 in., the film will not quite fit in the space allotted to it in the cassette, as a result of which double spots will appear on the precession photographs as noted at the end of Chapter 7.)

The cassette itself consists of a square metal frame which is made light-tight on the side toward the crystal by a taut piece of opaque paper and closed on the back by a metal plate. This mates with the frame by a stepped fit which renders this side of the cassette light-tight. The plate bears the dovetail, so it is the part of the cassette which fixes the location of the film. Two tiny holes drilled through the plate near each end of a horizontal centerline can be uncovered to expose two dots on the film; they allow the film's horizontal axis to be located. An additional hole placed nearer one corner produces another dot that makes it possible to identify that corner; its asymmetrical location permits distinguishing the front and back of the film.

(*g*) The last post carries the motor, driveshaft, and arc which cause the film normal to precess. Constant speed is assured by a synchronous motor which normally operates at 60 r.p.m. It is connected to the actual precession driveshaft by a worm and gear which reduce the speed by $\frac{1}{60}$, so that the driveshaft normally provides 1 precession cycle per minute. This speed can be varied, if necessary, by the use of a motor with different speed, or by employing a different drive gear.

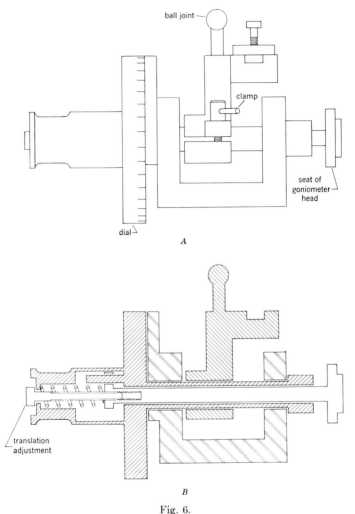

Fig. 6.
The dial-axis assembly of the precession instrument.

A. Front view.
B. Diagrammatic cross-section of *A*.

The normal to the film is represented by a steel shaft which fits into a socket in a slide on the arc. The arc is divided into degrees, while the slide carries a vernier which enables $\bar{\mu}$ to be read directly to 5 min. The slide can be clamped in any position from $\bar{\mu} = 0°$ to $30°$.

Other variations. Precession instruments are manufactured in many countries, but most are unimaginative copies of the original designs. An instrument in a different class has been designed by Dr. F. Hanic,

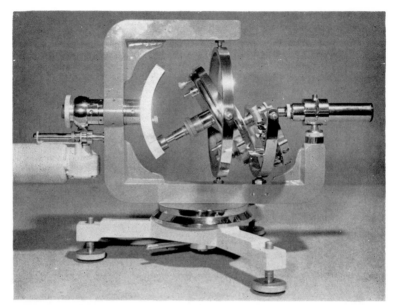

A

B

Fig. 7.
Variation of the Mark II precession instrument designed by Dr. F. Hanic, Dr. J. Maďar, and A. Kiss of Bratislava, Czechoslovakia (courtesy of Dr. F. Hanic).

Dr. J. Madar, and A. Kiss of the Institute of Inorganic Chemistry, Czechoslovakian Academy of Sciences, Bratislava, and is shown in Fig. 7. The most obvious feature of this instrument is the replacement of the upper base by a partial loop of metal and the mounting of the vertical axis of the camera across this loop rather than cantilever fashion, as in the conventional instruments.

5

The use of the precession apparatus

Appropriate x-ray tube and table

Any piece of single-crystal apparatus, including the precession instrument, should be used in conjunction with an x-ray tube whose axis is vertical. X-ray tubes whose axes are horizontal are not suitable for use with any standard single-crystal apparatus and seem to be designed by manufacturers unacquainted with modern single-crystal techniques. Furthermore, it is most convenient to have the vertical x-ray tube in the center of a circular table about 36 in. in diameter and about 41 in. high (≈ 104 cm). Any other arrangement causes discomfort and inconvenience to the operator of the apparatus. Tables much smaller do not give sufficient room for the base of the apparatus; those much larger prevent reaching some parts of the apparatus easily for adjustment. The corners of square tables are uncomfortable to lean against, and rectangular tables prevent reaching all parts of the apparatus for adjustment.

Aligning the instrument

The lower base of the precession apparatus is provided with three leveling screws to aid in adjusting it to the x-ray beam. To prevent the apparatus from slipping out of position accidentally after it is adjusted, the lower parts of the leveling screws are sometimes inserted into conical depressions in three small metal plates which rest directly on the surface of the table. A better arrangement is to use a T- or Y-shaped piece of flat metal whose three arms take the place of the three separate blocks. The arms should be machined at the proper locations to receive the ends of the leveling screws, one arm having a conical depression, another a V-shaped groove, and the third a small flat area. After the instrument is adjusted to the x-ray beam, the T or Y should be fixed to the table, either by partly surrounding it with plasticine or by some more elaborate mechanical means. With this arrangement the precession apparatus can be removed and later returned to the T or Y with the assurance that it will recover its original adjustment.

The first step in the adjustment of the precession instrument depends on whether the x-ray tube (with axis assumed vertical) has the target at the upper end (which is usual with commercial generator units) or at the lower end (which is preferable, but usually found only in home-made units. An example is seen in Fig. 2, Chapter 4). If the target is at the upper end, the x-rays issue from the window in a beam which slopes downward some 1° to 6° from the horizontal, whereas if the target is at the lower end, the beam slopes upward at the same angle. The leveling screws of the precession apparatus should be adjusted so that the base plate makes an angle of about 3° with the horizontal in the appropriate sense. The angle can be measured by use of a simple protractor and perhaps a small level.

Meanwhile the coarse collimator with its fluorescent screen should be in position. The end of the collimator should be placed about $\frac{1}{2}$ in. from the window of the x-ray tube and the height of the apparatus adjusted, as noted below, until the collimator points into the center of the window. To adjust the height, all leveling screws should be turned in the same direction by the same amount, thus leaving the slope of the instrument unaltered.

Before the x-ray beam is turned on now, or at any later time, an Azároff beam tunnel[†] should be inserted between the collimator and the x-ray tube to prevent exposure of personnel or film to scattered x-radiation. With no filter in the beam, the x-ray tube should now be turned on.

In making adjustments to align the apparatus to the x-ray beam, it is useful to adopt the following viewpoint: Alignment is achieved by pointing the collimator at the center of the focal spot on the target of the x-ray tube. This can be done by changing the direction toward which the collimator points. To raise or lower its viewpoint, both front leveling screws should be rotated by the same amount in the same direction. To shift the viewpoint left or right, they should be rotated by the same amount in opposite directions. These adjustments are made with one hand on each front leveling screw, and the turns should be made together and quickly. Neither adjustment appreciably alters the angle which the base of the instrument makes with the horizontal.

The procedure already recommended usually assures that the coarse collimator is pointing at a region of the target which includes the focal spot, so that the x-ray beam should be coming along the tube and illumi-

† L. V. Azároff. *A telescoping direct beam tunnel.* Rev. Sci. Instrum. **24** (1953) 872

nating the fluorescent screen. The front leveling screws should then be manipulated to maximize the illumination.

When this preliminary adjustment is finished, the x-rays should be turned off, the clamps which hold the upper base released, and the apparatus rotated so that the collimator is facing the operator. The plug which reduces the size of the outer opening is then inserted (as in Fig. 2*B*, page 51), and the instrument rotated back into position. Exact recovery of original direction is assured by turning the eccentric cam on the top of the lower base, after which the upper base should be locked. After restoring the Azároff beam tunnel and turning on the x-ray beam, the spot on the fluorescent screen will be seen to be smaller and may be uncentered. If so, it is adjusted to center by manipulating the front leveling screws.

Again the x-rays are turned off and the upper base rotated, but this time the coarse collimator is replaced by the 0.8-mm. pinhole system. When the apparatus is restored to position the pinhole system should appear to be approximately aligned. This time the alignment should be tested with the fluorescent screen slipped into the layer-line screen holder, after making sure that $\bar{\mu}$ is set at zero. If the fluorescent screen shows no spot, relatively small adjustments of the front leveling screws should cause it to appear. When this occurs, the position of maximum illumination should be determined by quick, short sweeps up and down, and right and left, and the instrument left in this orientation. It is now satisfactorily adjusted to the x-ray beam.

Mounting the crystal

The precession apparatus accepts the standard goniometer head which carries the crystal mount. The mount consists of a brass pin to which is attached a small glass capillary, at the end of which the crystal itself is mounted. While all this is standard practice, it will pay the user of the precession apparatus, particularly, to give attention to some of the details of making the mount.

It is worthwhile to have the brass pins machined to a simple design. To fit the goniometer head they should be $\frac{1}{8}$ in. (3.175 mm) in diameter. A length of $\frac{1}{2}$ in. ≈ 13 mm is recommended, and there should be no burred edges. A small hole (about $\frac{1}{2}$ mm in diameter and about 3 mm deep) should be drilled in one end to receive the glass capillary.

Maintaining the crystal in the x-ray beam during adjustment is much aided if the center of the crystal is always placed at the center of rotation of the two goniometer arcs. In the Supper goniometer heads this center is $\frac{1}{2}$ in. above the top of the pin receiver, Fig. 1. Thus, the length of the capillary plus the length of the brass pin showing above the receiver should be ½ in.

The capillary should be made of lead-free glass, such as Pyrex, drawn down to the smallest diameter which can be used conveniently, preferably of the order of 0.1-mm diameter. The reason for the small diameter is that whatever volume of glass there is in the beam scatters x-rays and so contributes to the background. The capillary should be inserted in the hole in the brass pin and fixed there with some adhesive; for example, that used to attach the crystal to the glass. For the latter use the adhesive must be amorphous so that it does not give rise to a powder pattern. It must also have the characteristic of not setting before one has finished manipulating the crystal, yet of not flowing after it has hardened. It should preferably be soluble in something so that, if the

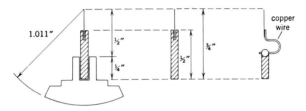

Fig. 1.
Dimensions of upper arc of the Supper goniometer head, and appropriate dimensions of pin and capillary to bring crystal to center of this arc.

mount proves unsatisfactory, the crystal can be removed and remounted. Some adhesives, like a thick mixture of shellac in methyl alcohol, are good except that during humid weather they tend to take on water and permit the crystal to change orientation. The two-component Araldite (CIBA, Duxford, Cambridge, England) has been used with some success. Other adhesives are du Pont's Duco (solvent: amyl acetate) and VYHH (solvent: cyclohexanone).

In sticking the crystal to the capillary, the crystal should touch and be supported as much as possible by the capillary. Only enough adhesive should be used to stick the crystal to the capillary. If an excess is used the adhesive will form a glob separating the crystal from the capillary. When this happens the crystal may shift as the adhesive sets or is affected by the atmosphere, and there is usually an excess of adhesive in the x-ray beam.

An alternative mount, which is convenient when the crystal orientation may have to be changed,[†] is shown at the right of Fig. 1. In this mount

---

[†] Fred Ordway. *Techniques for growing and mounting small single crystals of refractory compounds.* J. Res. Nat. Bur. Standards **48** (1952) 152–158.

the capillary is attached to a piece of copper wire, and this is soldered to a short brass pin. If the orientation of the crystal requires a change beyond the limits of the goniometer-head arc, this change can be readily made by bending the copper wire with pliers. More elaborate mounts that accomplish this purpose more elegantly have been described.[†]

Adjusting the crystal

Before a precession photograph is attempted, the crystal must be adjusted so that its center is in the center of the x-ray beam, and it must be oriented so that a selected translation is parallel to the x-ray beam when $\bar{\mu}$ is set at zero. These adjustments are to be carried out with the crystal attached to the precession apparatus. To attach it, the precession angle should first be set at zero, then the apparatus should be rotated out of the beam so the collimator can be removed. When this is done and when the beam stop is also snapped out of the way, the instrument is clear of protuberances which might otherwise foul the crystal. The goniometer head may then be screwed on the dial axis. In doing this the milled nut should be screwed only tight enough to assure that the goniometer head is seated properly.

Centering. If a goniometer is available, the crystal has presumably been examined on it and has been centered incidentally to the examination. When transferred from the goniometer to the precession instrument the crystal may be expected to remain approximately centered, but may prove to be slightly eccentric when tested as noted below. If so, it should be adjusted using the technique to be described.

On the other hand, if no attempt has been made as yet to center the crystal on a goniometer, the mounting technique described should assure that the crystal is not seriously eccentric. To test the centering, the coarse collimator is inserted and the lens cap slipped onto its front end. By looking through the lens the crystal will be found in focus, presumably framed in the opposite open end of the collimator. When the dial is rotated, the crystal, if somewhat eccentric, will appear to execute an up-and-down oscillation. To correct the eccentricity the dial should be rotated until one translation of the goniometer head is perpendicular to the line of sight. In this position the crystal, in general, will appear above or below the center of the field. The translation screw should be adjusted until the crystal is brought to the center of the field. Next, the dial should be rotated until the second translation of the goniometer head is perpendicular to the line of sight, and the adjustment routine repeated.

[†] H. J. Grenville-Wells. *Method of obtaining x-ray rotation photographs about three orthogonal axes from one crystal mounting.* Acta Cryst. **8** (1955) 519.

When the dial is then rotated a full 360° the center of the crystal ought to appear nearly or quite unmoved. If it does not, the procedure should be repeated, possibly with the following refinement: One translation is again placed perpendicular to the line of sight, then the dial quickly turned 180°. If this causes the crystal to rise in the field, it should be lowered by half its travel, and vice versa. This should be repeated with the other translation adjustment, and the whole procedure iterated as many times as necessary to cause the center of gravity of the crystal to remain unmoved during a full rotation. Finally, the translation parallel to the dial axis should be adjusted by means of the milled knob beyond the dial (extreme left center of Fig. 6B, Chapter 4) until the crystal is centered in this direction also.

This constitutes a preliminary adjustment with the coarse collimator, which should now be removed and replaced by the .8-mm. pinhole system. The centering tests described should be repeated, and, if necessary, further improvements of the centering should be made until the crystal center remains quite unmoved on complete rotation of the dial. When this has been accomplished, *the lens cap should be removed before turning on the x-ray beam.* If the Azároff beam tunnel is used, as recommended, failure to remove the lens will be noticed because the beam tunnel will fail to fit properly.

Study preliminary to orienting. Much time will be saved if advantage is taken of geometrical and optical methods of orienting the crystal before it is placed on the precession instrument. While it is true that a fragment can be oriented on the precession instrument without any auxiliary aid, the procedure does take time, and may lead to the necessity of remounting the fragment if it turns out to be in an orientation beyond the range the goniometer arcs are able to correct.

If partial or complete crystallographic data are available for the crystal, attention should be given especially to the known geometrical features which may help in determining the orientation of the crystal. These include the crystal habit, angles between faces, and cleavage (with further attention being paid to the possibility of twinning, which may require rejection of the sample selected). Any or all of these purely geometrical features may lead to a recognition of one or more rational crystallographic directions in the sample at hand. Relations between two or more such features present on the sample should be investigated with a goniometer if one is available. Such a study preferably concludes with a knowledge of at least one specific rational direction in the crystal, and this direction (or one of them if several become known) is to be set parallel to the precessing axis.

If no geometrical features are evident in the sample (and even if the geometrical study has achieved some success) the optical properties of the crystal may yield valuable clues to its orientation if the crystal is transparent. For this purpose the crystal should be studied with the aid of the polarizing microscope. Unless the crystal is isometric, such an examination usually establishes at least a rough knowledge of the symmetry directions in the crystal fragment, and if the optical properties of the crystal species are already well enough known to be listed in reference tabulations[†] the crystal directions may be established in considerable detail.

When this study is complete it usually has resulted in a partial or complete understanding of the rational directions of the crystal. One of these is accordingly chosen and set parallel to the direction of the x-ray beam when $\bar{\mu}$ is set at zero. It remains to check, and possibly to improve, this preliminary orientation.

Calibration of dial readings. When the dial of the precession apparatus reads zero, the pin in the seat into which the goniometer head fits is normal to the precessing axis. It is important that the relative directions of the pin and dial reading are known for the goniometer also. It is worth the trouble of arranging that the pin is normal to the line of sight when the dial reads zero; then the goniometer head can be transferred from goniometer to the precession instrument without the bother of making the transformation from one reading to another. But in any case the transformation should be known, and it should be noted whether the dial reading of the goniometer increases on clockwise rotation when facing the dial[§] (as it does on the precession instrument) or the reverse.

When the transformation of dial readings is known, the goniometer head can be transferred from goniometer to precession instrument without loss of information about the orientation of the crystal, except that there may be a small error (of the order of a degree in dial setting) incurred by the transfer due to the fact that the pins must fit the keyway in the goniometer head with a small tolerance. If the crystal has been perfectly oriented on the goniometer, therefore, it may be expected that it will still

---

[†] Charles Palache, Harry Berman, and Clifford Frondel. *The system of mineralogy.* (John Wiley and Sons, New York, 1944, 1951, 1962).

Esper S. Larsen and Harry Berman. *The microscopic determination of the non-opaque minerals.* U. S. Geol. Survey Bull. 848 (1934). 266 pages.

Alexander N. Winchell and Horace Winchell. *Elements of optical mineralogy, Part II, Descriptions of minerals.* (John Wiley and Sons, New York, 1951).

Alexander Newton Winchell. *The microscopic characters of artificial inorganic solid substances, or artificial minerals.* (John Wiley and Sons, New York, 1931).

Alexander N. Winchell. *The optical properties of organic compounds.* (Academic Press, New York, 2nd Ed., 1954).

[§] This is true of the goniometers made by LaPine, Nedinsco, Stoe, and Techne, and of the goniometer designed by C. R. Wolfe.

be oriented perfectly on the precession instrument except that there may be a small error in the dial setting remaining to be corrected.

Use of the autocollimator. The autocollimator attachment is a device which permits directing a light beam down the collimator while looking through the collimator at the same time to see if the light is reflected back by a plane surface. The design of a simple autocollimator is shown diagrammatically in Fig. 2*A*.

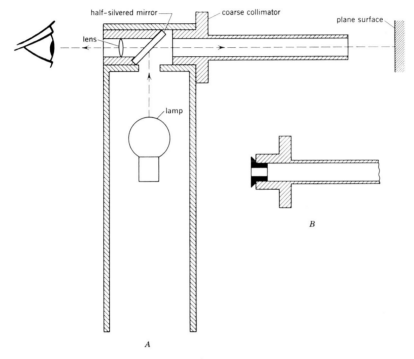

Fig. 2.

A. Diagram of a simple autocollimator for use in aligning a crystal plane perpendicular to the x-ray beam.

B. Insert (black) for use in reducing the aperture of the coarse collimator.

For use, this auxiliary device is slipped over the protruding front of the coarse collimator. A glass plate in the device then reflects the light from an electric bulb through the inside of the collimator. If a plane surface happens to lie perpendicular to the axis of the collimator, it reflects the light back to the eye and the surface appears bright. The aperture of the front opening of the coarse collimator as seen from the crystal is about 4°, so that a plane surface on the crystal, out of orientation by not more than 2°, will be noticed by its reflection when the dial is rotated. If such a reflection is found, it can be adjusted so that its normal lies very approximately in the axis of the collimator by turning the dial and angular-adjustment screws on the goniometer head until the brilliance of the reflection becomes a maximum. The precision can be improved by repeating the adjustment after reducing the front aperture of the collimator by inserting into it the plug with the smaller hole, as shown in Fig. 2B.

Crystallographic adjustment with the autocollimator. If the crystal has at least one plane surface, either growth plane or cleavage, the crystal can be quickly oriented for precession photographs with the aid of the autocollimator provided that the normal to the plane is a rational direction, preferably a crystallographic axis. It can also be oriented by this means if it has two such plane surfaces whose normals lie in a rational plane, preferably an axial plane. Therefore the orientation of many crystals other than triclinic can be carried out with the aid of the autocollimator alone. Neither of the conditions mentioned occurs generally in the triclinic system, so that every effort should be made to orient such crystals on a goniometer.

As a general rule, unless there is a compelling reason to proceed otherwise, the crystal should be mounted so that the plane surface (or one of several plane surfaces) is set parallel to one of the goniometer arcs. Then that face will be adjusted by the use of the other arc. Any further adjustment of the crystal, for example, by the use of a reflection from another face, should then be made by using the first arc only, because the face first adjusted is parallel to that arc and will remain parallel to itself when that arc is rotated.

The methods of adjustment can be illustrated by the typical examples shown in Fig. 3:

Orthorhombic crystal, one pinacoidal surface, Figure 3A. The required condition is satisfied if it is known that the crystal is orthorhombic and has a cleavage parallel to a pinacoid, say (100), as shown in Fig. 3A. The crystal should be mounted so that this surface is as nearly as possible parallel to the dial axis and also one of the two goniometer-head arcs. If the angle between the plane and the dial axis is less than about 2°, then the reflection from the surface will be picked up by looking through the autocollimator while the dial is slowly rotated, after which the face can be adjusted.

If a precession photograph is taken after adjustment, it will usually be found that both axes of the reciprocal cell make oblique angles with the dial axis, which is marked out by two dots on the photograph. If photographs of reciprocal-lattice planes parallel to this first photograph are all that is required, this feature may be ignored. But usually precession photographs are also required for stacks of planes parallel to a second plane of the reciprocal lattice. To bring the second set into orientation

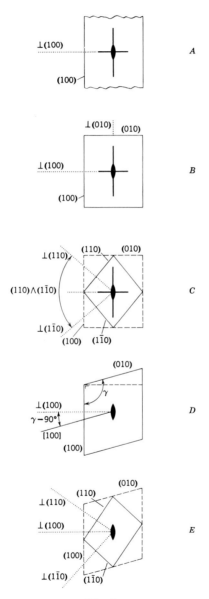

Fig. 3.
Adjustment of crystals in certain typical cases discussed in the text.   Views along the
dial axis of some crystal surfaces and the relations of these surfaces to crystal directions.

by a simple rotation of the dial, it is necessary that one axis of the reciprocal cell first be made parallel to the dial axes as suggested in Fig. 4. For this purpose the angle between the translation and the dial axis should be measured on the first precession photograph, and the amount of this misorientation corrected by the use of the arc parallel to the reflecting plane. A second photograph will probably show that this adjustment has disturbed the original orientation somewhat, so any required correction should be made before making any further photographs.

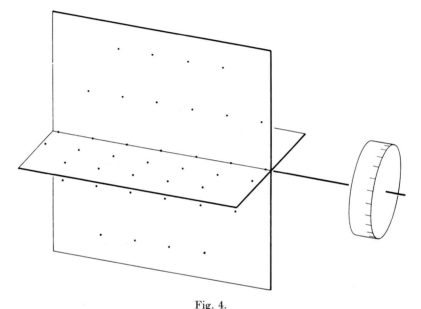

Fig. 4.

Appropriate relation of spots on two zero-level photographs with respect to the dial axis.

Orthorhombic crystal, two pinacoidal surfaces, Figure 3B. If an orthorhombic crystal displays two pinacoidal surfaces, the procedure is much simplified. Suppose that the surfaces are (100) and (010), as shown in the illustration. In mounting the crystal these two surfaces should be set as nearly as possible parallel to the axis of the mounting pin; then the latter should be rotated in the goniometer head until each surface is as closely as possible parallel to an arc. On the precession instrument, two reflections should be picked up 90° apart. Each is then adjusted in turn to maximum brilliance by using the arc normal to it. Finally, the dial should be clamped when either face gives a maximum reflection. The crystal is now perfectly set to give precession photographs parallel to one set of axial reciprocal-lattice planes. By rotating the dial 90° it should also be perfectly adjusted for photographs parallel to the second set of planes.

Orthorhombic crystal, two prismatic surfaces, Figure 3C. If an orthorhombic crystal displays two planes which are not 90° apart, the adjustment procedure is a little more difficult. The angles between various growth planes are usually available in reference works if the crystal has been studied goniometrically. The simplest situation occurs when the two surfaces are planes of the same prism; it is illustrated in Fig. 3C. As in the last example, the two surfaces should again be set as nearly as possible parallel to the axis of the mounting pin and also parallel to the dial axis; the pin should be rotated in the goniometer head until one surface (or else the inferred symmetry plane) is parallel to an arc. On the precession instrument the reflections from these surfaces are adjusted to maximum brilliance and the dial readings of these locations recorded. If the two faces do not belong to the same form, the indices of the surfaces which should come up for consideration may be found by reference to interfacial-angle tables, if available; from this information the location of the pinacoids may be deduced. In the symmetrical case shown in Fig. 3C, the surfaces are related by the symmetry planes of the orthorhombic lattice; in this case the average value of the dial readings locates the hypothetical pinacoid plane (100). The dial should be set and clamped in this position. The dial reading of the other pinacoid, (010), is, of course, $\pm 90°$ from this reading. These two positions give the information necessary for setting the dial for the required precession photographs parallel to two axial planes of the reciprocal lattice.

Monoclinic crystal, two pinacoidal surfaces parallel to unique axis, Figure 3D. The orientation of monoclinic crystals is a little more complicated than that of orthorhombic crystals. A monoclinic crystal can be easily oriented if it has two surfaces developed parallel to the unique axis. Using the first setting of the monoclinic system to bring out the contrast to the case already discussed, this axis is c and the two axial planes are (100) and (010). The crystal should be mounted so that the two surfaces are as nearly as possible parallel to the pin, and when the pin is set into the goniometer head it should be rotated until one surface is parallel to an arc. The two surfaces must be adjusted on the precession instrument as before, and their dial readings after adjustment recorded.

In contrast to the orthorhombic case, the normal to neither plane is rational. Let the dial readings of the two planes be $D_{(100)}$ and $D_{(010)}$. Figure 3D shows that the rational direction [100] has a dial reading $\gamma - 90°$ beyond that of the normal to (100). That is, the setting for [100] is $D_{(100)} + \gamma - 90°$. Similarly, the setting for [010] is $D_{(010)} - (\gamma - 90°)$. An alternative procedure is based upon the relations

(010) is parallel to a and c, so that $[100]\|(010)$,
(100) is parallel to b and c, so that $[010]\|(100)$.

If $D_{[100]}$ signifies the dial setting which brings [100] into the collimator axis, these relations lead to

$$D_{[100]} = D_{(010)} + 90°,$$
$$D_{[010]} = D_{(100)} - 90°.$$

Monoclinic crystal, two surfaces parallel to unique axis, Figure 3E. If the two surfaces of the monoclinic crystal are non-axial, the mounting of the crystal and the adjustment of the reflections of the two surfaces are still the same as in the last case. If the lattice of the crystal is unknown, the surfaces should be tentatively regarded as axial so that appropriate precession photographs can be taken by the last procedure in order to establish the lattice. Either this internal information, or data derived from reference works, may be used to establish the angles between the normals to the developed surfaces and the normals to (100) and (010). From this, $D_{(100)}$ and $D_{(010)}$ can be deduced, and these values can be used as in the last example to obtain axial photographs.

Correction of orientation errors. A precession photograph made with a crystal which is misoriented shows characteristic features. An error in the orientation of the crystal can be described as a rotation of the crystal about some axis. The axis also lies in the zero level of the reciprocal lattice, so the plane of this level is tipped about this axis. Only along the axis does the plane conform to the generalized de Jong-Bouman principle, so that along this axis only is the reciprocal lattice properly photographed. Off the axis the spots are, in general, doubled. Even if the misorientation is slight, such photographs are undesirable, and in any event should not be used for measurements expected to lead to accurate cell dimensions. If the orientation error is large the entire Laue cone cannot enter the annulus of the layer-line screen, so part of the record of the level will be missing. On the other hand, part of the Laue cone of some other level may enter the layer-line annulus, and so record part of that level. Photographs with severe orientation errors such as this are not only valueless but may be actually misleading.

To avoid such photographs a routine check of the orientation of the crystal using a special precession photograph should always be made, and any orientation error should be corrected before the regular precession photographs are made. Ordinarily this orientation check can be made with a short exposure (5 to 30 minutes usually being sufficient) because the required photograph is taken with a small precession angle, specifically $\bar{\mu} = 10°$. It is taken with a special layer-line screen that has an open circular hole (instead of the usual annulus) whose formal radius is 10 mm. Since the film area covered by the exposure is about 42 mm ($\approx 1\frac{5}{8}$ in.) in diameter, it is convenient to use for these orientation photographs the 2 x 5-in. film scraps left by trimming the commercial 5 x 7-in. stock to the 5 x 5-in. square required for regular precession photographs.

The making and interpretation of orientation photographs is discussed in Chapter 8. If the crystal has been oriented on a goniometer, the first orientation photograph may be expected to indicate, at most, a small error in the dial setting which can be determined from the orientation photograph and easily corrected. On the other hand, if the autocollimator has been used for orientation, there may be small errors, not only in the dial setting, but also in both of the goniometer-arc settings. These can also be determined and corrected as explained in Chapter 8. Finally, if the crystal has been oriented only roughly by eye there may be considerable errors in all three settings; in this case, after a first correction it is advisable to check the orientation again with a second photograph, and continue this iteration until the orientation is perfect.

Orientation errors can also be determined with the aid of cone-axis photographs. The theory of determining errors by this means is discussed in Chapter 9.

Cone-axis photographs

In order to take precession photographs of upper levels it is necessary to set the layer-line screen at the proper distance s and to set the film forward by the proper distance $M\zeta$. Both of these settings require a knowledge of ζ for each level to be photographed. These values are readily computed from measurements on a cone-axis photograph made for the same crystal orientation as the reciprocal-lattice levels to be photographed.

The direct computation of ζ is provided by (21) of Chapter 3:

$$\zeta_n = \cos \bar{\mu} - \cos \tan^{-1} \frac{r_n}{s}. \tag{1}$$

The cone-axis cassette slips into the layer-line screen holder at setting s. From (1) it can be seen that if s is taken as an integral number of centimeters, the computation of ζ can be made with computing facilities no more complicated than a table of trigonometric functions. Convenient values for s are 3 or 4 cm.

In Chapter 9 it will be shown that if $\bar{\mu}$ is set at $10°$, negative-order Laue cones will not be recorded, so that the innermost ring on the cone-axis photograph is the zero-order ring, which is a convenient feature. Thus the settings $s = 3.00$ cm. and $\bar{\mu} = 10°$ are recommended for cone-axis settings.

Refinements in making and interpreting cone-axis photographs are discussed in Chapter 9. In anticipation it should be noted, however, that a small constant should be added to the layer-line screen reading s when making cone-axis photographs.

Planning the precession photographs required

Purpose of photographs. Precession photographs are used in crystal-structure analysis for two chief purposes: first, to permit symmetry observations leading to determination of the space group, and measurements leading to a knowledge of the dimensions of the unit cell, and second, to provide data for the measurement of the intensities of the $|F_{hkl}|$'s. In planning the collection of precession photographs to be made, the particular requirements of these two objectives should be considered in advance. In this section the photographs desirable for space-group and unit-cell determination are considered. Discussion of the measurement of intensities is reserved for Chapter 10.

Requirements for geometrical determination. The determination of the space group and unit cell requires photographs which are individually good, especially in respect to the records of the geometries of the levels. The photographs of the set need not, however, be comparable with one another in intensity, although it is desirable that they be approximately so. The relative unimportance of exactly comparable intensities permits making photographs without careful attention to the exposure times or development procedures for different levels of the same dial setting, and also of different dial settings. It also leads to the possibility of using different $\bar{\mu}$ settings for different levels. Figure 6, Chapter 3, shows that the radius $\xi_{\max}$ of the recorded reciprocal lattice increases away from the zero level. With $\bar{\mu} = 30°$, the radius of the zero level is unity. On the photograph this is[†] $M \times 1 = 6$ cm ≈ 2.36 in. The diameter of this area, approximately $4\frac{3}{4}$ in., provides a circle which can just be inscribed in the useful area of the 5 x 5-in. film. On the other hand, the upper levels protrude beyond this area with the same setting of $\bar{\mu}$ so that it is permissible to set $\bar{\mu}$ to some smaller value (as suggested by Fig. 9, Chapter 3) for the upper levels. If this is done, the relative intensities of the upper levels are enhanced, for the same exposure time, but this variation is of no importance in space-group determination.

Space group. The determination of the space group is treated in Chapter 6. Briefly, the entire qualitative information which can be obtained from diffraction experiments is represented by the diffraction symbol. This consists of three parts. The first part is the Friedel symmetry, the second is the lattice type, and the last part is a record of the detection or non-detection of screw axes or glide planes permitted by the Friedel symmetry. (The Friedel symmetries are described in the next chapter, where they are listed in Table 1.) In a general way, each location of a symmetry axis of the Friedel symmetry should be explored

---

[†] The constant M was discussed in foregoing chapters. In instruments constructed at present it is ordinarily 6 cm.

by a set of precession photographs in order to fill in this portion of the diffraction symbol. A comparison of the zero level with one upper level also permits filling the last part of the symbol. The middle part of the symbol requires the comparison of a pair of adjacent levels.

Figure 5 shows representative settings of the crystal, as viewed along the precessing axis, which are desirable for studying the symmetry properties of crystals of various systems. The groups of settings are designed

Table 1A
Data for the zero-level record

$\bar{\mu}$	$\sin \bar{\mu}$	ξ_{max}	r_{max} (for $M = 6$ cm)
5°	.08716	.174	1.044 cm
10°	.17365	.347	2.084
15°	.25882	.518	3.106
20°	.34202	.684	4.104
25°	.42262	.845	5.071
30°	.50000	1.000	6.000

Table 1B
Values of the zero-level screen setting *s* for various screen radii *r* and precession angles $\bar{\mu}$

r	$\bar{\mu}$					
	5°	10°	15°	20°	25°	30°
5 mm	57.2 mm	28.4 mm	18.7 mm	13.7 mm	10.7 mm	8.7 mm
10		56.7	37.3	27.5	21.4	17.3
15			56.0	41.2	32.2	26.0
20				55.0	42.9	34.6
25					53.6	43.3
30						52.0

for the minimum number of mountings leading to space-group determination and unit-cell measurement. In the triclinic and orthorhombic cases there is no unique axis, so alternative arrangements are possible by interchanges of symbols.

Unit cell. While measurements leading to the determination of the dimensions of the unit cell can, in principle, be made on appropriate photographs of any level, it is desirable to use only zero-level photographs for this purpose because the settings for these photographs involve one less variable, namely the value of ζ for the level. Furthermore, in

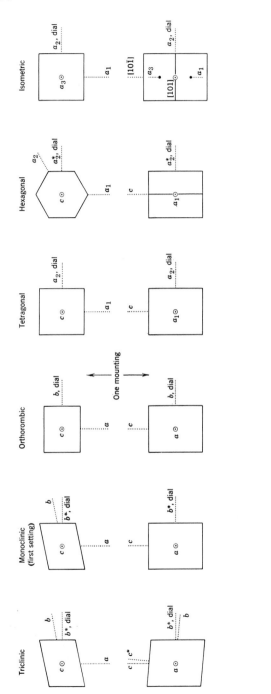

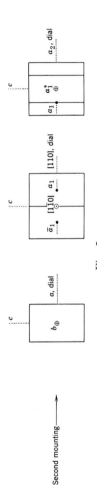

Fig. 5.

Representative settings of crystals viewed along the precessing axis, which are desirable for studying the symmetry properties of crystals of various systems. ⊙ represents a line going toward observer; ⊕ represents a line going away from observer.

order to give large distances which can be measured with good precision, it is advisable to use the maximum precession angle, namely $\bar{\mu} = 30°$, for photographs intended for the determination of cell geometry. For good results, special care should be exercised, first, that the crystal is sufficiently perfect to give single spots, and second, that the orientation of the crystal is excellent.

If the crystal is isometric, tetragonal, or hexagonal, one zero-level a-axis photograph suffices for measurements leading to the determination of the unit cell. If the crystal is orthorhombic or monoclinic, two zero-level photographs are required. Both can be made with the same mounting of the crystal. The dial axis of the orthorhombic crystal should be any of the three crystallographic axes, and a zero-level photograph should be made with each of the other two crystallographic axes adjusted to the precessing axis. The same strategy should be used with the monoclinic crystal, except that the dial axis should be specifically one of the two non-unique reciprocal-cell axes. For triclinic crystals, three zero-level photographs are required to establish directly the complete cell geometry, for which each of the three crystallographic axes, in turn, must be adjusted to the precessing axis. This can be done with two mountings of the crystal, two of the three reciprocal translations being set, in turn, parallel to the dial axis. The geometry can also be established less directly with one setting of the crystal as outlined in the next chapter.

Making precession photographs

Zero-level photographs. For zero-level photographs, ζ is zero, so the cassette is always in the zero position. The selection of $\bar{\mu}$ depends on how large an area of the zero level one wishes to explore, Table 1A. The exposure required increases with $\bar{\mu}$, so that by reducing $\bar{\mu}$ sufficiently very short exposures become possible. It is for this reason that, in taking zero-level orientation photographs, $\bar{\mu}$ is set at the comparatively small value of 10°. But for most other purposes it is important to record as large an area of the reciprocal lattice as possible, and this calls for using the maximum value of $\bar{\mu}$, namely 30°.

It is convenient to have separately available the zero-level settings for layer-line screens of various radii. These can be readily computed from (19) of Chapter 3 by requiring ζ to be zero. Table 1B lists some solutions for various radii and precession angles. The values enclosed in boxes are perhaps the most practical and are recommended.

Upper-level photographs. Before making an upper-level photograph, four instrumental settings or selections must be made: $M\zeta$, r_s, s, and $\bar{\mu}$. The distance $M\zeta$ by which the film must be set forward is dependent only on the value of ζ for that level; the other three and ζ are inter-

Table 2
Value of the screen setting, $s = r \cot \cos^{-1}(\cos \bar{u} - \zeta)$, as a function of ζ, for some discrete values of $\bar{u}$ and r

$\bar{u} = 15°$

r	ζ												
	−0.034	0	0.05	0.1	0.2	0.3	0.4	0.5	0.6	0.7	0.8	0.9	0.966
5 mm	∞	18.7	11.6	8.7	6.0	4.5	3.4	2.6	2.0	1.4	0.8	0.3	0
10	∞	37.3	23.2	17.3	11.9	8.9	6.9	5.3	3.9	2.8	1.7	0.7	0
15	∞	56.0	34.8	26.0	17.9	13.4	10.3	7.9	5.9	4.1	2.5	1.0	0
20	∞	74.6	46.4	34.6	23.8	17.9	13.7	10.5	7.8	5.5	3.4	1.3	0
25	∞	93.3	58.0	43.3	29.8	22.3	17.2	13.2	9.8	6.9	4.2	1.7	0
30	∞	112.0	69.6	51.9	35.7	26.8	20.6	15.8	11.8	8.3	5.0	2.0	0
35	∞	130.6	81.1	60.6	41.7	31.2	24.0	18.4	13.8	9.7	5.9	2.3	0
40	∞	149.3	92.7	69.2	47.6	35.7	27.5	21.1	15.7	11.0	6.7	2.6	0
45	∞	167.9	104.3	77.9	53.6	40.2	30.9	23.7	17.7	12.4	7.6	3.0	0

$\bar{u} = 20°$

r	ζ													
	−0.060	−0.05	0	0.05	0.1	0.2	0.3	0.4	0.5	0.6	0.7	0.8	0.9	0.940
5 mm	∞	34.6	13.7	9.8	7.7	5.5	4.2	3.2	2.5	1.8	1.2	0.7	0.2	0
10	∞	69.1	27.5	19.5	15.5	11.0	8.3	6.4	4.9	3.6	2.5	1.4	0.4	0
15	∞	103.7	41.2	29.3	23.2	16.5	12.5	9.6	7.4	5.4	3.7	2.1	0.6	0
20	∞	138.2	55.0	39.0	31.0	22.0	16.7	12.8	9.8	7.2	4.9	2.8	0.8	0
25	∞	172.8	68.7	48.8	38.7	27.5	20.8	16.1	12.3	9.1	6.2	3.5	1.0	0
30	∞	207.3	82.4	58.5	46.4	33.0	25.0	19.3	14.7	10.9	7.4	4.2	1.2	0
35	∞	241.9	96.2	68.3	54.2	38.5	29.2	22.5	17.2	12.7	8.6	4.9	1.4	0
40	∞	276.4	109.9	78.0	61.9	44.0	33.3	25.7	19.6	14.5	9.9	5.6	1.6	0
45	∞	311.0	123.6	87.8	69.7	49.5	37.5	28.9	22.1	16.3	11.1	6.3	1.8	0

Table 2 (Continued)

$\bar{\mu} = 25°$

ζ

r	0.906	0.8	0.7	0.6	0.5	0.4	0.3	0.2	0.1	0.05	0	−0.05	−0.094
5 mm	0	0.5	1.1	1.6	2.2	2.9	3.8	5.0	6.8	8.3	10.7	16.4	∞
10	0	1.1	2.1	3.2	4.4	5.9	7.6	10.0	13.6	16.6	21.4	32.7	∞
15	0	1.6	3.2	4.8	6.7	8.8	11.4	15.0	20.4	24.8	32.2	49.1	∞
20	0	2.1	4.2	6.4	8.9	11.7	15.2	19.9	27.2	33.1	42.9	65.4	∞
25	0	2.7	5.3	8.0	11.1	14.7	19.1	24.9	34.0	41.4	53.6	81.8	∞
30	0	3.2	6.3	9.6	13.3	17.6	22.9	29.9	40.8	49.7	64.3	98.1	∞
35	0	3.7	7.4	11.2	15.5	20.5	26.7	34.9	47.6	58.0	75.1	114.5	∞
40	0	4.3	8.4	12.8	17.9	23.5	30.5	39.9	54.4	66.2	85.8	130.8	∞
45	0	4.8	9.5	14.4	20.0	26.4	34.3	44.9	61.2	74.5	96.5	147.2	∞

$\bar{\mu} = 30°$

ζ

r	0.866	0.8	0.7	0.6	0.5	0.4	0.3	0.2	0.1	0.05	0	−0.05	−0.10	−0.134
5 mm	0	0.3	0.8	1.4	2.0	2.6	3.4	4.5	6.0	7.1	8.7	11.4	18.7	∞
10	0	0.7	1.7	2.8	3.9	5.3	6.7	8.9	11.9	14.1	17.3	22.8	37.4	∞
15	0	1.0	2.5	4.1	5.9	7.9	10.3	13.4	17.9	21.2	26.0	34.3	56.1	∞
20	0	1.3	3.4	5.5	7.9	10.5	13.7	17.9	23.8	28.2	34.6	45.7	74.7	∞
25	0	1.7	4.2	6.9	9.8	13.2	17.2	22.3	29.8	35.3	43.3	57.1	93.4	∞
30	0	2.0	5.0	8.3	11.8	15.8	20.6	26.8	35.8	42.4	52.0	68.5	112.1	∞
35	0	2.3	5.9	9.7	13.8	18.4	24.0	31.3	41.7	49.4	60.6	79.9	130.8	∞
40	0	2.6	6.7	11.0	15.7	21.1	27.4	35.7	47.7	56.5	69.3	91.3	149.5	∞
45	0	3.0	7.6	12.4	17.7	23.7	30.9	40.2	53.6	63.5	77.9	102.8	168.1	∞

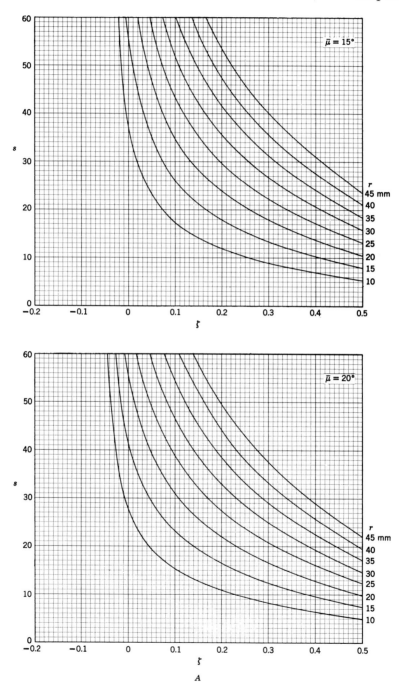

Fig. 6.
Variation of the screen setting s with ζ for various values of the radius r of the annulus of the layer-line screen.

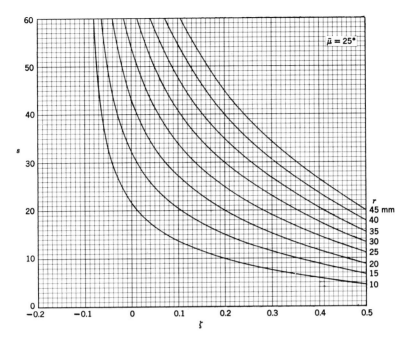

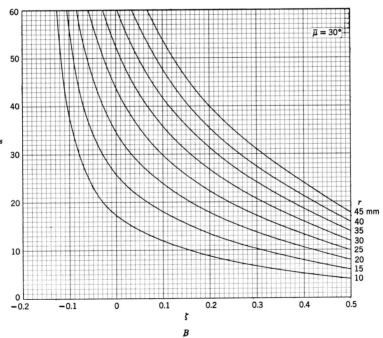

B

dependent in the manner given by (21) of Chapter 3. Solutions of r_s as a function of ζ for screen radii and precession angles commonly used are given in Table 2. The most convenient way to use these results is in graphical representations[†] of the variation of r_s with ζ. Such curves are

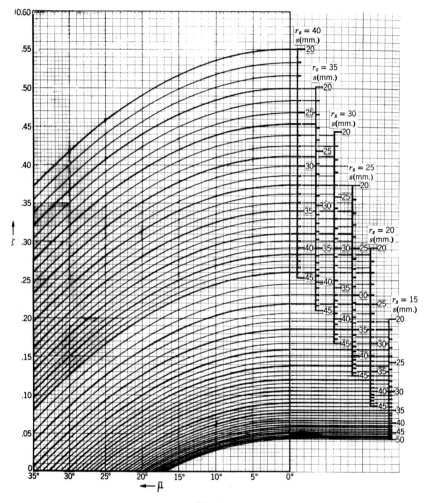

Fig. 7.

Bloss chart for selecting screen radii r_s and screen settings s for a required value of ζ.
(After Bloss.[53])

given in Figs. 6A and 6B. An alternative chart due to Bloss[53] is shown in Fig. 7. It is evident that for a particular value of ζ there are

---

[†] The solutions of (19) of Chapter 3 can also be found by the use of charts and nomograms; appropriate ones have been devised by Evans,[7,8,12] Tavora,[13] and King[15].

usually several solutions for s depending on the choice of r_s and $\bar{\mu}$. Some of the solutions suggested by Fig. 6 are impractical because they require settings in which the screen would foul the goniometer head or cassette. But within a certain limiting value of ζ (in the neighborhood of $\zeta = 0.4$) there is always at least one practical solution for s.

Before starting a series of precession photographs, it is well to tabulate the instrumental settings in some way. A convenient form is shown in Table 3. If the values of ζ_n for this table are examined in Fig. 6, it will be seen that with $\bar{\mu} = 30°$, levels 0, 1 and 2 can be isolated by various screens, but for the level 3 this value of $\bar{\mu}$ requires a screen setting so

Table 3
Example of computation of settings for upper-level precession photographs
(Andalusite, c-axis settings, $c = 5.60$ Å)

$$d^*_{001} = \frac{\lambda}{t_{001}} = \frac{0.7107}{5.60} = 0.127$$

Level n	$\zeta_n = nd^*_{001}$	$M\zeta_n$	s	r	$\bar{\mu}$
0	0	0	2.60 cm	15 mm	30°
1	0.127	0.762	2.75	20	30°
2	0.254	1.524	3.10	40	30°
3	0.381	2.286	$\begin{cases} 2.30 \\ 2.80 \end{cases}$	$\begin{matrix} 40 \\ 40 \end{matrix}$	$\left.\begin{matrix} 30° \\ 20° \end{matrix}\right\}$

small that the screen might foul the goniometer head. With $\bar{\mu} = 20°$, a large enough screen setting is available so that there is no danger of this.

Widths of slits in layer-line screens. The annular opening of the layer-line screen allows not only the reflections of the desired level but also undesired background to reach the photographic film. The narrower the slit, the less is the unwanted background on the film. If the slit is too narrow, however, it may cut off part of each individual reflection which it is designed to let through. It can be shown that a slit width of 2 mm will not cut off part of a reflection from an appropriate small crystal which is correctly oriented to within $\pm 5'$. On the other hand, the wider the slit, the greater the unwanted background and the more likely it is that diffraction from neighboring levels may reach the film, especially if the spacing between levels is small. The half width of a slit which will just permit a reflection from the next level to reach the film may be computed as follows:

From (18), Chapter 3:

r for the level being recorded:	$r_n = s \tan \cos^{-1} (\cos \bar{\mu} - n\zeta_1)$	
r for the next higher level:	$r_{n+1} = s \tan \cos^{-1} (\cos \bar{\mu} - [n+1]\zeta_1)$	(1)
r for the next lower level:	$r_{n-1} = s \tan \cos^{-1} (\cos \bar{\mu} - [n-1]\zeta_1)$	(2)

Slit half width for just recording the next higher level:

$$\Delta r_+ = s \tan \cos^{-1} (\cos \bar{\mu} - [n + 1]\zeta_1) - r_n, \quad (3)$$

Slit half width for just recording the next lower level:

$$\Delta r_- = -s \tan \cos^{-1} (\cos \bar{\mu} - [n - 1]\zeta_1) + r_n. \quad (4)$$

Values of ζ_1 (and the corresponding translations) for which various slit widths will just fail to properly screen out levels other than the one selected are listed in Table 4.

Table 4
Limiting values of the translation period for
non-recording of additional levels
$\bar{\mu} = 30°, n = 0$

Screen radius r	Slit width $2\Delta r$	ζ_1	t (for Mo$K\alpha$)
15 mm	2 mm	.01445	49.2 Å
	3	.02145	33.1
	5	.03523	20.2
20 mm	2	.01056	67.3
	3	.01582	44.9
	5	.02629	27.0

6

The geometrical interpretation of precession photographs

In the last chapter it was pointed out that precession photographs permit easy study of the geometry of the crystal and that they are also well adapted to the measurement of the intensities of the reflections. In this chapter the geometrical interpretation of precession photographs is considered, and in Chapter 10 the measurement of intensities is discussed.

If the suggestions of the last chapter have been followed, a set of photographs is available from which the space group and unit cell are readily determinable. In order to interpret them intelligently it is important that the investigator be familiar with the theory of reciprocal cells.[†]

Space group

Viewpoint. The interpretation of the space group of a crystal is independent of the dimensional aspects of the cell and can be carried out before the cell is measured. Precession photographs are especially suitable to space-group determination because they are scaled photographs of the reciprocal lattice whose geometrical features carry the space-group information.

The investigator has two choices in studying the space group by means of precession photographs. He can ignore the advantages of having a set of undistorted photographs of the reciprocal lattice and, instead, deal with the photographs as if they were mere lists of reflections, present or absent. If he does this he is treating space-group determination as it had to be treated in the bygone days of oscillating-crystal photographs. He is advised not to do this, but rather to take full advantage of his

---

[†] An appropriate background is given in M. J. Buerger. *X-ray crystallography.* (John Wiley and Sons, New York, 1942) Chapters 18 and 22.

Table 1
The Friedel symmetries and their distribution
among the point groups

Crystal		Symmetry of diffraction effect
System	Point group	
Triclinic	1	$\bar{1}$
	$\bar{1}$	
Monoclinic	2	$\dfrac{2}{m}$
	m	
	$\dfrac{2}{m}$	
Orthorhombic	2 2 2	$\dfrac{2}{m}\dfrac{2}{m}\dfrac{2}{m}$
	$m\,m\,2$	
	$\dfrac{2}{m}\dfrac{2}{m}\dfrac{2}{m}$	
Tetragonal	4	$\dfrac{4}{m}$
	$\bar{4}$	
	$\dfrac{4}{m}$	
	4 2 2	$\dfrac{4}{m}\dfrac{2}{m}\dfrac{2}{m}$
	$4\,m\,m$	
	$\bar{4}\,2\,m$	
	$\dfrac{4}{m}\dfrac{2}{m}\dfrac{2}{m}$	

superior material, for the set of precession photographs has a characteristic geometry whose interpretation does not require the assignment of indices to reflections. To encourage this point of view, the following outline of suggested interpretation is presented.

Diffraction symbols. All the qualitative information which can be derived from a set of x-ray diffraction photographs can be concentrated into a short sequence of symbols which together constitute the *diffraction symbol*. A diffraction symbol is determined by the Friedel symmetry, the lattice type, and the record of the direction of glide planes and screw axes. There are 122 such symbols, and they are of great utility in the determination of the space group of a crystal. The determination of the diffraction symbol is especially easy from precession photographs.

Table 1 (*Continued*)

Crystal		Symmetry of diffraction effect
System	Point group	
Hexagonal	3 $\bar{3}$	$\bar{3}$
	$3\ 2$ $3\ m$ $\bar{3}\ \dfrac{2}{m}$	$\bar{3}\ \dfrac{2}{m}$
	6 $\bar{6}$ $\dfrac{6}{m}$	$\dfrac{6}{m}$
	$6\ 2\ 2$ $6\ m\ m$ $\bar{6}\ m\ 2$ $\dfrac{6}{m}\ \dfrac{2}{m}\ \dfrac{2}{m}$	$\dfrac{6}{m}\ \dfrac{2}{m}\ \dfrac{2}{m}$
Isometric	$2\ 3$ $\dfrac{2}{m}\ \bar{3}$	$\dfrac{2}{m}\ \bar{3}$
	$4\ 3\ 2$ $\bar{4}\ 3\ m$ $\dfrac{4}{m}\ \bar{3}\ \dfrac{2}{m}$	$\dfrac{4}{m}\ \bar{3}\ \dfrac{2}{m}$

Friedel symmetry. Friedel's law[†] requires that the record of diffraction effects be centrosymmetrical, and therefore limits the observable diffraction from crystals to the symmetries of the 11 centrosymmetrical crystal classes. The symmetry of the x-ray diffraction effects of a crystal is known as its *Friedel symmetry.*[§] The 11 Friedel symmetries and their distribution among the crystal classes are shown in Table 1.

[†] G. Friedel. *Sur les symétries cristallines que peut révéler la diffraction des rayons Röntgen.* Comp. rend. **157** (1913) 1533–1536.

[§] This is also commonly called "Laue symmetry," but this designation gives the erroneous impression that the limitation was first pointed out by Laue. Actually the adjective "Laue" refers to the fact that, in the early days of x-ray diffraction, sym-

Table 2
The 10 point groups in a plane

1	*m*
2	2*mm*
3	3*m*
4	4*mm*
6	6*mm*

The first entry in the diffraction symbol is the Friedel symmetry. This can be determined by inspection from an appropriate set of precession photographs. Each rational direction of the crystal has one of the possible symmetries about a line in three-dimensional space. Each plane of the reciprocal lattice has a symmetry which is, in effect, the plane cross-section of this symmetry, and therefore one of the 10 point groups in a plane. These are listed in Table 2. One of these symmetries can be observed in each precession photograph as well as in the corresponding ring of the cone-axis photograph. The zero-level photograph is unique in two respects:

(*a*) It is the location of the inversion center of Friedel's law. This has the same symmetry properties as a 2-fold axis perpendicular to the plane of the level.

(*b*) It contains any other rotation axis parallel to the plane. An even-fold axis gives rise to additional symmetry in that level which has the appearance of a line of symmetry.

Thus, the zero level may have more symmetry than the upper levels of the reciprocal lattice.

Lattice type. The second entry of the diffraction symbol is the lattice type, designated P, A, B, C, I, F, or R. Each lattice type has a specific reciprocal. In particular, each lattice type, except I and F, is its own reciprocal. The reciprocal of I is F, and that of F is I. There is nothing very sophisticated about the identification of the lattice type; two adjacent photographs merely show enough of the space lattice in three dimensions to make obvious the lattice type of the reciprocal lattice.

To simplify the discussion it is convenient to assume a particular orientation of the crystal with respect to the precessing axis. Specifically, the precessing axis and film normal is taken as c; on the photographs b^* is horizontal so that a^* is vertical when $\gamma^* = 90°$. To determine the lattice

---

metry information could only be obtained from Laue photographs. If this view is followed, we are here dealing with "precession symmetry," a misnomer that misses the real point that the limitation is inherent in the diffraction phenomenon itself and therefore not a characteristic of the method.

type it is merely necessary to inspect the patterns of points on a pair of adjacent reciprocal-lattice levels. (If possible, it is well to select a pair of levels which does not include the zero level, because extinctions may cause some points of the zero level to be missing, and this may confuse the beginner.) If the photographs of two adjacent levels are superimposed in parallel position with the origins coincident, then if the plane lattices of the two levels coincide, and if the plane lattice is p, the space lattice is P, while if the plane lattice is c the space lattice is C. On the other hand if adjacent levels must be displaced relative to one another in order to bring the plane lattices into coincidence, then the space lattice is A, B, I, F, or R, depending on the plane-lattice type and the direction of the displacement required. The possible situations are outlined in Table 3 and illustrated in Figs. $1A$ and $1B$.

Glide planes and screw axes. The complete space-group symbol ends in a series of one to three fractions whose denominators are the symbols of symmetry planes isogonal with the corresponding mirrors of the point group, and whose numerators are the symbols of the symmetry axes isogonal with the rotation axes of the point group. The only point-group information x-ray photographs can give is the set of symmetry elements of the Friedel symmetry. To each entry in the Friedel symmetry symbol, a space-group symmetry element is possible; but it can be detected only if it has a translation component, when it leaves a record of itself in the form of a systematic extinction of certain reflections. In the reciprocal lattice the geometrical equivalent is the omission of a certain set of reciprocal-lattice points. A symmetry element which lacks a translation component leaves no specific record of itself, so that an observation that no special set of points is missing may mean either that the *translation-free* equivalent of the corresponding Friedel symmetry element is there, or that *no* symmetry element is there. The diffraction symbol takes this ambiguity into account. It ends with a list of fractions (or, for the abbreviated symbol, with a list of denominators only) in which every observable symmetry element is represented by its symbol, but every unobservable symmetry element is represented by a short dash.

The easiest way to find the required information about the nature of the symmetry plane or axis is to compare the zero level with one upper level of the reciprocal lattice parallel to the symmetry element in question. The possible patterns of missing points and their interpretations are shown in Table 4 (with Fig. 2) for symmetry planes, and in Table 5 (with Fig. 3) for symmetry axes. In these tables note the first horizontal row. This merely calls attention to the fact that if there is no pattern of missing points on the zero level no definite information is implied, so that the corresponding place in the diffraction symbol is to be filled in with a short dash.

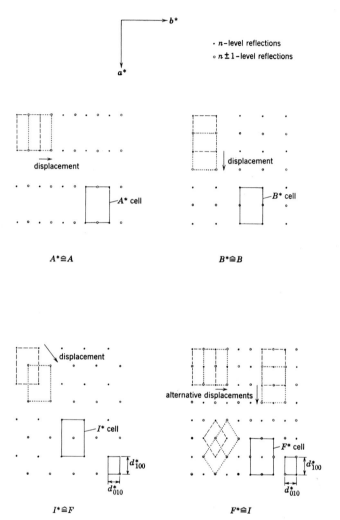

Fig. 1*A*.
Interpretation of the lattice type from the relative displacement of adjacent levels of
the reciprocal lattice.

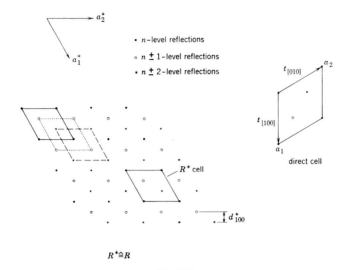

Fig. 1B.
Relative displacements of neighboring levels of the rhombhedral reciprocal lattice, and corresponding directions in the direct cell.

Table 3
Determination of the reciprocal-lattice type from precession photographs

Orientation: $\begin{cases} c \text{ normal to photographs} \\ b^* \text{ horizontal } (a_2^* \text{ for hexagonal crystals}) \\ a^* \text{ vertical when } \gamma^* \text{ is } 90° \end{cases}$

Displacement required to cause coincidence of plane-lattice levels	Plane-lattice type on level	
	p^*	c^*
0	$P^* \stackrel{\wedge}{=} P$	$C^* \stackrel{\wedge}{=} C$
$\frac{1}{2}t_{100}^*$	$B^* \stackrel{\wedge}{=} B \Big\}$ (Fig. 1A)	$F^* \stackrel{\wedge}{=} I \Big\}$ (Fig. 1A)
$\frac{1}{2}t_{010}^*$	$A^* \stackrel{\wedge}{=} A \Big\}$	$F^* \stackrel{\wedge}{=} I \Big\}$
$\frac{1}{2}t_{100}^* + \frac{1}{2}t_{010}^*$	$I^* \stackrel{\wedge}{=} F$ (Fig. 1A)	—
$\frac{1}{3}t_{100}^* + \frac{1}{3}t_{010}^*$	$R^* \stackrel{\wedge}{=} R^†$ (Fig. 1B)	—

† For an isometric crystal the same distribution occurs for P, I, and F if the precessing axis is [111], but it then also occurs for [$\bar{1}$11], [1$\bar{1}$1], and [11$\bar{1}$]. For a set of photographs normal to only one such axis, the distinction between R, I, and F can be determined from the relation between the translation of the plane lattice and the spacing.

Determination of the space group. There are 122 diffraction symbols. In general, each one is consistent with several space groups having the same Friedel symmetry and lattice type. When the diffraction symbol has been determined, therefore, the possible space groups which come up for consideration are limited and can be found by consulting appropriate tables.[†] Of the 122 diffraction symbols, 58 of them are consistent with only one space group (or with one enantiomorphic pair of space groups). In these fortunate cases the knowledge of the diffraction symbol implies a unique determination of the space group for purposes of x-ray crystallography or crystal-structure analysis.

Unit cell

Measurable geometrical features. Since precession photographs provide an undistorted picture of the reciprocal lattice, it is evident that the proper reciprocal cell can be selected by examination of an appropriate set of such photographs, and when selected its geometrical features can be measured. The fundamental quantities required are the edge lengths and interaxial angles of the reciprocal cell. Once the reciprocal cell has been measured the results can be readily transformed into edge lengths and interaxial angles of the direct cell by using standard relations between the two cells.

If the linear elements of the direct cell are to be expressed in Ångström units, the usual reciprocity formulae, with a proportionality constant of unity implied, require the linear elements of the reciprocal cell to be expressed in $Å^{-1}$ units. These are usually referred to as "absolute" units for the reciprocal cell. In discussing diffraction experiments, however, it is usual to express the reciprocal cell in λ units; i.e., in transforming the direct cell to the reciprocal, a constant λ is required. In addition, the precession instrument introduces a magnification factor M, so that measurements made on precession photographs involve a constant λM. For such measurements to be transformed to absolute units, they must be divided by this constant.

Measuring device for precession photographs. The measurement of both angular and linear features of precession photographs requires the use of a measuring device like that shown in Fig. 4 (p. 80). It consists of three chief parts: a metal base, a disk mounted on the base so that it can be rotated and which carries the photograph, and a slider which slides horizontally along the base and maintains a hairline etched on its glass face accurately vertical in all positions. The edge of the disk is graduated in degrees, and its angular position can be read directly to

[†] See Table 34, pages 511–516, M. J. Buerger. *X-ray crystallography.* (John Wiley and Sons, New York, 1942.)

Table 4
Types of symmetry planes with translation components, indicated
by various patterns of missing reciprocal-lattice points on the
zero level

Fig. 2, Pattern of missing points 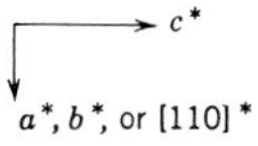	Reciprocal lattice:	P^*	A^*	B^*	C^*	I^*	F^*	R^*
	Direct lattice:	P	A	B	C	F	I	R

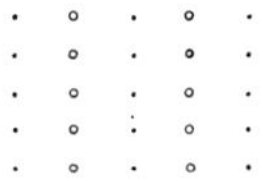

$\longrightarrow c^*$

a^*, b^*, or [110]*

	c		a	c			c
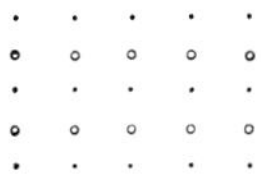	a	b		—			
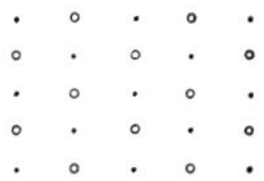	n	(d)	(d)		d		
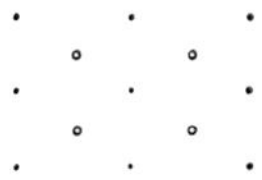	$c=b$	$c=a$		$c=a$ $c=b$			

Table 5

Types of symmetry axes with translation components, indicated by various patterns of missing reciprocal-lattice points on the zero level

(Axes for unconventional choices of cells are enclosed in parentheses)

Reciprocal lattice:	P^*	A^*	B^*	C^*	I^*	F^*	R^*
Direct lattice:	P	A	B	C	F	I	R
	2_1						
	4_2						
	6_3						
	2_1			2_1	$(4_1, 4_3)$	$4_1, 4_3$	
	4_2			(4_2)			
	6_3			(6_3)			

Fig. 3,
Pattern of missing points

$a^*, b^*,$ or $[110]^*$ → c^*

$(3_1, 3_2)$ $(6_2, 6_4)$ $(4_1, 4_3)$ $(6_1, 6_5)$ $(4_1, 4_3)$ $4_1, 4_3$

$3_1, 3_2$ $6_2, 6_4$ $4_1, 4_3$ $6_1, 6_5$

5 min. by means of a vernier on the base.   The position of the slider is provided by a commercial centimeter scale graduated to millimeters and which can be read by means of a vernier directly to 0.01 cm (or, to 0.005 cm).

To use the measuring device, it is placed against the illuminated surface of a viewing box.   The film is placed on the surface of the disk and stuck there by means of small bits of cellophane tape.   The disk can be rotated freely so that any line of reciprocal-lattice points can be set vertical.   In

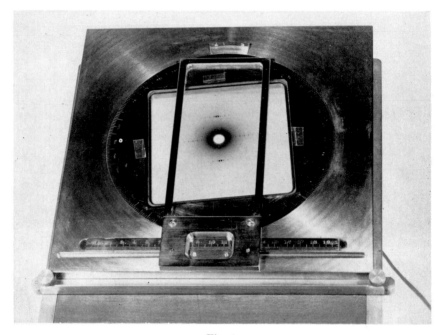

Fig. 4.
Device for measuring angles and distances on precession photographs.
(After Buerger.[3])

this position of the film the angular position of the row is read from the graduated disk and vernier, and its linear position is indicated by the reading of the slider.

Measurement of angles

Angles in the plane of the photograph.   Since a precession photograph is a scaled picture of a part of a level of the reciprocal lattice, it faithfully preserves the angular relations in that plane.   To measure an angle between reciprocal-lattice rows in this plane, the photograph should be attached to the disk or table of the measuring device and the table rotated until a row of spots is accurately aligned with the hairline of the slider as in Fig. 5. The angular position of the table is then read to the nearest 5 min. by means of the scale and vernier. This sequence of operations is repeated for another row of spots; the difference between the two readings is an accurate measure of the angle between the two rows. Ordinarily the two rows are along the axes chosen for the cell of the reciprocal lattice, in which case the measured angle is α^*, β^*, or γ^*.

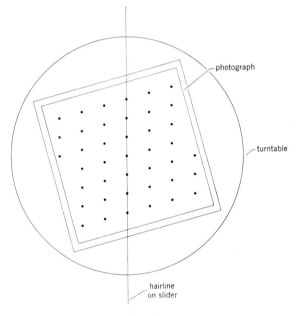

Fig. 5.

Angles between the planes of two photographs. In Chapter 5 it is recommended that an axis of the cell of the reciprocal lattice be set accurately parallel to the dial axis (for example, see Fig. 4, Chapter 5). When this is done the two axial planes of the reciprocal lattice containing this common row can be brought, one after another, parallel to the film, and thus these axial planes can be photographed. The accurate adjustment of the planes parallel to the film can be accomplished, for example, with the aid of orientation photographs, discussed in Chapter 8. Now the angles between two such axial *reciprocal*-lattice planes is a *direct*-lattice interaxial angle. Figure 6 as well as the left-hand parts of Figs. 8 and 9 show that this angle can be easily measured as the difference in dial settings when photographing the two axial planes.

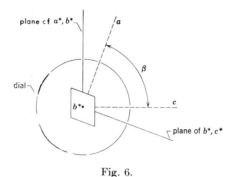

Fig. 6.

Measurement of distances

Measurement of translations in the reciprocal lattice. The most general problem of measurement of distances occurs when the plane lattice of the level has a parallelogram cell as in Fig. 7. The most general immediate result required from the measurements are the lengths of two translations of the reciprocal plane lattice. The problem can be solved in two ways. In the most direct way, the disk of Fig. 5 is first rotated until the translation is parallel to the hairline, and a reading is taken of the angular position of the disk. The disk is then rotated through exactly 90° and the hairline is set on two spots in the row separated by n translation intervals, as suggested by Fig. 7A. The difference in readings divided by n then gives the required reciprocal translation directly (scaled by λM, of course). This method gives relatively poor precision because it depends on setting the hairline on only one spot for each setting. The method described next is recommended.

Measurement of row spacings. Figure 7B illustrates an alternative and better method. Instead of measuring the translation $t_1{}^*$ directly, the spacing δ_2 of the rows corresponding to some other translation $t_2{}^*$ is measured, as well as the angle ϕ between the two translations. Then the required translation is given by

$$t_1{}^* = \delta_2{}^* \cos(90° - \phi)$$
$$= \delta_2{}^* \sin \phi. \tag{1}$$

For greater precision the multiple interval $n\delta_2{}^*$ is actually measured. The angle ϕ is determined by methods already described for measurement of angles between rows.

Determination of the cell of the direct lattice

Determination from one setting of the crystal. It is convenient to be able to determine the cell from one setting of the crystal. The discussion falls into three cases. It is assumed that the crystals are mounted as shown in the upper two rows of Fig. 5, Chapter 5. For clearness, it is assumed that b^* (or its equivalent in more symmetrical crystal systems) is set parallel to the dial axis, so that the view along the dial axis is like that shown in Fig. 6.

In all cases rough values of two direct-lattice translations can be measured from the following cone-axis photographs (see Chapter 9):

a axis: from the a-axis cone-axis photograph,
c axis: from the c-axis cone-axis photograph.

More accurate values of these and other aspects of the cell geometry can be obtained in the following way.

Orthogonal systems. For orthorhombic, tetragonal, and isometric crystal systems, $\alpha = \beta = \gamma = \alpha^* = \beta^* = \gamma^* = 90°$, so that no angles need be measured. This geometry further provides that there is a reciprocal-cell edge normal to each axial plane of the reciprocal cell. Therefore any spacing δ between rows in the axial planes is also the spacing d^* of the plane of the reciprocal lattice which contains the row and the orthogonal cell edge. These spacings are directly measurable on the precession photograph, and to each measurement the translation parallel to a reciprocal-lattice spacing can always be computed from the fundamental reciprocity relation

$$t_{uvw} = \lambda \frac{1}{d^*_{uvw}}. \tag{2}$$

For the most general orthogonal system, the orthorhombic, this becomes,

A   B

Fig. 7.

for the axial translations,

$$a = t_{100} = \lambda \frac{1}{d^*_{100}} \tag{3}$$

$$b = t_{010} = \lambda \frac{1}{d^*_{010}} \tag{4}$$

$$c = t_{001} = \lambda \frac{1}{d^*_{001}}. \tag{5}$$

After measurement of the appropriate d^*'s using the precession-photograph measuring device, the lengths of the axes are readily computed from (3)–(5). For tetragonal crystals $b \to a_2 = a_1$, so that (4) is unnecessary, and, in addition, for isometric crystals, $c \to a_3 = a_1$, so that only (3) is necessary.

Hexagonal and monoclinic crystals. For hexagonal and monoclinic crystals (first setting), symmetry requires that α-$\beta = 90°$, and so need not be measured. A more detailed illustration of the relation between crystal and reciprocal cell is given in Fig. 8 for a monoclinic crystal. For the monoclinic case, γ ($= 180° - \gamma^*$) has a general value which can be measured in the a^*b^* plane; i.e., on the c-axis precession photograph; hexagonal crystals are a special case in which symmetry requires that $\gamma = 120°$, $\gamma^* = 60°$.

In Fig. 8 it can be seen that the cell edge c^* is orthogonal to the plane a^*b^*. Therefore any spacing δ between rows in this net is also a spacing d^* of the plane of the reciprocal lattice which contains the row and the orthogonal c^* axis. Accordingly, to determine a and b, the spacing δ_{b^*} of the b^* row and the spacing δ_{a^*} of the a^* row are measured, and from these measurements a and b are computed as follows:

$$a = t_{100} = \lambda \frac{1}{d^*_{100}} = \lambda \frac{1}{\delta_{b^*}} \tag{6}$$

$$b = t_{010} = \lambda \frac{1}{d^*_{010}} = \lambda \frac{1}{\delta_{a^*}}. \tag{7}$$

The magnitude of c is determined by measuring d^*_{001} in the b^*c^* plane, i.e., on the a-axis precession photograph. The computation is like those above, specifically

$$c = t_{001} = \lambda \frac{1}{d^*_{001}} = \lambda \frac{1}{\delta_{b^*}}. \tag{8}$$

Triclinic crystals. In Fig. 9 the relations are shown between a triclinic crystal, as mounted in Fig. 5, Chapter 5, and the corresponding reciprocal cell. In the two illustrations on the lower right the reciprocal-

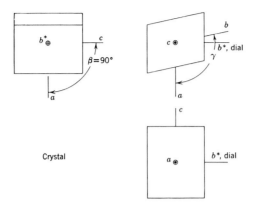

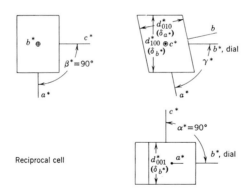

Fig. 8.
Monoclinic crystal, mounted for determining cell dimensions, and labeled in first
setting.

Left: View looking at the free end of the crystal along the dial axis.
Right: View along the precessing axis, oriented at the two desired dial orientations.

lattice planes are parallel to the plane of the paper, and correspond to two precession photographs, namely

Upper illustration: c-axis precession photograph, a^*b^* plane.
Lower illustration: a-axis precession photograph, b^*c^* plane.

In both these planes measurement of angles between appropriate rows establish interaxial angles, and measurements of row spacings corresponding to (1) can establish the lengths of all reciprocal-cell edges, specifically:
In the a^*b^* plane,

$$\gamma^* = a^* \wedge b^* \tag{9}$$

$$a^* = \delta_{b^*} \sin \gamma^* \tag{10}$$

$$b^* = \delta_{a^*} \sin \gamma^*. \tag{11}$$

In the b^*c^* plane,

$$\alpha^* = b^* \wedge c^* \tag{12}$$

$$b^* = \delta_{c^*} \sin \alpha^* \tag{13}$$

$$c^* = \delta_{b^*} \sin \alpha^*. \tag{14}$$

The lower left part of the illustration shows that the difference in dial settings for photographing the a^*b^* and the b^*c^* planes is the direct-lattice angle β or its supplement. The following measured values are now available:

$$
\begin{array}{cc}
a^* & \alpha^* \\
b^* & \beta \\
c^* & \gamma^*.
\end{array}
$$

In the triclinic case the determination of the geometry of the cell from one setting of the crystal (as compared with using two settings of the crystal) involves the acceptance of possibly a somewhat inferior accuracy because one of the reciprocal-cell angles (β^*, in this example) cannot be directly measured, although a quite good value of the corresponding direct angle (β, in this case) can be derived from dial readings. This mixed set of reciprocal- and direct-cell dimensions can be transformed to the geometry of the direct cell by the use of the following relations. The unavailable β^* can be computed by solving the standard relation

$$\cos \beta = \frac{\cos \alpha^* \cos \gamma^* - \cos \beta^*}{\sin \alpha^* \sin \gamma^*} \tag{15}$$

for β^*, giving

$$\beta^* = \cos^{-1}(\cos \alpha^* \cos \gamma^* - \sin \alpha^* \sin \gamma^* \cos \beta). \tag{16}$$

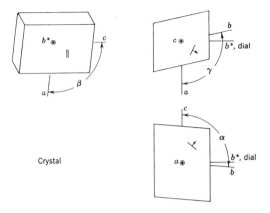

Crystal

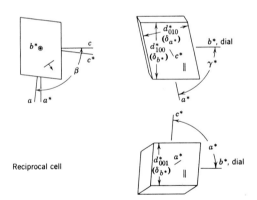

Reciprocal cell

Fig. 9.
Triclinic crystal, mounted for determining cell dimensions.
Left: View looking at the free end of the crystal along the dial axis.
Right: View along the precessing axis, oriented at the two desired dial orientations.

The following standard relations are available for deriving direct-cell dimensions from these data:

$$V^* = a^*b^*c^* \sin \alpha^* \sin \beta \sin \gamma^* \tag{17}$$

$$V = \frac{1}{V^*} \tag{18}$$

$$a = \frac{b^*c^* \sin \alpha^*}{V^*} \tag{19}$$

$$b = \frac{c^*a^* \sin \beta^*}{V^*} \tag{20}$$

$$c = \frac{a^*b^* \sin \gamma^*}{V^*} \tag{21}$$

$$\cos \alpha = \frac{\cos \beta^* \cos \gamma^* - \cos \alpha^*}{\sin \beta^* \sin \gamma^*} \tag{22}$$

$$\cos \gamma = \frac{\cos \alpha^* \cos \beta^* - \cos \gamma^*}{\sin \alpha^* \sin \beta^*}. \tag{23}$$

An example of the accuracy which can be attained for triclinic crystals by the methods described is given in Table 6.

Table 6
Comparison[†] of cell dimensions obtained by the precession method and back-reflection Weissenberg method. **(Turquois, $CuAl_6(PO_4)_4(OH)_8 \cdot 4H_2O$**

Cell dimension	Value obtained by the precession method	Value obtained from measurements of a set of back-reflection Weissenberg photographs, refined by 6 least-squares cycles
a^*	0.15285	0.15257 ± 0.00005
b^*	0.14948	0.14956 ± 0.00003
c^*	0.11167	0.11132 ± 0.00002
α^*	104°45′	104°53′ ± 1′
[β^*]		
γ^*	109°40′	109°43′ ± 2′
[α]		
β	69°42′	69°42′ ± 2′
[γ]		

[†] Courtesy of Dr. Hilda Cid-Dresdner.

Accuracy of the results

General appraisal. The accuracy of the cell dimensions resulting from measurements of precession photographs has been considered by several authors.[8-11, 14, 42] It is generally agreed that, if reasonable care is taken in orienting the crystal, the interaxial angles should be accurate to about 5 minutes, and the cell edges to about 0.2% to 0.3%. This is adequate for the normal requirements of x-ray crystallography and crystal-structure analysis.

The precision obtainable by the precession method without special precautions is superior to that obtainable with the oscillating-crystal and Weissenberg methods chiefly because it is possible to set the hairline of the measuring device in the position which represents a good average for the centers of spots of an entire row instead of in a position which represents the center of a single spot. Barnes et al.[14] note that measurements made on the same photograph by different people usually differ by less than 0.1%, and never by more than 0.25% even for the poorer photographs. They believe that, if film shrinkage is taken into account, the maximum probable error in the unit-cell edges should not exceed 0.3% and should seldom be more than 0.2%.

Direct measurement of angular relationships cannot be made by any other method except the de Jong-Bouman method.

Precautions. The accuracy of the results can be improved by observing certain precautions, several of which are of an obvious nature. In particular the accuracy is affected by the accuracy of the knowledge of M, the crystal shape and absorption, the centering of the crystal, and the shrinkage of the film. Some remarks on these matters follow.

Knowledge of M. In the precession instruments currently available, the distance from the center of crystal rotation about the dial axis to the center of the photographic film is set by the manufacturer. On the Supper apparatus this distance is 6.000 ± 0.003 cm, so that M is known to about 0.05%. A serious error will certainly result in this important distance if the operator attempts in any way to make adjustments or repairs on his instrument. Adjustments or repairs should be made only by the manufacturer, who has unusual facilities for adjustment. If there is any doubt about the crystal-to-film distance, the manufacturer or a competent instrument maker should establish it by direct measurement. This distance can also be determined by calibration with a crystal of accurately known cell geometry,[11, 14] a method that is less desirable because it involves other factors such as those described below.

Crystal size and shape. So that the hairline may be set accurately along a row of spots, the spots should be small. This requires the crystal to be small. If the crystal is large, it produces large spots whose centers are not readily located. If the crystal is much elongated (for example, a prismatic crystal elongated along the dial axis), it produces spots which are longer in one direction than the other; this gives rise to different precisions for different row measurements.

It is desirable to use a small crystal for a second reason. If the crystal has much absorption, the intensity of each spot is reduced by absorption on the side toward the center of the film. This tends to shift the apparent center of the spot away from the film center, giving rise to measurements slightly too high which, in turn, lead to cell edges slightly too low. Fortunately the use of Mo radiation with the precession camera is nearly standard procedure, and usually absorption for Mo radiation is less than that for Cu radiation, sometimes by an order of magnitude. Doubtless even this error could be removed by extrapolation against an appropriate function, but extrapolation techniques have not yet been developed for precession photographs.

Crystal centering. If, as recommended above, a crystal which is small enough to give rise to small diffraction spots is used, it is also small enough to be centered in the x-ray beam to less than a tenth of a millimeter, which is near the accuracy of the knowledge of M. On the other hand, if the crystal is rather large, a larger error in its centering can be made. If the direction of this error is not perpendicular to the x-ray beam the component of the error in that direction produces an error in the effective M.

Orientation errors. Barnes et al.[14] have empirically investigated the error in measuring Md^* which results from an error in the orientation of the crystal. They found that an error of orientation of 0.1° and 0.2° did not result in an error of Md^* of more than 0.1%, and that even an error of 2° did not give rise to an error exceeding 0.3%. Probably these favorable conclusions depend on the fact that an orientation error about an axis normal to a row does not change the location of the center of the row, and merely separates each spot into a doublet centered on the true row line. If the error is small, the doublet is not resolved but appears like a wider spot.

Film shrinkage. Apparently the greatest inaccuracy in determining cell dimensions by the precession method arises from film shrinkage. Barnes et al.[14] have made a careful investigation of the shrinkage of the photographic film which occurs during the process of development. It turned out that the shrinkage is different in the 5-in. and in the 7-in. direction of the 5 x 7-in. film from which the precession film is cut. To investigate this Barnes et al. used the two tiny holes in the back of the cassette which mark out the horizontal direction of the photograph. After the diffraction exposure was complete, they exposed the film through these holes in the normal way, then turned the back of the cassette through 90° (in the darkroom) and exposed the film again, thus giving rise to a pair of fiducial spots separated in a vertical direction on the film. The distance between holes in the cassette was measured on a traveling microscope.

The shrinkages in the two directions of the film were found to be different, regardless of which direction was placed horizontally in the developing frame. The amount of shrinkage of films from boxes of the same lot number was the same, except that vertical and horizontal shrinkages were sometimes interchanged for different parts of the same box. The value of the shrinkage was of the order of 0.15% to 0.45% for the direction of higher shrinkage, but occasionally was as high as 0.9%. The value was only 0.05% to 0.15% for the direction of lower shrinkage, but occasionally it was as much as 0.3%. Over a period of 2 months the dried x-ray photographs did not measurably change further.

These results show that, to take full advantage of the accuracy of the precession instrument, the photographs should be calibrated for shrinkage.

Error analysis. Patterson and Love[42] have discussed the errors that occur in making measurements of precession photographs and the statistics of deriving from these measurements their probable errors. From this analysis it is possible to estimate the errors to be expected in the cell dimensions derived from precession photographs. On the basis of their discussion they concluded that, provided manufacturing accuracy and adjustment of the instrument are maintained, the fractional errors resulting from measurement of films of high quality can be expected to be 0.2%. When careful calibration is carried out this can be reduced to 0.12% or 0.14% when using a measuring device with a 0.10-mm vernier, and to 0.063 to 0.089% with a 0.05-mm vernier. In the latter case, the wavelength error becomes much more important. This accuracy corresponds to an error in the carbon single-bond length of about 0.002 Å, which is adequate for all but the most precise analyses.

7

Errors in satisfying the generalized de Jong-Bouman condition

To make a photograph of an upper level, the film must be set forward from the suspension center by a distance $M\zeta$. If an error is made in this setting, the generalized de Jong-Bouman condition is not fulfilled, so the photograph suffers from distortion; it is also characterized by doubling of the spots.

More generally, doubling of the spots on any precession photograph is an indication that, in some way, the generalized de Jong-Bouman condition has not been satisfied. This situation may be caused by various possible errors; they are discussed in this chapter. All are best understood if the result of an error in setting $M\zeta$ is first considered.

Errors in setting $M\zeta$

General features. To simplify the illustrations it is assumed for the purposes of the present discussion that the magnification factor M is unity. Under these circumstances the photographic film, when correctly positioned, coincides with the reciprocal-lattice plane being photographed. No loss of generality is incurred by this assumption, since the actual photographic record is the same as shown in the illustrations except that it is scaled up by the particular value of M selected.

In order to focus attention on the geometry of the plane of the photograph, Fig. 1*A* shows a view normal to the plane of the reciprocal lattice being photographed. This requires that, in the view parallel to the plane, Fig. 1*B*, the x-ray beam must be shown inclined to the horizontal.

The zero level, drawn lightly in Fig. 1*B*, will not be further considered. The vector ζ from the origin O normal to the levels determines the location of O_n; the upper level should have its origin here. This location is shown

as a heavy line in Fig. 1*B* and as a solid circle in Fig. 1*A*. Actually,
due to an error of magnitude $+e$ the photographic film has been placed
at the end of a vector $\zeta + e$; this location is shown dashed in Figs. 1*B*
and 1*A*. The ray SP should ideally record at P but is intercepted by
the film at P'. The recorded spot therefore occurs nearer to the origin
O_n than it should. It also does not occur on the line O_nP which radiates
from the level origin, but rather in the line SP which radiates from the
projection of the center of the sphere. The obvious result of the setting

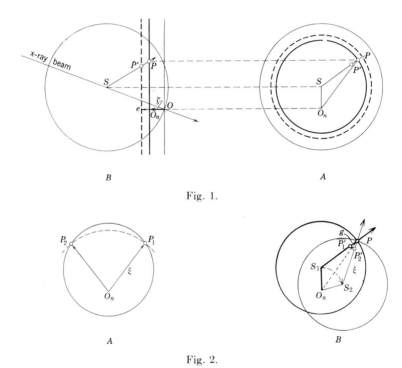

Fig. 1.

Fig. 2.

error $+e$, therefore, is that the spot appears too near the origin and its
position is also shifted sideways towards S. The setting error gives rise
to a distortion of the record.

The mislocation of the spot causes it to appear double in the complete
record. The reason for this is illustrated in Fig. 2. The center of the
circle S in Fig. 1*A* is always the projection of the center of the sphere.
The level origin O_n is eccentric with respect to the center of the circle.
The point P lies on a circle of radius ξ whose center is at O_n. These two
circles intersect in the two points P_1 and P_2, as shown in Fig. 2*A*. In
Figs. 1*A* and 2*B* the view is normal to the levels, so that O_n always
appears at the origin. In Fig. 1*A* the motion of precession appears as a

$\Delta M \zeta = 0.$

$\Delta M \zeta = +2$ mm.

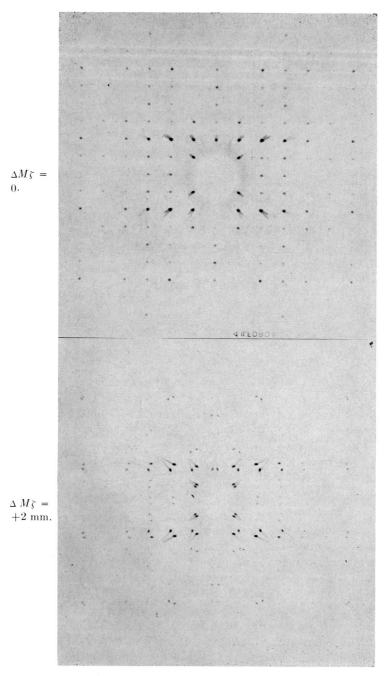

Fig. 3.
Precession photographs, illustrating the result of missetting $M\zeta$ for an upper level.

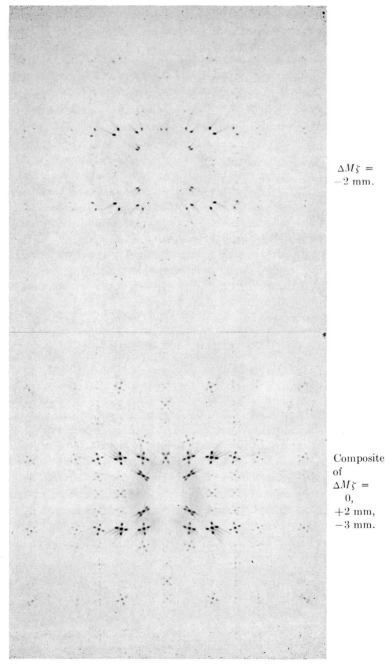

$\Delta M \zeta =$
-2 mm.

Composite
of
$\Delta M \zeta =$
$0,$
$+2$ mm,
-3 mm.

(Monticellite, $CaMgSiO_4$, b axis, 2nd level, $\bar{\mu} = 30°$; $MoK\alpha$, 35 kV, 12 mA, 15 hours)

precession of the x-ray beam about the vector ζ, so that in Fig. $1B$ the center S appears to rotate about O_n. The situation of Fig. $1A$ is shown heavy in Fig. $2B$. In this situation the circle is making contact with point P for the first time. During the precession motion the circle appears to rotate about O_n carrying the center S_1 in the same direction. The circle eventually makes contact with P a second time, and when this occurs S has position S_2. The reciprocal-lattice point enters the circle when S is at S_1, and gives rise to reflected ray S_1P which records as a spot at P_1'; it leaves the circle when S is at S_2, and gives rise to a reflected ray S_2P which records as a spot at P_2'. If the photographic film is correctly placed, Fig. 1 shows that P' coincides perfectly with P, so that in Fig. $2B$, P_1' and P_2' coincide perfectly. But if there is a setting error of $+e$, Fig. $2B$ shows that the two spots record separately and too near the center; conversely, if there is a setting error of $-e$, the two spots record separately and too far from the center.

These results are seen in a set of actual precession photographs in Fig. 3. This illustration shows photographs which were made with three different conditions: with $M\zeta$ correctly set, with $M\zeta$ set with an error $+Me$, and with $M\zeta$ set with an error $-Me$. It also shows a superposition of all three photographs. The correspondence with theory is evident. In these photographs it can be observed that the doublets corresponding to setting errors $+Me$ and $-Me$ mark out the arms of a cross symmetrical in the ray ξ and in the single spot of the correct setting. The angle of the cross is $2\psi = 2\angle S_1PO_n$ of Fig. $2B$. Its magnitude depends on the angular separation of points where the reciprocal-lattice point P enters and leaves the circle of reflection, which can be readily derived graphically as shown in Fig. $1A$. It is twice the angle subtended by points S and O_n at the edge of the circle of reflection. Its magnitude is zero at the outer edge of the record which occurs when P is located at the upper end of the diameter containing O_nS in Fig. $1A$, increases to a maximum, then declines rapidly and becomes zero at the edge of the inner blind spot which occurs when P is located at the lower end of the diameter containing O_nS in Fig. $1A$. The spots of the doublet can be found by drawing equal circles centering on the ideal location of the spot, as shown later.

Quantitative discussion. In Fig. 4 the same geometry is displayed as in Fig. 1, but with an additional view of the sphere in which SP is in the plane of the paper. This permits adding some quantitative features.

Figure $4C$ shows that the setting error e and the resulting displacement g of the spot are related by

$$\tan \bar{\nu} = \frac{g}{e}. \tag{1}$$

Thus, for a given setting error and cone angle, the displacement is constant all over the film, namely, $g = e \tan \bar{\nu}$. This feature is seen in Fig. 3.

It is also evident that the triangle O_nPS is scalene, having sides ξ, $\sin \bar{\nu}$, and $\sin \bar{\mu}$. If the generalized Pythagorean theorem is applied to this triangle, the relation between these sides is seen to be

$$(\sin \bar{\mu})^2 = \xi^2 + (\sin \bar{\nu})^2 - 2\xi \sin \bar{\nu} \cos \psi. \tag{2}$$

From this the required angle ψ is given by

$$\cos \psi = \frac{\xi^2 + \sin^2 \bar{\nu} - \sin^2 \bar{\mu}}{2\xi \sin \bar{\nu}}. \tag{3}$$

Determination of the setting error. The quantitative features just derived can be used to determine the setting error e from a measure-

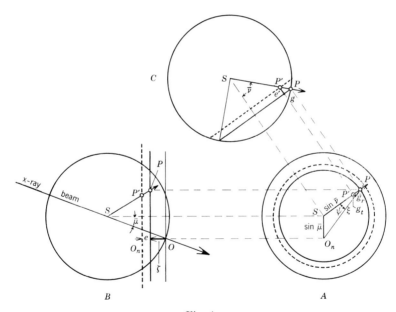

Fig. 4.

ment of the displacement g. In Fig. 4A it is seen that the tangential component (normal to O_nP) of the displacement is

$$g_t = g \sin \psi. \tag{4}$$

This value can be readily measured because Fig. 2B shows that $2g_t$ is the separation P_1P_2 of the members of the doublet. When (1), (4), and (3)

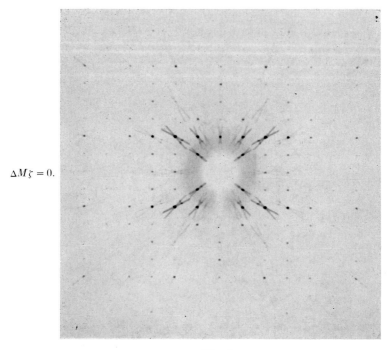

$\Delta M \zeta = 0.$

Fig. 5.

The use of general-radiation streaks in correcting the missetting of $M\zeta$ for an upper level. (Monticellite, $CaMgSiO_4$, b axis, 2nd level, $\bar{\mu} = 30°$; $MoK\alpha$, 35 kV, 12 mA, $5\frac{1}{2}$ hours.)

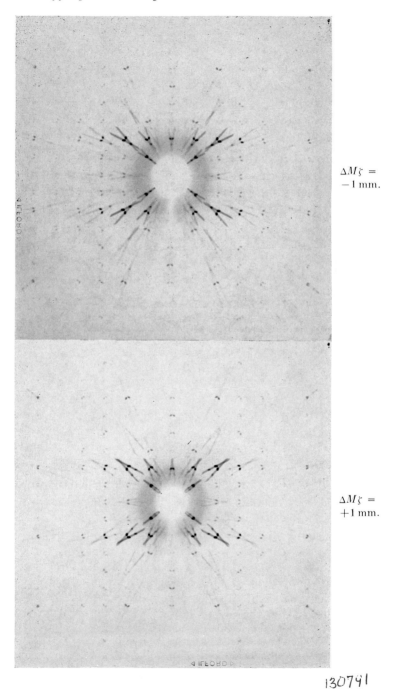

$\Delta M \zeta = -1$ mm.

$\Delta M \zeta = +1$ mm.

130741

are combined, there results

$$e = g \cot \bar{\nu}$$

$$= \frac{g_t}{\sin \psi} \cot \bar{\nu} \tag{5}$$

$$= g_t \cot \bar{\nu} \csc \cos^{-1} \frac{\xi^2 + \sin^2 \bar{\nu} - \sin^2 \bar{\mu}}{2\xi \sin \bar{\nu}}. \tag{6}$$

In this relation, $\bar{\mu}$ and $\bar{\nu}$ are experimental constants. For any specific doublet, ξ is measurable (either by the use of general-radiation streaks, as described later, or by comparison with the zero level). Thus, if the doublet separation $2g_t$ is measured, the setting error e can be determined from (6).

Figure 4A also shows that the radial component (parallel to $O_n P$) of the displacement of the spot is

$$g_r = g \cos \psi. \tag{7}$$

When (1), (7), and (3) are combined there results

$$e = g \cot \bar{\nu}$$

$$= \frac{g_r}{\cos \psi} \cot \bar{\nu} \tag{8}$$

$$= g_r \cot \bar{\nu} \frac{2\xi \sin \bar{\nu}}{\xi^2 + \sin^2 \bar{\nu} - \sin^2 \bar{\mu}}$$

$$= g_r \frac{2\xi \cos \bar{\nu}}{\xi^2 + \sin^2 \bar{\nu} - \sin^2 \bar{\mu}}. \tag{9}$$

If the displacement g_r of any particular spot from its ideal position is determined, for example by comparisons with the zero level, the setting error e can be computed from (9).

Use of general-radiation streaks. If the radiation used for making the precession photograph contains a good deal of general radiation (as it does when the β filter is omitted) the general-radiation streaks which occur on the photograph can be used to provide experimental values for some quantities in (5) and (8), leading to easy solutions of these relations. The basis of this is as follows. The value of ζ is a function of wavelength, specifically

$$\zeta_n = n d^*_{uvw}$$

$$= n \frac{\lambda}{t_{uvw}}. \tag{10}$$

If, therefore, the wavelength is varied in the neighborhood of that of the characteristic radiation a decrease in wavelength reduces ζ_n in (10) and hence shifts the erroneous (dashed) location of the plane in Fig. 4 toward the correct location. At the same time in Fig. 2B, P' approaches P. In fact, if λ is varied, the two lines in Fig. 2B which cross at P are traced out by the general radiation record. A precession photograph illustrating this point is shown in Fig. 5. It is evident not only that the point where the two general-radiation streaks cross locates the ideal position of the spot, but that the streaks cross at the angle 2ψ. If this angle and the

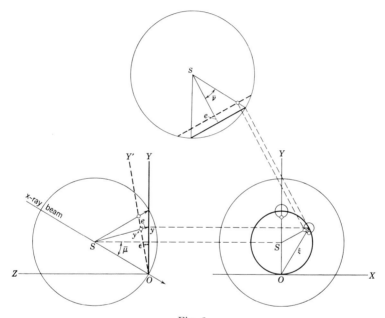

Fig. 6.

doublet displacement are measured, data are at hand to solve (5) for the setting error e. In a similar manner (8) can be solved for e, but with less accuracy, since the radial displacement g_r can be less precisely determined than g_t because it is difficult to determine the exact crossing point. Finally, g itself can be determined from measurements on various parts of the photograph, and from this value e is given by (1).

Use of β spots. Qurashi and Barnes[23] have derived a method of estimating the setting error based upon calibrations using the α and β spots which are both present when employing unfiltered radiation. The distance q of the α spot from the crossover is measured; this is proportional to the scaled error, Me. They also measure the distance D between the corresponding reflections due to the α and β radiations; this is propor-

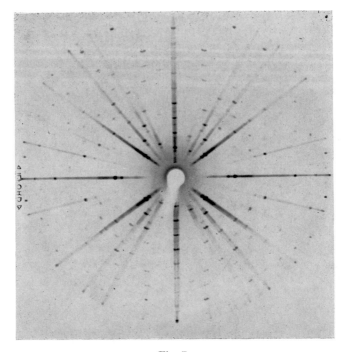

Fig. 7.

Precession photograph made with an angular error between the reciprocal-lattice plane and the plane of the photograph of $\epsilon = 2°$ about the dial axis. (Wollastonite, CaSiO$_3$, c axis, zero level, $\bar{\mu} = 30°$, MoK, 35 kV, 15 mA, 5 hours.)

tional to $M\xi_\alpha - M\xi_\beta$. These two proportionalities provide the ratio

$$\frac{D}{q} = \frac{M\xi_\alpha - M\xi_\beta}{Me} = \frac{M\xi_\alpha(1 - \lambda_\beta/\lambda_\alpha)}{Me}. \tag{11}$$

From this the setting error is given by

$$Me = \frac{q}{D} M\xi_\alpha \left(1 - \frac{\lambda_\beta}{\lambda_\alpha}\right). \tag{12}$$

The value of $1 - \lambda_\beta/\lambda_\alpha$ is approximately 0.1, so that a rough estimate of q/D gives an accurate value of Me.

Angular errors

If the crystal is set on the precession apparatus in such a way that the reciprocal-lattice plane to be photographed is not quite parallel with the film, some characteristic features occur in the zero-level photograph which can be understood in terms of the discussion already given. Figure 6 is

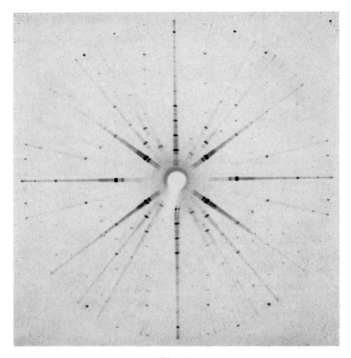

Fig. 8.

Precession photograph made with photographic film deliberately bulged in the center by insertion of a thin circular card $1\frac{3}{4}$ in. in diameter. Note that the spot doubling is confined to the center of the film. (Wollastonite, $CaSiO_3$, c axis, zero level, $\bar{\mu} = 30°$, MoK; 35 kV, 15 mA, 5 hours.)

drawn like Fig. 4 to illustrate the relations involved. In Fig. 6 the correct location of the reciprocal-lattice plane is drawn in full lines and the actual position in dashed lines. These two planes intersect in a line OX. Along the line OX the generalized de Jong-Bouman condition is perfectly satisfied, but departure from this condition increases with distance from OX. For example, along OY there is no error at O, so there is no displacement or resulting doublet. But at other positions there is an error amounting to

$$e \approx y \tan \epsilon, \tag{13}$$

which is proportional to y. Thus all displacement circles at equal distances y are equal. But the doublet occupies points on the arms of a cross symmetrical with the ray (of length ξ) from the origin to the point. A photograph illustrating the situation is shown in Fig. 7. It is characterized by doubled spots. As pointed out earlier, the angular separation of the doublet vanishes at the inner edge and outer edge of the recorded region. The inner edge for the zero level is the center of the record, so that these spots lie on narrow closed loops radiating from the center and which can be marked out by general radiation, as in Fig. 7.

Bulging of the film

When photographic film is used in a humid atmosphere it absorbs moisture and expands.   If the expansion occurs, as it often does, after the film is clamped between the metal parts of the cassette, the edges of the film are not free to expand, so that release of the strain takes place by the bulging of the center away from the metal back of the cassette. When this occurs the bulged part of the film does not fulfill the generalized de Jong-Bouman condition.   The result is a photograph in which many of the spots are doublets whose separation is large near the center but vanishes at the edges, as shown in Fig. 8.

Doubled spots are commonly caused by using a piece of photographic film cut too large for its place in the cassette.   For example, it is sometimes assumed that the cassette is intended for a 5-in. square film, while it is actually designed for a $4\frac{15}{16}$-in. square film (because film whose nominal width is 5 in. is actually only $4\frac{15}{16}$ in. wide).   A film cut too large for its place bulges in the center and gives rise to a result like that shown in Fig. 8.

Elimination of doubling by non-recording

It is evident from the foregoing discussion that doubled spots will not appear unless there is some flaw in the technique.   They can also be

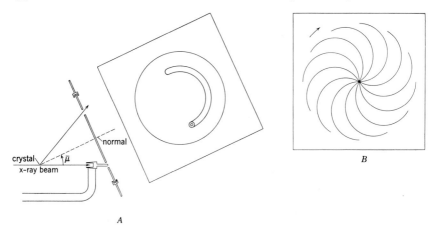

A

B

Fig. 9.
Diagrams illustrating the Zoltai device for recording only one of the two diffraction spots corresponding to each point of the reciprocal lattice.

avoided by permitting the recording of the reflection only when the reciprocal-lattice point is entering (or leaving) the sphere of reflection. This strategy may be useful when the crystal is so imperfect that it is difficult to orient correctly. Zoltai[54] has shown how one spot of the doublet can be eliminated in this way. The annular layer-line screen is replaced by a plate with a semicircular slit which is free to rotate about its center in a fixed plate. The screen is caused to rotate in synchronism with the precession motion by fixing the point where the direct beam would strike the rotating layer-line screen. The mechanism for doing this can be visualized as an extension of the direct-beam catcher. The extension plugs into a hole in the rotating member, as suggested in Fig. 9A. Thus for a layer-line screen to be used for recording the zero level, one end of the slit is maintained in the extension of the direct-beam. As the precession motion progresses, the normal to the layer-line screen holder is caused to rotate around the direct beam, and this causes the center of the rotating member to move around the direct beam. But the extension of the direct-beam catcher keeps one end of the semicircular slit at the center, so the semicircle takes the successive positions suggested in Fig. 9B.

8

Orientation errors

An *orientation photograph* is a particular kind of precession photograph made with a special technique.   It is useful in assessing the error in parallelism between the reciprocal-lattice plane and the photographic film and between a reciprocal-lattice line and the dial axis.   With the aid of this kind of photograph, the direction and magnitude of an orientation error can be determined and therefore corrected.

Orientation photographs[2]

Technique.   Orientation photographs are made with x-radiation containing as much general radiation as possible in addition to the usual characteristic radiation.   Under normal operating conditions the target metals used for the longer-wavelength characteristic radiations, namely Cu, Ni, Co, and Fe, are comparatively lacking in general radiation and are not recommended.   Those used for shorter wavelengths contain a larger proportion of general radiation and consequently are preferred. Molybdenum radiation, which is most widely used with a β filter for ordinary precession photographs, is appropriate for orientation photographs when used without a filter.   Unfiltered Ag radiation is also appropriate.

The theory and practice of making orientation photographs is simplest for the zero level.   Short exposures[†] (say 5 to 30 minutes) are possible if small values of $\bar{\mu}$ are used; in most cases $\bar{\mu} = 10°$ is recommended.   When dealing with small orientation errors it is customary to eliminate any recording of upper levels by using a special layer-line screen.   This contains a circular (not annular) opening of about 10-mm radius.   The

[†] Even shorter exposures can be obtained if a Polaroid film is used.[51,56]   This also has the advantage that the development time is only 10 seconds.

annular-type opening is not necessary because Table 1 of the next chapter shows that for $\bar{\mu} = 10°$, no negative-order levels will record (and therefore cause confusion in the center of the zero-level record) unless $t > 46.8$ Å with Mo radiation. If the translation normal to the layers is larger than this, Table 1 of Chapter 9 should be consulted for guidance in selecting a more appropriate value of $\bar{\mu}$.

General-radiation streaks. For diffraction purposes, the reciprocal lattice of a crystal is a collection of points at distances λ/d_{hkl} from the origin. Each point lies on a ray parallel to d_{hkl} in the crystal. For characteristic radiation, λ is discrete, so that λ/d_{hkl} determines a single point of the reciprocal lattice. But for general radiation, λ is continuous, so that λ/d_{hkl} determines a continuous path of points along the same ray as the spot caused by the characteristic radiation. Every plane of the reciprocal lattice that contains the origin (these are known as *central planes* of the reciprocal lattice) is characterized by such radial straight lines of general radiation in which are embedded the characteristic points.

As a consequence of this, when a zero-level plane is tipped into the sphere of reflection, the part of the plane which passes through the surface of the sphere is marked out on the photographic record, not only by containing the characteristic lattice points, but also by containing the general-radiation streaks. These shaded portions of the photographic record reveal the limits to which the reciprocal-lattice plane has entered the sphere during the motion of precession. Some examples are shown in Figs. 1 and 2. It is evident that if the reciprocal-lattice plane is truly perpendicular to the precessing axis, the plane enters the sphere equally in all directions, thus producing general-radiation streaks in a circular area centered at the origin. On the other hand, if the reciprocal-lattice plane is not quite normal to the precessing axis, the shaded area is eccentric but still nearly circular. The direction and magnitude of the eccentricity provide a delicate means of judging the orientation error, and so permit correcting it.

Quantitative relations.[2] With this general background the relation of the displacement to the orientation error can be considered. The situation is illustrated diagrammatically in Figs. 3A and 3B. Both show sections of the sphere in the plane of the orientation-error angle ϵ. Figure 3A shows the condition during the precession cycle when the precessing axis ST is in the plane of the error angle, and on the same side of the x-ray beam, while Fig. 3B shows the condition during the precession cycle when the precessing axis ST is on the side opposite to the error.

First consider Fig. 3A. The directions of the crystal translation normal to the reciprocal-lattice plane ought to lie along ST, making an angle $\bar{\mu}$ with the x-ray beam; actually it lies along ST' and makes an angle $\bar{\mu} + \epsilon$ with the x-ray beam. As a consequence the reciprocal-lattice plane lies

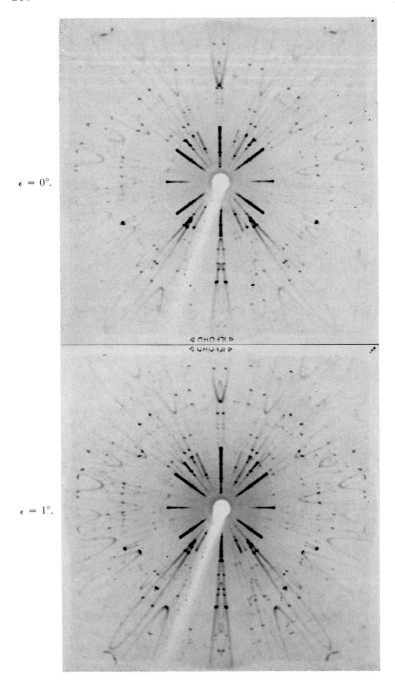

$\epsilon = 0°.$

$\epsilon = 1°.$

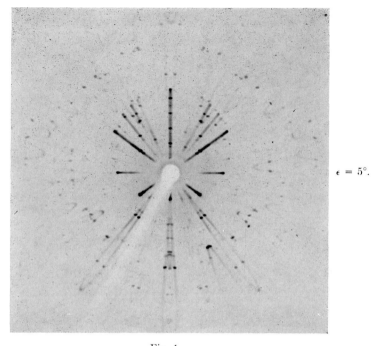

$\epsilon = 5°.$

Fig. 1.
Orientation photographs made without layer-line screens.
(Wollastonite, CaSiO$_3$, c axis, zero level, $\bar{\mu} = 10°$; MoK, 35 kV, 15 mA, $\frac{3}{4}$ hour.)

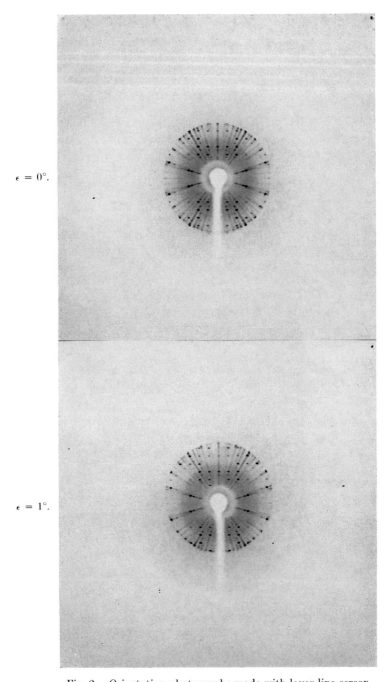

$\epsilon = 0°.$

$\epsilon = 1°.$

Fig. 2. Orientation photographs made with layer-line screen.

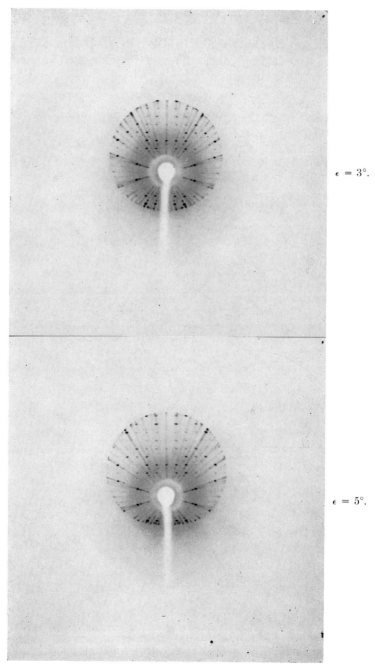

$\epsilon = 3°.$

$\epsilon = 5°.$

(Berthierite, $FeSb_2S_4$, c axis, zero level, $\bar{\mu} = 10°$; MoK, 35 kV, 12 mA, $1\frac{1}{3}$ hours.)

along the heavy dotted line instead of the heavy full line and intersects
the sphere at W instead of U. The reflections due to this reciprocal-
lattice plane project onto the film (which is parallel to the correct position
of the reciprocal-lattice plane, OU) as if they arose from points on the

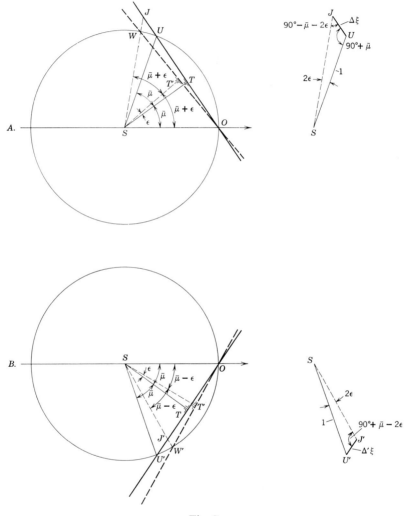

Fig. 3.

correct position of the reciprocal-lattice plane. Thus the reflection due
to limiting point W appears to have arisen at point J of the correct
position of the plane. Accordingly, the margin of the area of reflection
appears to have been moved from U to J.

The magnitude of this displacement $\Delta\xi = UJ$ can be evaluated as follows: If rays SU and SWJ are drawn, then

$$\angle OSU = 2\bar{\mu}, \tag{1}$$

$$\angle OSW = 2(\bar{\mu}+\epsilon); \tag{2}$$

subtracting, $\qquad\qquad \angle USW = 2\epsilon. \tag{3}$

The error ϵ and the consequent shift $\Delta\xi$ of the shaded area can be evaluated from the geometry of triangle SUJ, which is isolated for clearness at the right of Fig. 3A. The angle U is $90° + \bar{\mu}$. The remaining angle J is $180° - 2\epsilon - (90° + \bar{\mu}) = 90° - 2\epsilon - \bar{\mu}$. If the law of sines is applied to this triangle the result is

$$\frac{\Delta\xi}{1} = \frac{\sin 2\epsilon}{\sin (90°-2\epsilon-\bar{\mu})}, \tag{4}$$

so that $\qquad\qquad \Delta\xi = \frac{\sin 2\epsilon}{\cos (2\epsilon+\bar{\mu})}. \tag{5}$

If the denominator is expanded this can be expressed as a function of ϵ, as follows:

$$\Delta\xi = \frac{\sin 2\epsilon}{\cos 2\epsilon \cos \bar{\mu} - \sin 2\epsilon \sin \bar{\mu}},$$

$$\frac{1}{\Delta\xi} = \cot 2\epsilon \cos \bar{\mu} - \sin \bar{\mu},$$

$$\cot 2\epsilon = \frac{1}{\Delta\xi} \sec \bar{\mu} + \tan \bar{\mu}; \tag{6}$$

also, $\qquad\qquad \tan 2\epsilon = \frac{\Delta\xi \cos \bar{\mu}}{1 + \Delta\xi \sin \bar{\mu}}. \tag{7}$

When the precession motion has advanced half a cycle beyond that shown in Fig. 3A, the situation is as shown in Fig. 3B. If the law of sines is applied to triangle $SU'J'$ in that figure the result is

$$\frac{\Delta'\xi}{1} = \frac{\sin 2\epsilon}{\sin (90°-2\epsilon+\bar{\mu})}. \tag{8}$$

Thus $\qquad\qquad \Delta'\xi = \frac{\sin 2\epsilon}{\cos (2\epsilon-\bar{\mu})}. \tag{9}$

Expanding the denominator gives

$$\Delta'\xi = \frac{\sin 2\epsilon}{\cos 2\epsilon \cos \bar{\mu} + \sin 2\epsilon \sin \bar{\mu}}$$

$$\frac{1}{\Delta'\xi} = \cot 2\epsilon \sin \bar{\mu} + \sin \bar{\mu}$$

$$\cot 2\epsilon = \frac{1}{\Delta'\xi} \sec \bar{\mu} - \tan \bar{\mu}, \tag{10}$$

also, $$\tan 2\epsilon = \frac{\Delta'\xi \cos \bar{\mu}}{1 - \Delta'\xi \sin \bar{\mu}}. \tag{11}$$

These functions are sensitive measures of the orientation error, as will be seen presently. For small values of $\bar{\mu}$ both (7) and (11) are approximately linear, for

$$\tan 2\epsilon \approx \Delta\xi \approx \Delta'\xi \qquad (\bar{\mu} \text{ small}). \tag{12}$$

When the error is also small these both reduce to

$$\epsilon \approx \frac{\Delta\xi}{2} \approx \frac{\Delta'\xi}{2} \qquad (\bar{\mu}, \epsilon \text{ both small}). \tag{13}$$

Appearance of photographs. The change in the appearance of a zero-level photograph due to a small orientation error is suggested in

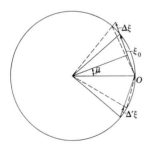
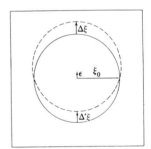

Fig. 4.

Fig. 4. If there were no error, the record would be contained within a circle concentric with the center of the film, whose radius is $r_0 = M\xi_0 = M(2 \sin \bar{\mu})$. For $\bar{\mu} = 10°$ and $M = 6$ cm this radius is $6 \times 2 \times 0.1737 = 2.084$ cm. When an orientation error occurs, the ray from the origin to the edge of the shaded area is extended in the direction of the error by amount $\Delta\xi$ and the ray in the opposite direction is shortened by $\Delta'\xi$. The diameter of the shaded area in the plane of the error is

$$(\xi_0 + \Delta\xi) + (\xi_0 - |\Delta'\xi|) = 2\xi_0 + \Delta\xi - |\Delta'\xi|. \tag{14}$$

The increase in the diameter in the direction of the error is

$$
\Delta\xi - |\Delta'\xi| = \frac{\sin 2\epsilon}{\cos (2\epsilon+\bar{\mu})} - \frac{\sin 2\epsilon}{\cos (2\epsilon-\bar{\mu})}
$$

$$
= \sin 2\epsilon \left[\frac{1}{\cos (2\epsilon+\bar{\mu})} - \frac{1}{\cos (2\epsilon-\bar{\mu})} \right]
$$

$$
= \sin 2\epsilon \left[\frac{\cos (2\epsilon-\bar{\mu}) - \cos (2\epsilon+\bar{\mu})}{\cos (2\epsilon+\bar{\mu}) \cos (2\epsilon-\bar{\mu})} \right]
$$

$$
= \frac{\sin 2\epsilon\, (2 \sin 2\epsilon \sin \bar{\mu})}{\cos^2 2\epsilon - \sin^2 \bar{\mu}}
$$

$$
= \frac{2 \sin^2 2\epsilon \sin \bar{\mu}}{\cos^2 2\epsilon - \sin^2 \bar{\mu}}. \tag{15}
$$

So long as ϵ is small enough so that $\cos^2 2\epsilon > \sin^2 \bar{\mu}$, the denominator of (15) is a positive quantity; in this case (15) indicates that the radius in the direction of the error is greater than the radius ξ_0 of the circular area characteristic of no error. The distance from the origin to the edge in a direction normal to the displacement is unaffected by the error and is equal to $r_0 = 2\,M \sin \bar{\mu}$, Fig. 4.

Orientation photographs may be taken with or without a layer-line screen. When taken without a layer-line screen, then, in addition to the desired zero-level record, they also show spots and streaks due to upper levels, as seen in Fig. 1. The nature of these general features is discussed in a later section, "Orientation photographs for large errors."

Ordinarily these additional features are not useful and merely cause confusion, which may be so great as to prevent ready interpretation of the orientation photograph. To avoid them, a special layer-line screen that has a circular, rather than an annular, opening should be used. When such a layer-line screen is used, it may cut off the record if the orientation error is too large for the screen opening. The condition under which this just begins to occur can be found as follows.

In Fig. 5 a circular screen of radius r, set at distance s from the crystal, is seen to subtend a cone of half-opening angle χ, so

$$
\chi = \tan^{-1} \frac{r}{s}. \tag{16}
$$

If the crystal were in adjustment, its rational axis would lie along ST; actually it makes an error ϵ with ST and lies along ST'. The entire zero-level Laue cone must fit within the angle OSU; i.e., the half-opening angle of the Laue cone is limited by the layer-line screen to $\frac{1}{2}(\bar{\mu} + \chi)$.

But the maximum half-opening angle of the Laue cone of the crystal is $\bar{\mu} + \epsilon$. When this just passes through the layer-line screen, the angles just mentioned are equal, that is,

$$\bar{\mu} + \epsilon = \tfrac{1}{2}(\bar{\mu}+\chi), \tag{17}$$

so that the permissible error is limited to

$$\epsilon = \tfrac{1}{2}(\chi-\bar{\mu}). \tag{18}$$

If the value given by (16) is substituted in (18), there results

$$\epsilon = \frac{1}{2}\left(\tan^{-1}\frac{r}{s} - \bar{\mu}\right). \tag{19}$$

Some values of the allowable error ϵ as a function of s for screen radii $r = 5$, 10, and 15 mm are given in Table 1.

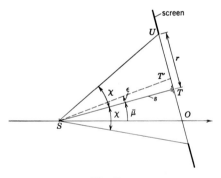

Fig. 5.

Of course, the error ϵ is not ordinarily known until the photograph has been taken. If an orientation photograph has already been taken using the special layer-line screen, and if the shaded part of the zero level shows an unnatural flattening of the most distant part of the oval, the interpretation of ϵ from the photograph should be based upon $\Delta'\xi$ alone, and not on $\Delta\xi$ or $\Delta\xi + |\Delta'\xi|$.

Determination of the error

There are two general methods of determining the orientation error. In both methods the direction of the error is that of the direction of shift of the center of the shaded area. In one method the displacement $M\Delta\xi$

of the far edge, or $M\Delta'\xi$ of the near edge, is measured, and ϵ computed from $\Delta\xi$ using (7), or from $\Delta'\xi$ using (11). A nomogram for the evaluation of these functions for any value of $\bar{\mu}$ has been provided by King.[27] But, since the value of $\bar{\mu}$ selected for the precession angle is arbitrary, it is more convenient to transform the measurement to the error by means of a graph of the function. Such graphs have been provided by Fisher.[21] Since (7) and (11) reduce to $\tan 2\epsilon = \Delta\xi = \Delta'\xi$ when $\bar{\mu} = 0$, these graphs are asymptotic to a tangent function.

An alternative method, due to Evans,[15] makes use of both maximum and minimum displacements at the same time. In making use of both

Table 1

Allowable orientation error, ε, as a function of screen setting s for screens with circular openings

Screen setting s	$\bar{\mu} = 5°$			$\bar{\mu} = 10°$		
	Screen radius r			Screen radius r		
	5 mm	10 mm	15 mm	5 mm	10 mm	15 mm
20 mm	4° 31′	10° 47′	15° 56′	2° 01′	8° 17′	13° 26′
22	3° 54′	9° 44′	14° 39′	1° 24′	7° 14′	12° 09′
24	3° 23′	8° 49′	13° 30′	0° 53′	6° 19′	11° 00′
26	2° 57′	8° 01′	12° 30′	0° 27′	5° 31′	10° 00′
28	2° 34′	7° 20′	11° 36′	0° 04′	4° 50′	9° 06′
30	2° 14′	6° 43′	10° 47′	—	4° 13′	8° 17′
32	1° 57′	6° 11′	10° 04′	—	3° 41′	7° 34′
34	1° 41′	5° 42′	9° 25′	—	3° 12′	6° 55′
36	1° 27′	5° 16′	8° 49′	—	2° 46′	6° 19′
38	1° 15′	4° 53′	8° 16′	—	2° 23′	5° 46′
40	1° 04′	4° 31′	7° 47′	—	2° 01′	5° 17′
42	0° 54′	4° 12′	7° 20′	—	1° 42′	4° 50′
44	0° 45′	3° 54′	6° 55′	—	1° 24′	4° 25′

$\Delta\xi$ and $\Delta'\xi$ together, confusion can arise due to the possibility of using various coordinate systems. In discussing the reciprocal lattice it is usual to use a cylindrical coordinate system, so that a polar coordinate system is used for one level. When this is done, $\Delta\xi$ is positive while $\Delta'\xi$ is negative. Nevertheless $\Delta\xi$ and $\Delta'\xi$ are displacements in the same direction, and Evans' function makes use of the sum of the magnitudes of these, namely $\Delta\xi + |\Delta'\xi|$. The average of these two displacements of the ends of the diameter of the shaded area is the shift of the middle of the diameter,

$$\text{Shift of diameter center} = \frac{\Delta\xi + |\Delta'\xi|}{2}, \tag{20}$$

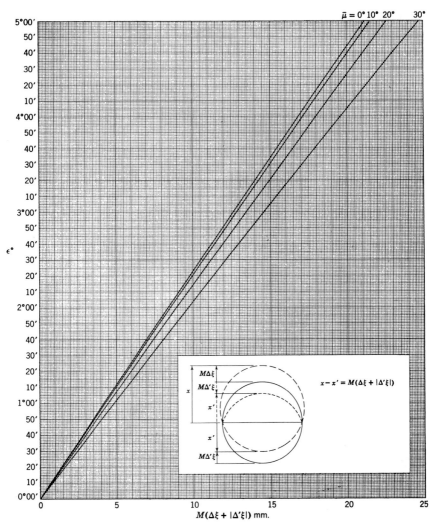

Fig. 6.

Graph for determining the orientation error ϵ from the shifts, $M(\Delta\xi + |\Delta'\xi|)$, of the shaded area.   (For an instrument with $M = 6$ cm.)

Insert: Some quantities involved in the shift of the shaded area.   Measurements $x - x'$ determine $M(\Delta\xi + |\Delta'\xi|)$.

so the sum of the shifts, $\Delta\xi + |\Delta'\xi|$, is twice the shift of this diameter. This sum can easily be related to the error ϵ by substituting from (5) and (9):

$$\Delta\xi + |\Delta'\xi| = \frac{\sin 2\epsilon}{\cos (2\epsilon + \bar{\mu})} + \frac{\sin 2\epsilon}{\cos (2\epsilon - \bar{\mu})} \tag{21}$$

$$= \sin 2\epsilon \, \frac{\cos \, (2\epsilon - \bar{\mu}) \, + \, \cos \, (2\epsilon + \bar{\mu})}{\cos \, (2\epsilon + \bar{\mu}) \, \cos \, (2\epsilon - \bar{\mu})}$$

$$= \frac{\sin 4\epsilon \, \cos \, \bar{\mu}}{\cos^2 2\epsilon \, - \, \sin^2 \bar{\mu}}. \tag{22}$$

Values of $\Delta\xi + |\Delta'\xi|$ as a function of ϵ are listed in Table 2 for precession angles commonly used, and graphs of $M(\Delta\xi + |\Delta'\xi|)$ are shown in Fig. 6. To make use of this graph the sum of the magnitudes of the

Table 2A

Displacement (×2, in reciprocal-lattice units) of the center of the shaded area in orientation photographs, as a function of the orientation error, ε

Orientation error ϵ	$\bar{\mu}$			
	$0°$	$10°$	$20°$	$30°$
$0°$	0	0	0	0
$\frac{1}{2}°$	.03492	.03545	.03715	.04031
$1°$	.06984	.07092	.07435	.08068
$1\frac{1}{2}°$	.10482	.10645	.11158	.12115
$2°$	.13986	.14203	.14892	.16174
$2\frac{1}{2}°$	.17498	.17772	.18640	.20257
$3°$	.21020	.21353	.22403	.24363
$3\frac{1}{2}°$	.24556	.24948	.26246	.28497
$4°$	.28108	.28559	.29990	.32671
$4\frac{1}{2}°$	.31676	.32191	.33822	.36885
$5°$	.35266	.35844	.37683	.41148

Table 2B

Displacement (×2, in distance on the film, M = 6 cm) of the center of the shaded area in orientation photographs, as a function of the orientation error, ε

Orientation error ϵ	$\bar{\mu}$			
	$0°$	$10°$	$20°$	$30°$
$0°$	0.00 mm	0.00 mm	0.00 mm	0.00 mm
$\frac{1}{2}°$	2.10	2.13	2.23	2.42
$1°$	4.10	4.26	4.46	4.84
$1\frac{1}{2}°$	6.29	6.39	6.70	7.27
$2°$	8.39	8.52	8.94	9.70
$2\frac{1}{2}°$	10.50	10.66	11.18	12.15
$3°$	12.61	12.81	13.44	14.62
$3\frac{1}{2}°$	14.73	14.97	15.75	17.10
$4°$	16.86	17.14	17.99	19.60
$4\frac{1}{2}°$	19.01	19.31	20.29	22.13
$5°$	21.16	21.51	22.61	24.69

shifts $\Delta\xi$ and $\Delta'\xi$ are needed. If, as suggested in the insert of Fig. 6, a point on the nearer edge of the shaded area is transferred to the opposite side of the center[†] by means of a pair of dividers, the distance from the transferred point to the farther edge of the shaded area is the required M ($|\Delta'\xi| + \Delta\xi$). (Since $\Delta\xi$ and $\Delta'\xi$ are in opposite directions it may also be noted that $\Delta\xi + |\Delta'\xi| = \Delta\xi - \Delta'\xi$.)

Fisher[21] determines the shift of the shaded area somewhat differently: He makes use of the fact that the shifted shaded area is approximately circular, as noted beyond. He places the film on a glass positive print of polar coordinate paper, on which the center is easily found and recorded by a pin prick; its distance from the direct beam spot is related to (20).

Correction of orientation errors

Routine procedure. Any errors in the orientation of the crystal can be corrected by means of the two arcs on the goniometer head, plus the dial, provided the errors are less than the corresponding adjustment ranges. The adjustment possible on the dial is unlimited, but most goniometer arcs are limited to $\pm 25°$ from their central positions.

The most strategic position for the goniometer arcs when beginning the adjustment of a crystal is shown in Fig. 9, as seen from the back of the precession instrument. Specifically, the crystal should be so mounted on the goniometer head that (*a*) both arcs read $0°$; (*b*) the outermost arc lies in a vertical plane, and (*c*) the arc upon which it rests lies in a horizontal plane. These orientations of the arcs will be accurately attained if, after the goniometer head is attached to the spindle, the dial is set to read $0°$. The advantage of this initial position is that in the adjustment procedure each adjustment does not disturb one already made. The orientation error ϵ has components

$$\Delta V, \text{ on the vertical arc}$$

$$\Delta H, \text{ on the horizontal arc}$$

$$\Delta D, \text{ on the dial.}$$

In Chapter 5 it was pointed out that in planning the collection of precession photographs to be made about different precessing axes, it is most desirable to orient some specific axial row of the reciprocal lattice along the dial axis. This row can usually be seen on the orientation photograph, and in Fig. 7 it is taken as the nearly horizontal full line. Some features of the orientation photograph are shown in Fig. 7, which shows that this line makes an angle with the horizontal line of the film (marked

---

[†] The center can be marked out, if necessary, by a momentary exposure of the direct beam when $\bar{\mu}$ is set at $0°$.

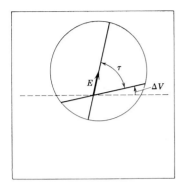

Fig. 7.

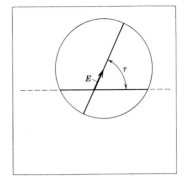

Fig. 8.

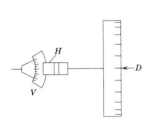

Fig. 9.

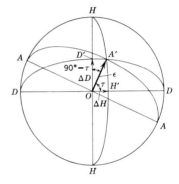

Fig. 10.

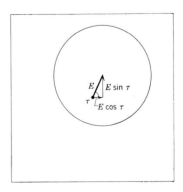

Fig. 11.

out by two dots, as described in Chapter 5) that is very approximately
equal to ΔV. Accordingly this error is substantially corrected first by
turning the vertical arc through the angle $-\Delta V$. If another orientation
photograph were taken after adjustment, it would appear as in Fig. 8.
(The photograph need not, of course, be made.)

The angular relations, plotted on the surface of a sphere, would now
appear as in Fig. 10. The direction of the x-ray beam is represented by
a point at the center of the diagram while the error ϵ is an arc of a great
circle beginning at the center. Its components on the horizontal arc and
dial arc are also arcs of great circles, each beginning at the center. Their
magnitudes can be understood in the following way: The error ϵ, represented as the arc ϵ, is also a rotation of angle ϵ about axis AA. This
rotation would carry a great circle AOA to $AA'A$. Its component ΔH
about the horizontal arc is a rotation about axis HH such that it would
carry great circle HOH to $HA'H'H$; i.e., it must include point A'. Similarly the component ΔD of the error ϵ on the dial would carry a great
circle DOD to $DD'A'D$; i.e., it must include point A' also. With this
construction, as the horizontal component ΔH is removed by rotating arc
$HA'H'H$ about axis HH by amount $-\Delta H$, the end of the vector ϵ travels
along the arc $DA'D'A$, from point A' to point D'. There remains then
only the component ΔD, which can be removed by a rotation about axis
DD by $-\Delta D$.

The magnitudes of ΔH and ΔD can be computed as follows: In right
spherical triangle $OA'H'$,

$$\cos \tau = \frac{\tan \Delta H}{\tan \epsilon} \tag{23}$$

so
$$\tan \Delta H = \tan \epsilon \cos \tau. \tag{24}$$

In right spherical triangle $OA'D'$

$$\cos (90° - \tau) = \frac{\tan \Delta D}{\tan \epsilon} \tag{25}$$

so
$$\tan \Delta D = \tan \epsilon \sin \tau. \tag{26}$$

When ϵ is small, ΔH and ΔD are also small, and good approximations to
(24) and (26) are

(24):
$$\Delta H = \cos \tau, \tag{27}$$

(26):
$$\Delta D = \sin \tau. \tag{28}$$

To correct these errors, corrections $-\Delta H$ and $-\Delta D$ are made on the
horizontal goniometer arc and dial, respectively.

After the correction $-\Delta V$ has been made, an approximately equivalent
procedure is to utilize the components of the film displacement E, as indi-

cated in Fig. 11. If, instead of measuring the displacement E, its components $E \cos \tau$ and $E \sin \tau$ are measured on the film, these can be transformed into angles using Fig. 6, and the reverse angles used for corrections.

A different procedure for correcting an orientation error is illustrated in Fig. 12. In using relation (22), the straightforward procedure is to determine the extreme values of $\Delta \xi + |\Delta' \xi|$ and using (22) transform this into

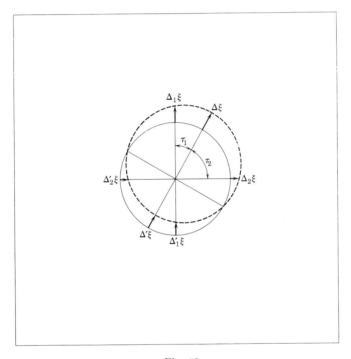

Fig. 12.
The quantities involved in correcting an orientation error not parallel to an arc. $\Delta \xi$ is the maximum shift. $\Delta_1 \xi$ and $\Delta'_1 \xi$ are shifts parallel to the plane of the dial while $\Delta_2 \xi$ and $\Delta'_2 \xi$ are shifts parallel to the plane of the horizontal arc of the goniometer head.

the corresponding angular error ϵ in the direction of $\Delta \xi$. Now suppose a plane is passed normal to the zero level through its center, but along some arbitrary direction (such as the vertical and horizontal lines in Fig. 12). Let the dihedral angle in this plane which the misoriented plane makes with the correctly oriented plane be ϵ'. It is shown later that the shifts of the shaded area along the intersection of this plane with the correctly oriented plane bear the same relation to ϵ' as the extreme shifts do to ϵ. If this relation is applied to Fig. 12, the sum of the shifts $\Delta_1 \xi + |\Delta_1' \xi|$ can

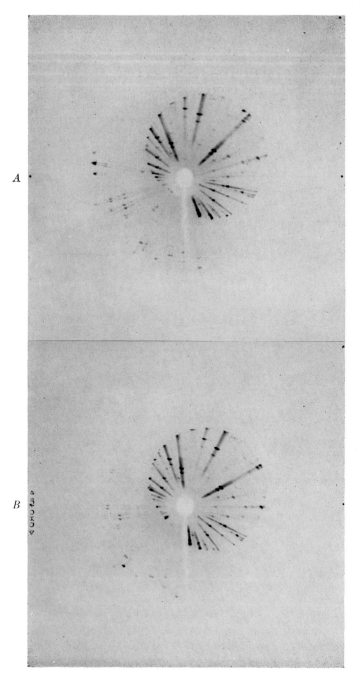

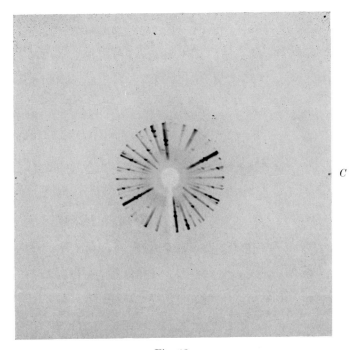

C

Fig. 13.
Sequence of orientation photographs ($\bar{\mu} = 10°$), demonstrating the adjustment of an axis of a triclinic crystal to the precessing axis (Rhodonite, $Mn_4CaSi_5O_{15}$, c axis; MoK, 35 kV, 12 mA, $\frac{3}{4}$ hour.)

A. Precessing axis set perpendicular to (001) cleavage (photograph corresponding to Fig. 7).

B. Appropriate reciprocal-lattice row brought parallel to dial axis by use of goniometer arc V (photograph corresponding to Fig. 8).

C. Final orientation accomplished by adjusting dial and goniometer arc H.

be used to correct the angular error ϵ_1' along the vertical line (by changing the dial reading by $-\epsilon_1'$), while the shifts $\Delta_2\xi + |\Delta_2'\xi|$ can be used to correct the angular error ϵ_2' along the horizontal line (by changing the horizontal arc reading by $-\epsilon_2'$).

Some orientation photographs, illustrating the correction of errors, are shown in Fig. 13.

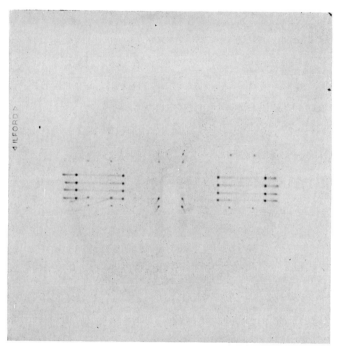

Fig. 14.

Example of an orientation photograph made by the Laves method, using a layer-line screen. (Zircon, $ZrSiO_4$, a axis, MoK, 35 kV, 15 mA, four exposures of 20 minutes each.)

Laves' method. Fisher[21,33] has described a method of orientation, due to Fritz Laves, that has been used in adjusting into exact orientation a crystal which is already nearly in correct orientation. The method involves taking four exposures (each of about 5–20 min) on the same film, the cassette being raised after each exposure about 2 or 3 mm to permit identification of each exposure. The arcs are placed in vertical and horizontal planes. If, for example, they are set initially with the plane of the outer arc vertical, as in Fig. 9 where the dial reads 0°, photographs are taken for dial readings 0°, 180°, 90°, and 270°. An example of such a multiple correction photograph is shown in Fig. 14. The pair taken for $D = 0°$ and $D = 180°$ show two nearly horizontal streaks whose divergence is $2\Delta V$. The pair taken for $D = 90°$ and $D = 270°$ show two nearly horizontal streaks whose divergence is $2\Delta H$. In the specific procedure described by Fisher these angles are not measured, but rather the horizontal displacements Δx_V and Δx_H of the ends of the horizontal general-radiation streaks. If these are measured in millimeters, the corrections are given by

$$M = 6 \text{ cm:} \begin{cases} \Delta V = \dfrac{60}{q}\, \Delta x_V \text{ minutes} \\[2mm] -\Delta H = \dfrac{60}{q}\, \Delta x_H \text{ minutes,} \end{cases}$$

where the values of q for various values of $\bar{\mu}$ are

$$\bar{\mu} = 3° \qquad 10° \qquad 20° \qquad 25°$$

$$q = 4.20 \qquad 4.26 \qquad 4.494 \qquad 4.625 \text{ mm}$$

After these corrections, the horizontal reciprocal-lattice line should remain invariant for any dial setting. The procedure does not correct any error in dial setting, however. This must be effected with the aid of the vertical displacement of the shaded area.

Orientation photographs for large errors

Technique. On some occasions a large orientation error may be expected. Then it is desirable to omit the layer-line screen since this will cut off the outer part of the record if the error is large enough. The size of the shaded area increases with the error so that with large errors the far edge of the area is liable to lie outside the film. To reduce this difficulty a small area is called for; this can be approached by using a small precession angle, say $\bar{\mu} = 5°$. With such a small angle few reciprocal-lattice points produced by characteristic radiation should be expected, but the exposure times will be relatively short.

Appearance of photographs. An example of a photograph made with this alternative technique is shown in Fig. 15. In general such photographs differ in several respects from those already considered:

(*a*) Since a layer-line screen is not used, the photograph contains, in addition to zero-level features, upper-level spots and streaks.

(*b*) The general-radiation streaks on the zero-level record are essentially straight lines radiating from the origin only if the zero-level plane is nearly in orientation. If it is out of orientation the radial straight line is replaced by a narrow ellipse-like streak. This occurs because the zero level is no longer truly a zero level; the reciprocal-lattice points depart from the generalized de Jong-Bouman condition in the same way that they would if they were on upper levels as described more completely in Chapter 7.

(*c*) There are usually evidences of more than one central reciprocal-lattice plane close enough to zero-level orientation to be recognized. Each is marked out by a shaded area which is more or less oval. For reasons to be noted later, each such area has a chord in common with a diameter of a hypothetical correctly adjusted zero-level plane. This chord is normal to the displacement direction of the shaded area. The diameter of the correctly adjusted zero-level plane is $2r_0 = 2M\xi_{max} = 4M \sin \bar{\mu}$. Values of this common chord for various precession angles are listed in Table 3, page 133.

When several reciprocal-lattice planes lie in a zone, they have in common a rational line in the reciprocal lattice. When this line lies in the zero-level plane, the several reciprocal-lattice planes may be regarded as planes departing from the zero-level position by different error angles ϵ. The shaded areas of the planes of such a set have the common rational line as the common chord. Examples are seen in Fig. 15.

(*d*) If the angle between the reciprocal-lattice plane and the photographic film exceeds a certain limit, specifically $\epsilon > \bar{\mu}$, the shaded area contains a central blind region as shown in Fig. 17. The reason for this is supplied by Fig. 16, which shows the ideal and misoriented zero-level plane at the upper and lower limits of the precession cycle. When $\epsilon = \bar{\mu}$, the misoriented plane becomes just tangent to the sphere at the lower limit of the cycle. If $\epsilon > \bar{\mu}$, it fails to attain this tangency, and a blind spot results. This extends from the origin to a distance ξ_b in the direction of the error. The outer limit can be evaluated by applying the law of sines to the small triangle isolated at the right of Fig. 16:

$$\frac{\xi_b}{2 \sin (\epsilon - \bar{\mu})} = \frac{\sin (90° + \epsilon - \bar{\mu})}{\sin (90° - 2\epsilon + \bar{\mu})} = \frac{\cos (\epsilon - \bar{\mu})}{\cos (2\epsilon - \bar{\mu})} \tag{29}$$

$$\xi_b = \frac{2 \sin (\epsilon - \bar{\mu}) \cos (\epsilon - \bar{\mu})}{\cos (2\epsilon - \bar{\mu})}$$

$$= \frac{\sin 2(\epsilon - \bar{\mu})}{\cos (2\epsilon - \bar{\mu})}. \tag{30}$$

This blind spot is not circular, but is a drop-shaped area (as derived later) elongated in the direction of the error. The general-radiation streaks in the shaded area appear as long quasi-elliptical streaks which begin at the edge of the blind region, extend radially away from the origin, and terminate at the outer edge of the shaded area. This is a feature of a tipped zero-level plane, discussed in Chapter 7.

Theory of the common chord. It has been noted that the shaded area of a misoriented reciprocal-lattice plane has a chord in common

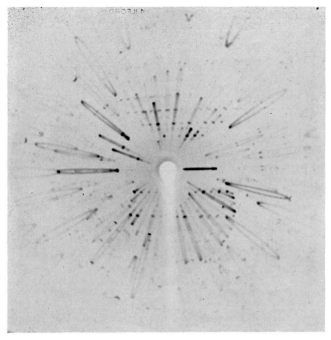

Fig. 15.

Example of a precession photograph taken with $\bar{\mu} = 5°$ for an arbitrary orientation of the crystal. Below the center is a well-outlined shaded plane. A number of zero-level planes can also be discerned outlined by sets of narrow loops. The blind region of such a plane is the area between the inner ends of the loops and the center of the photograph. (Kaliborite, $KMg_2B_{11}O_{19}\cdot 9H_2O$; MoK, 35 kV, 15 mA, 45 minutes.)

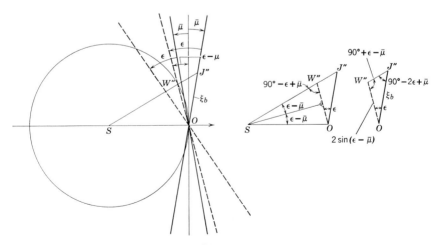

Fig. 16.

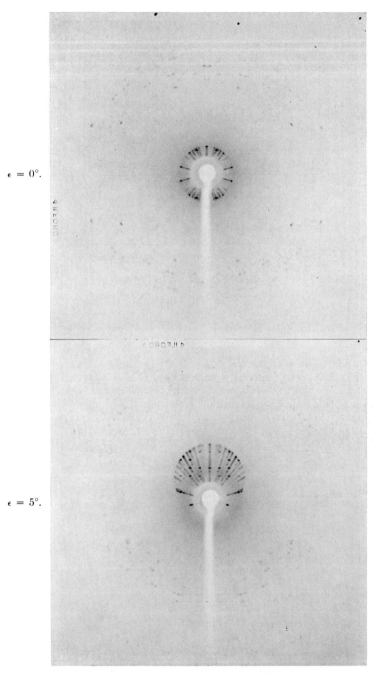

$\epsilon = 0°.$

$\epsilon = 5°.$

Fig. 17.   Orientation photographs; $\bar{\mu} = 5°.$

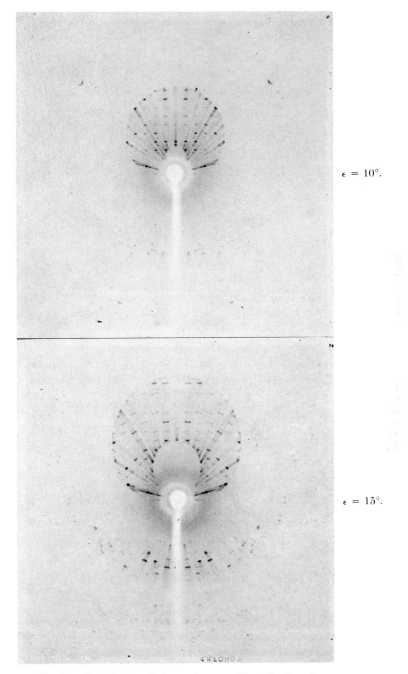

$\epsilon = 10°.$

$\epsilon = 15°.$

Fig. 17.   Orientation photographs; $\bar{\mu} = 5°$.   (*Continued*)

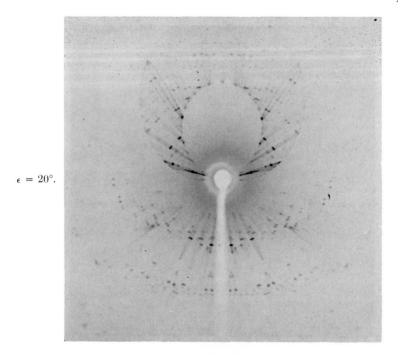

$\epsilon = 20°.$

Fig. 17.
Set of orientation photographs made with $\bar{\mu} = 5°$ and no layer-line screen, showing the appearance of some characteristics of large orientation errors. (Bertherite, $FeSb_2S_4$, c axis; MoK, 35 kV, 12 mA, 1 hour.)

Table 3
Common chord of zero-level shaded areas in orientation photographs

Precession angle, $\bar{\mu}$	Chord of shaded area $2M\xi_{max}$ $M = 6$ cm	Precession angle, $\bar{\mu}$	Chord of shaded area $2M\xi_{max}$ $M = 6$ cm
1°	0.419 cm	16°	6.615 cm
2°	0.838	17°	7.017
3°	1.256	18°	7.416
4°	1.674	19°	7.814
5°	2.092	20°	8.208
6°	2.509	21°	8.601
7°	2.925	22°	8.991
8°	3.340	23°	9.378
9°	3.754	24°	9.762
10°	4.167	25°	10.143
11°	4.579	26°	10.521
12°	4.990	27°	10.896
13°	5.399	28°	11.267
14°	5.806	29°	11.635
15°	6.212	30°	12.000

with its correctly oriented equivalent. The reason for this is shown in Fig. 18. In this and similar figures an attempt is made to illustrate the intersection of the Laue cone with the sphere of reflection and how it migrates over the surface of the sphere during the precession cycle.

In Fig. 18A the places where the rational axis of the crystal pierce the sphere at four selected phases of the precession cycle are shown by four "open points." The Laue cone has constant half-opening angle $\bar{\mu}$, so the intersection with the sphere is a circle of constant diameter. During the precession cycle, this Laue circle sweeps out a circular area on the sphere. Since the photographic film is normal to the direction from the

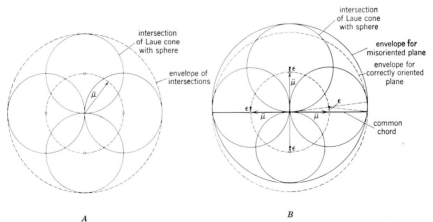

Fig. 18.

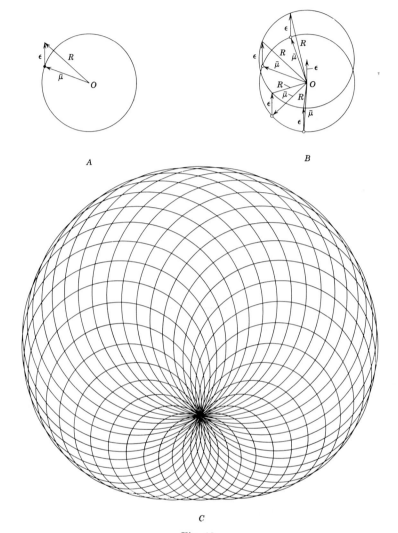

C

Fig. 19.
Construction of the intersections of the Laue cones with the misoriented plane.

A. Basis for determining the radius of the Laue intersection.
B. Variation of the radius of the Laue intersection with direction.
C. Laue intersections for $\epsilon < \bar{\mu}$: $\bar{\mu} = 10°$, $\epsilon = 5°$.

center of the sphere at the "open points," the photographic film also displays a circular shaded area.

In Fig. 18B the rational axis makes an angle ϵ with the normal to the film. The rational axis therefore pierces the sphere at the "solid points," which are displaced from the "open points" by arcs ϵ. It is evident that

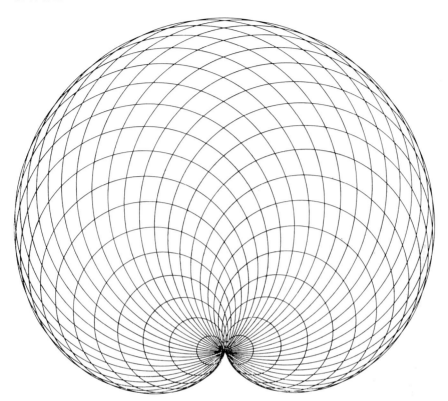

Fig. 20.   Laue intersections for $\epsilon = \bar{\mu}$: $\bar{\mu} = 10°$, $\epsilon = 10°$.

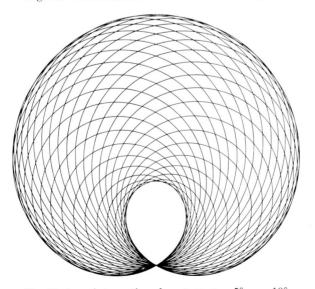

Fig. 21. Laue intersections for $\epsilon > \bar{\mu}$: $\bar{\mu} = 5°$, $\epsilon = 10°$.

the Laue cone has a half-opening angle $\bar{\mu} + \epsilon$ at the upper phase but only $\bar{\mu} - \epsilon$ at the lower phase, so the size of the Laue cone varies continuously during the cycle. The solid line shows the envelope of the Laue-cone intersections. This envelope, projected from the center of the sphere to the film, becomes the shaded area. The geometry at the right and left phases is such that the horizontal diameter of the envelope is constant regardless of the error. This diameter, projected to the film, becomes the common chord.

Theory of the shape of the shaded area. The general shape of the shaded area can be understood by referring to the general type of construction already used in Fig. 18. This can be turned into a suitable routine as suggested in Fig. 19. The routine is based upon the fact, as noted in Fig. 19A, that the radius of the intersection of the Laue cone is found by adding arc ϵ to arc $\bar{\mu}$. A resulting radius R of the intersection of a Laue cone is seen to be given, as noted in Fig. 19B, by the distance from the origin to a point on a circle of radius $\bar{\mu}$ (on the sphere of reflection) which is displaced from the origin by arc ϵ. In other words, the Laue-cone intersections are constructed by using points of the displaced circle as centers, and arcs from these points to the origin as radii. The envelope of all such Laue-cone intersections, as shown in Fig. 19C, is the representation on the sphere of reflection of the border of the dark area on the film.

This construction is carried out for a comparatively small orientation error (that is, for $\epsilon < \bar{\mu}$) in Fig. 19C. The corresponding constructions for larger errors are given for $\epsilon = \bar{\mu}$ in Fig. 20 and for $\epsilon > \bar{\mu}$ in Fig. 21. It is seen that in both cases the shaded areas depart markedly from circular form since the circumferences are cusped. Fig. 21 shows that when $\epsilon > \bar{\mu}$ a blind area occurs within the shaded area.

The first part of this chapter dealt with small orientation errors, and there it was convenient to derive $\Delta\xi$ and $\Delta'\xi$, the radial departures of the shaded area from the circle which corresponded to a perfectly oriented plane. When considering large orientation errors the resemblance of the shaded area to a circle is no longer so close, so it is more convenient to derive the maximum radius ξ_{max} and minimum radius ξ_{min} of the shaded area.

The geometries involved are shown in Fig. 22. The situation at the upper extreme of the precession motion is shown in the upper part of the figure. The angular values required are shown for clearness in a separate sketch of triangle SOJ. Another triangle, OJW, is also illustrated separately. Similarly, the lower extreme of the precession motion is shown in the lower part of the figure, and triangles SOW' and $OJ'W'$ are shown separately. If the law of sines is applied to these two cases the following relations can be derived:

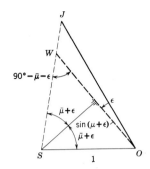

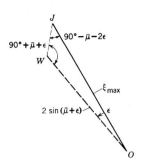

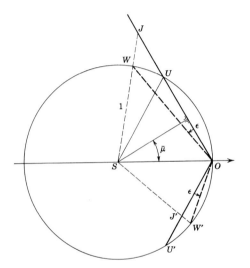

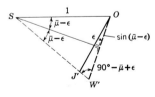

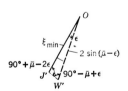

Fig. 22.

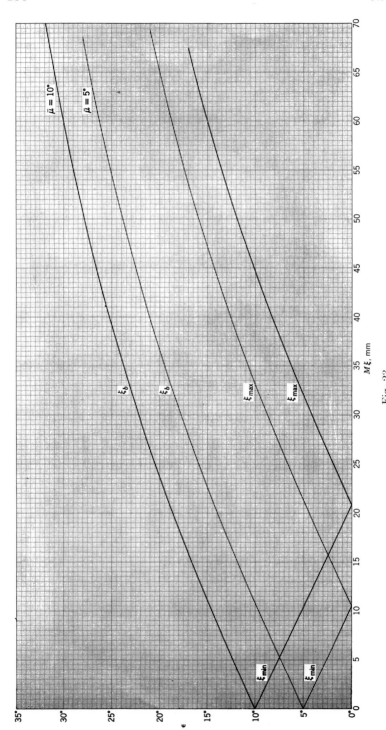

Fig. 23.

Graph for determining the orientation error ϵ as a function of the distances to the outer edge of the recorded region (lower right curves), to the inner edge of the recorded region (curves at left) and to the edge of the blind region (upper curves).

Table 4
Radii, in direction of orientation error, of recorded region of reciprocal-lattice plane for various orientation errors

Orientation error ϵ	$\bar{\mu}$					
	5°			10°		
	Shorter radius, ξ_{min}	Radius to edge of blind region, ξ_b	Longer radius, ξ_{max}	Shorter radius, ξ_{min}	Radius edge of blind region, ξ_b	Longer radius, ξ_{max}
0°	10.46 mm		10.46 mm	20.84 mm		20.84 mm
1°	8.36		12.57	18.72		22.98
2°	6.27		14.70	16.63		25.15
3°	4.19		16.87	14.55		27.36
4°	2.10		19.03	12.48		29.62
5°	0.0	0.0 mm	21.25	10.42		31.93
6°		2.11	23.50	8.36		34.29
7°		4.24	25.81	6.29		36.73
8°		6.39	28.17	4.21		39.24
9°		8.57	30.60	2.11		41.84
10°		10.79	33.10	0.0	0.0 mm	44.53
11°		13.04	35.68		2.14	47.87
12°		15.35	38.36		4.31	50.27
13°		17.72	41.14		6.52	53.35
14°		20.14	44.05		8.78	56.58
15°		22.64	47.08		11.09	60.00
16°		25.23	50.27		13.45	63.62
17°		27.90	53.63		15.89	67.48
18°		30.68	57.19		18.40	71.61
19°		33.59	60.97		21.00	76.04
20°		36.62	65.00		23.70	80.84
21°		39.81	69.33		26.50	86.05
22°		43.17	73.99		29.44	91.75
23°		46.73	79.04		32.51	98.02
24°		50.51	84.55		35.75	104.98
25°		54.54	90.59		39.16	112.76
26°		58.87	97.27		42.78	121.55
27°		63.53	104.71		46.64	131.57
28°		68.58	113.06		50.77	143.13
29°		74.09	122.54		55.21	156.67
30°		80.13	133.41		60.00	172.76
31°						
32°					70.91	

Upper extreme:

$$\frac{\xi_{\max}}{2 \sin (\bar{\mu}+\epsilon)} = \frac{\sin (90°+\bar{\mu}+\epsilon)}{\sin (90°-\bar{\mu}-2\epsilon)} = \frac{\cos (\bar{\mu}+\epsilon)}{\cos (\bar{\mu}+2\epsilon)} \tag{31}$$

$$\xi_{\max} = \frac{2 \sin (\bar{\mu}+\epsilon) \cos (\bar{\mu}+\epsilon)}{\cos (\bar{\mu}+2\epsilon)} \tag{32}$$

$$= \frac{\sin 2(\bar{\mu}+\epsilon)}{\cos (\bar{\mu}+2\epsilon)}, \tag{33}$$

Lower extreme:

$$\frac{\xi_{\min}}{2 \sin (\bar{\mu}-\epsilon)} = \frac{\sin (90°-\bar{\mu}+\epsilon)}{\sin (90°+\bar{\mu}-2\epsilon)} = \frac{\cos (\bar{\mu}-\epsilon)}{\cos (\bar{\mu}-2\epsilon)} \tag{34}$$

$$\xi_{\min} = \frac{2 \sin (\bar{\mu}-\epsilon) \cos (\bar{\mu}-\epsilon)}{\cos (\bar{\mu}-2\epsilon)} \tag{35}$$

$$= \frac{\sin 2(\bar{\mu}-\epsilon)}{\cos (\bar{\mu}-2\epsilon)}. \tag{36}$$

In (33) both numerator and denominator are always positive. In (36) the denominator is always positive but the numerator becomes negative when $\epsilon > \bar{\mu}$; under these circumstances $\xi_{\min}$ becomes negative. But the condition $\epsilon > \bar{\mu}$ is also the condition under which a blind spot develops; it is not surprising, therefore, that a comparison of (36) with (30) shows that these results are the same provided $\xi_{\min} = -\xi_b$. In other words, when $\epsilon > \bar{\mu}$, then $\xi_{\min}$ gives the origin distance of the edge of the blind spot measured along the radius but in a negative direction.

Relations (33) and (36) are very useful in estimating the orientation error, especially when large, of a reciprocal-lattice plane. Table 4 presents $M\xi_{\min}$, $M\xi_b$ and $M\xi_{\max}$ as functions of the error ϵ, for precession angles $\bar{\mu} = 5°$ and $\bar{\mu} = 10°$. The functions are also presented in graphical form in Fig. 23.

The following discussion gives a more general view of the whole situation. In Fig. 24, some geometrical aspects of the motion of precession are illustrated on a reference sphere (*not* the sphere of reflection). The three views of the sphere represent three different phases of the precession cycle. In each view the x-ray beam is the horizontal line, and the views are each seen looking parallel to the plane of the error ϵ. In the upper drawing the precession arc $\bar{\mu}$ is horizontal; i.e., it is normal to the plane of the error ϵ. The diagonal line is the trace on the sphere of the correctly oriented zero-level plane, while the dashed line is the trace of the same plane misoriented by angle ϵ. In the middle view the precession phase has advanced to a general position, and in the bottom view the

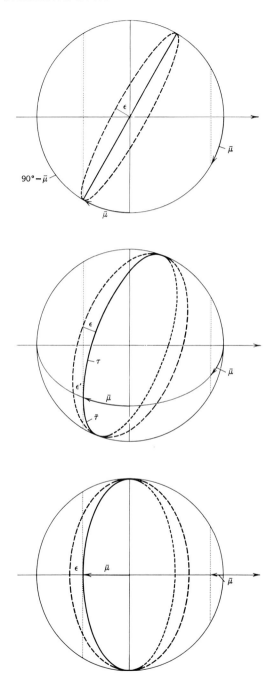

Fig. 24.

precession phase is 90° beyond that of the top view; i.e., the precession arc $\bar{\mu}$ is vertical, and accordingly is in the plane of the error ϵ.

A characteristic of precession motion is that the plane of the arc $\bar{\mu}$ is always normal to the correctly oriented reciprocal-lattice plane. Therefore in the middle view the arcs ϵ' and $\bar{\tau}$ are orthogonal. The spherical triangle having these two orthogonal arcs as sides is shown enlarged to the right. In this right spherical triangle the relation between ϵ', $\bar{\tau}$, and ϵ is

$$\tan \epsilon' = \sin \bar{\tau} \tan \epsilon. \tag{37}$$

When ϵ is small, a good approximation is

$$\epsilon' \approx \epsilon \sin \bar{\tau}, \tag{38}$$

or $$\epsilon' \approx \epsilon \cos \tau, \quad \text{where} \quad \tau = 90° - \bar{\tau}. \tag{39}$$

The angle τ is the azimuth of ϵ' as measured from ϵ in the correctly oriented plane.

Now, along the great circle containing the arcs ϵ' and $\bar{\mu}$ in the middle view of Fig. 24, all the conditions shown in Fig. 22 are satisfied provided ϵ' is substituted for ϵ in Fig. 22. Therefore the distance ξ (to the outer edge of the recorded region) is related to $\bar{\mu}$ and ϵ' as in (33); specifically

$$\xi = \frac{\sin 2(\bar{\mu} + \tan^{-1} [\tan \epsilon \cos \tau])}{\cos (\bar{\mu} + 2 \tan^{-1}[\tan \epsilon \cos \tau])}. \tag{40}$$

Some computed values of this function are given in Table 5. An approximate form of (40), valid when ϵ is small, is given by substituting (39) into (40), specifically

$$\xi = \frac{\sin 2(\bar{\mu} + \epsilon \cos \tau)}{\cos (\bar{\mu} + 2\epsilon \cos \tau)}. \tag{41}$$

Relation (40) and the approximation (41) provide the equation of the edge of the recorded region in polar coordinates, ξ_{max} (radial), as a function of its azimuth τ. Note that when $\epsilon > \bar{\mu}$, the numerators of these functions are negative in the neighborhood of $\tau = 180°$; this corresponds to the blind region. Graphs of the approximate function (41) are shown in Fig. 25. These should correspond with the construction of Figs. 19C and 21 and with the photograph in Fig. 17.

The curvature of the boundary of the recorded region. An alternative measure of the shape of the recorded region is the curvature of its boundary. The customary measure of the curvature of a plane curve expressed in polar coordinates is the external angle ψ between the radius vector ξ and the tangent to the curve. This is generally given by

$$\tan \psi = \xi \left/ \frac{d\xi}{d\tau}. \right. \tag{42}$$

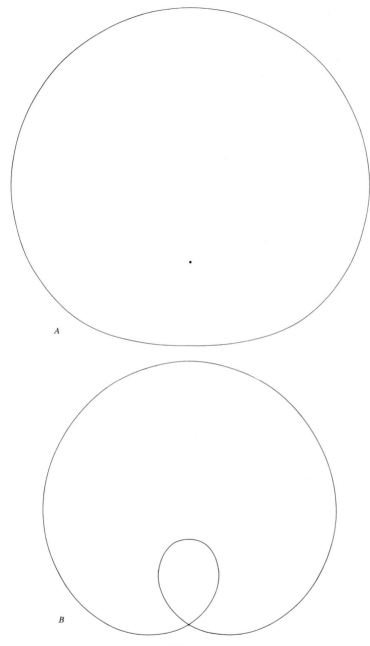

Fig. 25.
Shapes of shaded areas on orientation photographs, as plotted from (41).
A. $\epsilon < \bar{\mu}$: $\bar{\mu} = 10°$, $\epsilon = 5°$.   (Compare with Fig. 19C).
B. $\epsilon > \bar{\mu}$: $\mu = 5°$, $\epsilon = 10°$.   (Compare with Fig. 21).

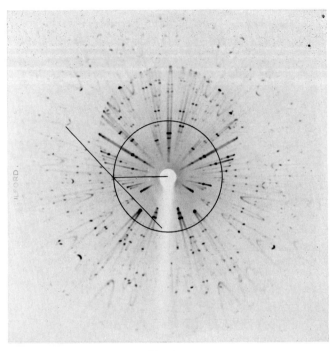

Fig. 26.

Orientation photograph illustrating the determination of the orientation error ($\epsilon = 9°$) by making use of the boundary curvature at the end of the common chord. (Apatite, $Ca_5(OH)(PO_4)_3$, c axis, zero level, $\bar{\mu} = 10°$; MoK, 35 kV, 15 mA, 2 hours.)

The denominator of the right of (42), in this instance, is obtained by differentiating (40) with respect to τ for constant $\bar{\mu}$ and ϵ:

$$\frac{d\xi}{d\tau} = \frac{2\tan\epsilon\cos\bar{\mu}\sin\tau}{\cos^2(\bar{\mu} + 2\tan^{-1}[\tan\epsilon\cos\tau])(1 + \tan^2\epsilon\cos^2\tau)}. \tag{43}$$

When this is substituted into (42) the specific form for the curvature of the boundary of the recorded region at the end of the radius vector ξ is seen to be

$$\tan\psi = -\frac{\xi\cos^2(\bar{\mu} + 2\tan^{-1}[\tan\epsilon\cos\tau])(1 + \tan^2\epsilon\cos^2\tau)}{2\tan\epsilon\cos\bar{\mu}\sin\tau}. \tag{44}$$

A useful special case of this occurs at $\tau = 90°$. There the radius vector coincides with half of the common chord. For this case (44) reduces to

$$\tan\psi_{\tau=90°} = \frac{\xi\cos\bar{\mu}}{2\tan\epsilon} \tag{45}$$

$$= \frac{\sin 2\bar{\mu}}{2\tan\epsilon}. \tag{46}$$

The angle $\psi_{\tau=90°}$ can easily be measured as shown in Fig. 26. The error can be determined from this value by solving (46) for ϵ:

$$\epsilon = \tan^{-1}\left(\frac{\sin 2\bar{\mu}}{2\tan\psi}\right).$$ (47)

When this boundary-curvature method is used the orientation error can be determined regardless of the magnitude of the error. Errors approaching $\epsilon = 90°$, for example, can be determined, although the method is less sensitive at large errors than at small ones.

Application to oblique crystals. A simple application of orientation photographs occurs in connection with oblique crystals, especially monoclinic and triclinic. Suppose, for example, that a monoclinic crystal is oriented by obtaining a reflection from a (100) cleavage in the autocollimator. Since (100) is not normal to [100], but makes an angle $\gamma - 90°$ (first setting) with it, an orientation picture shows an error $\epsilon = \gamma - 90°$ for [100]. The orientation photograph therefore provides the necessary information to make an immediate correction of the orientation (probably using only one arc) so that a precession photograph with [100] as the precessing axis can be made next.

For triclinic crystals a similar strategy can be used. The orientation must generally be corrected by using components on two arcs. An illustration of this is given in Fig. 13.

Application to unoriented crystal fragments. With the aid of the theory already presented it is possible to start with a fragment of completely unknown orientation and orient it for further examination. In this connection the following reasoning is helpful.

Every central reciprocal-lattice plane is shaded by general-radiation streaks. Since a streak occurs between each reciprocal-lattice point and the origin, the shading of a zero-level plane is directly proportional to its spacing and inversely proportional to the translation of the direct lattice normal to the plane. If one can pick out a dense reciprocal-lattice plane by means of shading, he has also found a translation of small interval, and consequently a likely crystallographic axis.

Suppose that a crystal of random orientation is placed on the precession apparatus. The motion tips many reciprocal-lattice planes into the sphere, but only relatively dense planes provide shading dark enough to attract attention. If a sequence of precession orientation photographs is taken for dial readings at, say, 15° intervals, several dense planes will come within range of recognition. The most intensely shaded one can be selected and brought into orientation. Once in orientation, the unit cell and other features can be quickly determined by normal precession methods.

Table 5

Radius, ξ, of the edge of the recorded region in orientation photographs ($\bar{u} = 5°$), as a function of its angle τ from the direction of maximum error, for various error angles ε

τ	0°	1°	2°	3°	4°	5°	6°	10°	15°	20°	25°	30°
0.0°	0.1743	0.2095	0.2449	0.2808	0.3171	0.3541	0.3917	0.5517	0.7847	1.0834	1.5099	2.2235
5.0	0.1743	0.2093	0.2447	0.2804	0.3166	0.3534	0.3909	0.5501	0.7819	1.0785	1.5011	2.2052
10.0	0.1743	0.2089	0.2439	0.2792	0.3149	0.3513	0.3883	0.5454	0.7735	1.0640	1.4751	2.1519
15.0	0.1743	0.2083	0.2425	0.2771	0.3122	0.3478	0.3840	0.5376	0.7596	1.0405	1.4332	2.0674
20.0	0.1743	0.2073	0.2406	0.2743	0.3084	0.3429	0.3781	0.5269	0.7407	1.0085	1.3772	1.9578
25.0	0.1743	0.2062	0.2383	0.2707	0.3035	0.3368	0.3706	0.5133	0.7169	0.9689	1.3095	1.8296
30.0	0.1743	0.2047	0.2354	0.2664	0.2977	0.3294	0.3616	0.4970	0.6888	0.9228	1.2324	1.6895
35.0	0.1743	0.2031	0.2321	0.2613	0.2909	0.3208	0.3511	0.4783	0.6567	0.8712	1.1484	1.5433
40.0	0.1743	0.2012	0.2283	0.2556	0.2832	0.3111	0.3394	0.4573	0.6213	0.8152	1.0598	1.3957
45.0	0.1743	0.1991	0.2241	0.2493	0.2747	0.3004	0.3263	0.4343	0.5829	0.7557	0.9684	1.2501
50.0	0.1743	0.1969	0.2196	0.2424	0.2655	0.2887	0.3122	0.4095	0.5421	0.6937	0.8759	1.1087
55.0	0.1743	0.1944	0.2147	0.2350	0.2555	0.2762	0.2971	0.3832	0.4993	0.6299	0.7834	0.9730
60.0	0.1743	0.1919	0.2095	0.2272	0.2450	0.2630	0.2811	0.3555	0.4549	0.5651	0.6916	0.8434
65.0	0.1743	0.1891	0.2040	0.2190	0.2340	0.2491	0.2644	0.3268	0.4093	0.4996	0.6013	0.7200
70.0	0.1743	0.1863	0.1983	0.2104	0.2226	0.2348	0.2470	0.2971	0.3629	0.4339	0.5125	0.6022
75.0	0.1743	0.1834	0.1925	0.2016	0.2108	0.2200	0.2292	0.2669	0.3159	0.3684	0.4256	0.4896
80.0	0.1743	0.1804	0.1865	0.1926	0.1987	0.2049	0.2111	0.2362	0.2687	0.3031	0.3403	0.3813
85.0	0.1743	0.1774	0.1804	0.1835	0.1866	0.1896	0.1927	0.2053	0.2214	0.2384	0.2566	0.2765
90.0	0.1743	0.1743	0.1743	0.1743	0.1743	0.1743	0.1743	0.1743	0.1743	0.1743	0.1743	0.1743
95.0	0.1743	0.1713	0.1682	0.1651	0.1621	0.1590	0.1559	0.1435	0.1276	0.1109	0.0932	0.0739
100.0	0.1743	0.1682	0.1621	0.1561	0.1500	0.1439	0.1378	0.1131	0.0815	0.0483	0.0130	−0.0255
105.0	0.1743	0.1652	0.1562	0.1471	0.1381	0.1290	0.1199	0.0832	0.0361	−0.0134	−0.0664	−0.1245
110.0	0.1743	0.1623	0.1504	0.1384	0.1265	0.1145	0.1025	0.0541	−0.0083	−0.0740	−0.1451	−0.2239
115.0	0.1743	0.1595	0.1448	0.1300	0.1152	0.1005	0.0856	0.0258	−0.0515	−0.1335	−0.2231	−0.3239

Table 5 (*Continued*)

ϵ

τ	0°	1°	2°	3°	4°	5°	6°	10°	15°	20°	25°	30°
120.0	0.1743	0.1568	0.1394	0.1219	0.1045	0.0870	0.0695	-0.0013	-0.0932	-0.1915	-0.3002	-0.4249
125.0	0.1743	0.1542	0.1342	0.1142	0.0942	0.0742	0.0541	-0.0272	-0.1332	-0.2478	-0.3763	-0.5268
130.0	0.1743	0.1518	0.1294	0.1070	0.0846	0.0622	0.0397	-0.0517	-0.1713	-0.3020	-0.4508	-0.6292
135.0	0.1743	0.1496	0.1249	0.1003	0.0757	0.0510	0.0262	-0.0744	-0.2071	-0.3536	-0.5233	-0.7316
140.0	0.1743	0.1475	0.1208	0.0941	0.0675	0.0407	0.0139	-0.0954	-0.2404	-0.4021	-0.5928	-0.8327
145.0	0.1743	0.1457	0.1171	0.0886	0.0601	0.0315	0.0028	-0.1144	-0.2707	-0.4471	-0.6584	-0.9309
150.0	0.1743	0.1440	0.1139	0.0837	0.0536	0.0233	-0.0070	-0.1312	-0.2978	-0.4878	-0.7190	-1.0243
155.0	0.1743	0.1426	0.1111	0.0795	0.0480	0.0163	-0.0155	-0.1457	-0.3214	-0.5236	-0.7733	-1.1103
160.0	0.1743	0.1415	0.1087	0.0760	0.0433	0.0105	-0.0225	-0.1578	-0.3412	-0.5539	-0.8201	-1.1862
165.0	0.1743	0.1406	0.1069	0.0733	0.0397	0.0059	-0.0280	-0.1674	-0.3568	-0.5782	-0.8580	-1.2491
170.0	0.1743	0.1399	0.1056	0.0713	0.0371	0.0026	-0.0320	-0.1742	-0.3682	-0.5960	-0.8861	-1.2963
175.0	0.1743	0.1395	0.1048	0.0702	0.0355	0.0007	-0.0344	-0.1784	-0.3751	-0.6068	-0.9032	-1.3256
180.0	0.1743	0.1394	0.1045	0.0698	0.0349	-0.0000	-0.0352	-0.1798	-0.3774	-0.6104	-0.9090	-1.3356

Table 6

Radius, ξ, of the edge of the recorded region in orientation photographs ($\bar{u} = 10°$), as a function of its angle τ from the direction of maximum error, for various error angles ε

τ	0°	1°	2°	3°	4°	5°	6°	10°	15°	20°	25°	30°
0.0°	0.3473	0.3830	0.4192	0.4560	0.4936	0.5321	0.5715	0.7422	1.0000	1.3473	1.8794	2.8794
5.0	0.3473	0.3828	0.4189	0.4556	0.4931	0.5314	0.5706	0.7405	0.9968	1.3415	1.8680	2.8519
10.0	0.3473	0.3824	0.4181	0.4543	0.4913	0.5291	0.5679	0.7354	0.9873	1.3242	1.8343	2.7721
15.0	0.3473	0.3818	0.4167	0.4522	0.4885	0.5255	0.5634	0.7270	0.9717	1.2962	1.7804	2.6477
20.0	0.3473	0.3808	0.4148	0.4493	0.4845	0.5204	0.5572	0.7154	0.9504	1.2583	1.7091	2.4895
25.0	0.3473	0.3796	0.4124	0.4456	0.4795	0.5140	0.5494	0.7008	0.9239	1.2119	1.6238	2.3091
30.0	0.3473	0.3782	0.4094	0.4412	0.4734	0.5063	0.5399	0.6833	0.8925	1.1581	1.5282	2.1173
35.0	0.3473	0.3765	0.4060	0.4360	0.4664	0.4974	0.5290	0.6633	0.8571	1.0986	1.4256	1.9230
40.0	0.3473	0.3746	0.4022	0.4301	0.4585	0.4873	0.5167	0.6410	0.8181	1.0345	1.3192	1.7325
45.0	0.3473	0.3725	0.3979	0.4237	0.4498	0.4762	0.5032	0.6165	0.7761	0.9673	1.2113	1.5500
50.0	0.3473	0.3702	0.3933	0.4166	0.4402	0.4642	0.4885	0.5903	0.7318	0.8980	1.1040	1.3778
55.0	0.3473	0.3677	0.3883	0.4091	0.4301	0.4513	0.4729	0.5626	0.6858	0.8276	0.9985	1.2167
60.0	0.3473	0.3651	0.3830	0.4010	0.4193	0.4377	0.4563	0.5336	0.6384	0.7567	0.8957	1.0667
65.0	0.3473	0.3623	0.3774	0.3927	0.4080	0.4235	0.4391	0.5036	0.5901	0.6861	0.7961	0.9273
70.0	0.3473	0.3594	0.3717	0.3839	0.3963	0.4088	0.4213	0.4729	0.5413	0.6161	0.7000	0.7972
75.0	0.3473	0.3565	0.3657	0.3750	0.3843	0.3937	0.4031	0.4417	0.4924	0.5470	0.6072	0.6754
80.0	0.3473	0.3535	0.3596	0.3658	0.3721	0.3783	0.3846	0.4102	0.4436	0.4791	0.5177	0.5606
85.0	0.3473	0.3504	0.3535	0.3566	0.3597	0.3628	0.3660	0.3787	0.3951	0.4125	0.4312	0.4516
90.0	0.3473	0.3473	0.3473	0.3473	0.3473	0.3473	0.3473	0.3473	0.3473	0.3473	0.3473	0.3473
95.0	0.3473	0.3442	0.3411	0.3380	0.3349	0.3319	0.3288	0.3162	0.3002	0.2835	0.2658	0.2466
100.0	0.3473	0.3411	0.3350	0.3289	0.3227	0.3166	0.3105	0.2857	0.2541	0.2212	0.1864	0.1487
105.0	0.3473	0.3381	0.3290	0.3199	0.3108	0.3017	0.2925	0.2559	0.2092	0.1605	0.1089	0.0528
110.0	0.3473	0.3352	0.3231	0.3111	0.2991	0.2871	0.2751	0.2269	0.1655	0.1015	0.0331	−0.0418
115.0	0.3473	0.3324	0.3175	0.3026	0.2878	0.2731	0.2583	0.1190	0.1234	0.0442	−0.0410	−0.1354

Table 6 (*Continued*)

τ	0°	1°	2°	3°	4°	5°	6°	10°	15°	20°	25°	30°
						ε						
120.0	0.3473	0.3296	0.3120	0.2945	0.2771	0.2596	0.2422	0.1723	0.0830	−0.0112	−0.1134	−0.2283
125.0	0.3473	0.3270	0.3069	0.2868	0.2669	0.2469	0.2270	01.470	0.0444	−0.0643	−0.1838	−0.3205
130.0	0.3473	0.3246	0.3020	0.2796	0.2573	0.2350	0.2127	0.1232	0.0081	−0.1150	−0.2519	−0.4116
135.0	0.3473	0.3223	0.2976	0.2729	0.2484	0.2239	0.1994	0.1011	−0.0259	−0.1629	−0.3173	−0.5011
140.0	0.3473	0.3203	0.2934	0.2668	0.2402	0.2137	0.1873	0.0808	−0.0573	−0.2075	−0.3793	−0.5880
145.0	0.3473	0.3184	0.2897	0.2613	0.2329	0.2046	0.1764	0.0625	−0.0858	−0.2485	−0.4372	−0.6711
150.0	0.3473	0.3168	0.2865	0.2564	0.2264	0.1966	0.1667	0.0464	−0.1111	−0.2854	−0.4901	−0.7489
155.0	0.3473	0.3153	0.2837	0.2522	0.2209	0.1897	0.1585	0.0325	−0.1331	−0.3176	−0.5371	−0.8159
160.0	0.3473	0.3142	0.2813	0.2488	0.2163	0.1840	0.1516	0.0209	−0.1514	−0.3448	−0.5772	−0.8810
165.0	0.3473	0.3132	0.2795	0.2460	0.2127	0.1795	0.1462	0.0118	−0.1659	−0.3664	−0.6096	−0.9315
170.0	0.3473	0.3126	0.2782	0.2441	0.2101	0.1762	0.1424	0.0053	−0.1763	−0.3822	−0.6333	−0.9690
175.0	0.3473	0.3122	0.2774	0.2429	0.2086	0.1743	0.1400	0.0013	−0.1827	−0.3917	−0.6478	−0.9922
180.0	0.3473	0.3121	0.2772	0.2425	0.2080	0.1736	0.1393	0.0000	−0.1848	−0.3949	−0.6527	−1.0000

9

Cone-axis photographs

The cone-axis photograph bears the same general relation to the precession photograph that the rotating-crystal photograph does to the Weissenberg photograph. Its most obvious use is the determination, from measurements made on it, of the translation of the crystal axis which is the axis of the Laue cone. But it has other useful properties. Most important, it provides information about the crystal symmetry, for the symmetry of each ring of the photograph is the Friedel symmetry of the corresponding level of the reciprocal lattice. The spots on a cone-axis photograph can also be indexed. If there is an error in the orientation of the axis, the photograph contains data for determining the error. Furthermore, the cone-axis photograph made with radiation containing general radiation is related to the Laue photograph. These matters are discussed in this chapter.

Determination of the translation

Relevant relations. The determination of the translation along the axis of the Laue cone from measurements of the diameters of the rings on the cone-axis photograph has been discussed in Chapter 2 and again, from a reciprocal-lattice point of view, in Chapter 3. Some of the basic relations developed there were the following:

Chapter 2:

(1): $$\frac{n\lambda}{t} = \cos \bar{\mu} - \cos \bar{\nu}_n \qquad (1)$$

(2): $$\tan \bar{\nu}_n = \frac{r_n}{s} \qquad (2)$$

Chapter 3:

(22): $$\zeta_n = nd^* = n\,\frac{\lambda}{t}$$ (3)

(15): $$\zeta = \cos \bar{\mu} - \cos \bar{\nu}$$ (4)

(21): $$\zeta = \cos \bar{\mu} - \cos \tan^{-1} \frac{r_n}{s}$$ (5)

(19): $$s = r_n \cot \cos^{-1} (\cos \bar{\mu} - \zeta)$$ (6)

Techniques. The cone-axis cassette as currently made holds a film $3\frac{3}{4}$ in. square. Some cone-axis photographs are shown in Fig. 1. Each is characterized by reflections located on a set of concentric circles which mark the intersections of the Laue cones with the film, which is set perpendicular to the cone axis. The order of the Laue cone is specified by n in (1). When $n = 0$, then $\bar{\mu} = \bar{\nu}$, and (2) shows that the radius of this zero-order ring is $s \tan \bar{\mu}$. When n is positive, (1) shows that $\cos \bar{\mu} > \cos \bar{\nu}$ so that $\bar{\nu} > \bar{\mu}$; accordingly, rings for positive n are found outside the zero-order ring, while those for negative n are found inside this ring. To index the order of the ring, it is convenient to be able to distinguish the zero-order ring on sight. Although this ring does have some distinguishing features, it is easy to arrange the technique so that the innermost ring is always the zero-order ring.

In order that the zero ring should be innermost, it is required that negative-order rings should not record. The limiting conditions for this is that the first negative-order ring just barely records, i.e., that the radius of the ring for which $n = -1$ is just zero. If this value of r_{-1} is substituted into (5), or if $\bar{\nu} = 0$ is substituted into (4), these equations reduce to $\zeta_{-1} = \cos \bar{\mu} - 1$. Values of d^* and t corresponding to this condition are listed in Table 1 for various useful radiations. It can be seen

Table 1

Values of the translation t for which the first negative-order Laue cone just appears on cone-axis photographs

		t			
			Radiation		
$\bar{\mu}$	ζ	Ag$K\alpha$	Mo$K\alpha$	Cu$K\alpha$	Fe$K\alpha$
		$\lambda = 0.5608$ Å	0.7107 Å	1.5418 Å	1.9373 Å
5°	−0.00381	147. Å	187. Å	405. Å	508. Å
10°	−0.01519	36.9	46.8	102.	128.
15°	−0.03407	16.5	20.9	45.3	56.9
20°	−0.06031	9.30	11.78	25.6	32.1
25°	−0.09369	5.99	7.59	16.5	20.7
30°	−0.13397	4.19	5.30	11.5	14.5

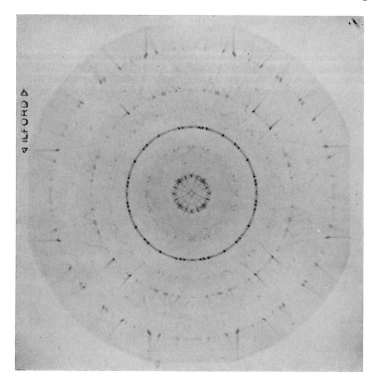

Fig. 1.1.

Example of cone-axis photograph. The darkest ring is the zero level. Odd-numbered levels are faint. Levels shown are −2 (near center), −1, 0, 1, 2, 3, 4. (Garnet from Oregon beach sand; a axis, $\bar{\mu} = 30°$, $s = 30$ mm; $MoK\alpha$, 35 kV, 15 mA, 40 minutes.)

that if $\bar{\mu}$ is set at 10°, there will be no negative-order rings when using Mo radiation unless t exceeds 46.8 Å, a most unlikely condition for most crystals except biological compounds with very large cells.

Calibration of s. If precautions are not taken, the values of t obtained from cone-axis photographs are not very accurate. This error is not ordinarily connected with setting $\bar{\mu}$, for this angle is set by a vernier reading directly to 5 min., so the angle can be set accurately to $2\frac{1}{2}$ min. This involves an error of less than 0.02% at $\bar{\mu} = 10°$, 0.03% at $\bar{\mu} = 20°$, and 0.05% at $\bar{\mu} = 30°$. Thus the first term in (5) does not contribute a substantial error.

The measurement of s in (5) may, however, involve a small error. One reason is that the cone-axis cassette slips into the holder for the layer-line screen, and the plane of the film is not necessarily coincident with the plane of the layer-line screen. Usually a small constant must be added to the reading of the layer-line screen to obtain the correct s for

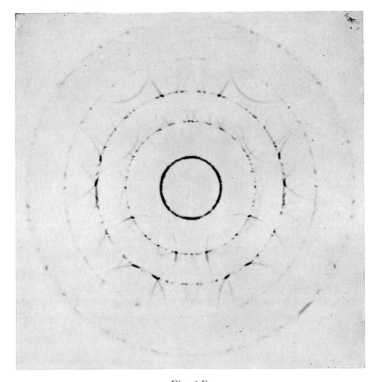

Fig. 1*B*.
Example of cone-axis photograph. Levels shown are 0 (nearest center), 1, 2, 3, 4.
(Wollastonite, $CaSiO_3$; c axis, $\bar{\mu} = 15°$, $s = 30$ mm; $MoK\alpha$, 35 kV, 15 mA, 45 minutes.)

computation of ζ or t. To determine this, the radius of the zero-level circle should be measured. For $n = 0$, $\bar{\nu} = \bar{\mu}$, so s is then given by (2) as

$$s = \frac{r_0}{\tan \bar{\mu}}. \tag{7}$$

If this value is used in (5), more consistent values of ζ are obtained from the various rings.

Calculation of ζ. In setting the camera forward by distance $M\zeta$ when making an upper-level precession photograph, ζ_n can be determined individually for each precession photograph from the corresponding cone-axis ring. But better values can be obtained by combining the values computed from the measurement of all rings. According to (3),

$$d^* = \frac{1}{n} \zeta_n. \tag{8}$$

If this is combined with (5), the following computing form is obtained:

$$d^* = \frac{1}{n}\left(\cos\bar{\mu} - \cos\tan^{-1}\frac{r_n}{s}\right). \tag{9}$$

An example of the computation involved in this procedure is given in Table 2.

Table 2
Example of computation of d^* from cone-axis data
(Molybdophyllite, d^*_{001})

$$\bar{\mu} = 10°$$

$$s = \frac{\tan\bar{\mu}}{r_0} = 40.00 \text{ mm}$$

$$d^*_{001} = \frac{1}{n}\zeta_n = \frac{1}{n}\left(\cos\bar{\mu} - \cos\tan^{-1}\frac{r_n}{s}\right)$$

Level n	r_n	$\dfrac{r_n}{s}$	$\cos\bar{\mu}$	$\cos\tan^{-1}\dfrac{r_n}{s}$	$nd^*_{001} = \zeta_n$	$d^*_{001} = \dfrac{1}{n}\zeta_n$
0	7.10 mm	.1775	.9848	.9848	0	—
1	18.59	.4646	.9848	.9069	.0779	.0779
2	27.00	.6750	.9848	.8287	.1561	.0781
3	35.08	.8769	.9848	.7519	.2329	.0776

$$6\big|.4669$$

Weighted average, $d^*_{001} = .07782$

$$t_{[001]} = \lambda\frac{1}{d^*_{001}} = 9.13 \text{ Å}$$

In a set of computations like those of Table 2, a drift of the computed value of d^* with n is often noted. Instead of computing an average value of d^*, the values can be extrapolated against some function of the measured value of r on the grounds that some systematic error is involved in this measurement. Qurashi and Barnes[23] suggest extrapolating d^* against $r_n{}^2$. An example of such an extrapolation is shown in Fig. 2.

From the best value of d^*_{wvw}, t_{uvw} can be computed from (3).

Indexing cone-axis photographs

If one has a precession instrument the occasion to index a cone-axis photograph will arise most infrequently. On the other hand, if one does *not* have a precession instrument a cone-axis camera can be constructed very easily. The instrument is more suitable to crystallographic investigations than a rotating-crystal camera. For example, it provides not only the length of the translation along a rational axis, but its symmetry also. Under these circumstances it may be useful to index the photographs. Furthermore, there are occasions where this procedure may even be worth knowing with a precession instrument, for example, in the correction of orientation errors. Indexing such photographs is consequently treated here. Fisher[20] was the first to point out how cone-axis photographs can be indexed.

The plane of the cone-axis is parallel to the planes of the precession photograph and of the reciprocal lattice. These three planes differ from one another in distance from the crystal. For indexing purposes either the scale of each level of the reciprocal lattice or the scale of the

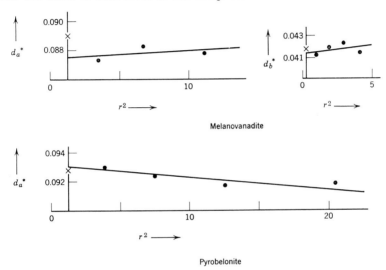

Melanovanadite

Pyrobelonite

Fig. 2.
Graphs of d^* against r^2 for cone-axis photographs of melanovanadite and pyrobelonite; crosses indicate values of d^* obtained from zero-level precession photographs.
(After Qurashi and Barnes.[23])

cone-axis photograph must be changed, so that both have the same effective distance from the crystal. Since the arrangement of points on each level of any lattice is the same, except for a possible shift of origin, it is convenient to regard the level pattern as invariant and so to change the scale of the cone-axis ring to correspond with that required by the particular level in question. More specifically, the distance from the crystal to the n-level film is $M \cos \bar{\nu}$, while the distance from the crystal to the cone-axis film is s. The cone-axis geometry must be enlarged differently for each level in order to scale s to become $M \cos \bar{\nu}$, i.e., the radius of the ring for each level must be multiplied by a factor $(M \cos \bar{\nu})/s$.

The theory of indexing can be understood with the aid of Fig. 3, which is a representation like that of Fig. 1, Chapter 7. Figure 3B is drawn in the plane of the reciprocal lattice. This means that the view is always along the precessing axis, which is also the axis of the Laue cones. This axis appears as point S, the center of the reflecting circle, whose distance from the origin is always sin $\bar{\mu}$. During precession the origin remains fixed, but S appears to rotate around O along the dotted path of Fig. 3.

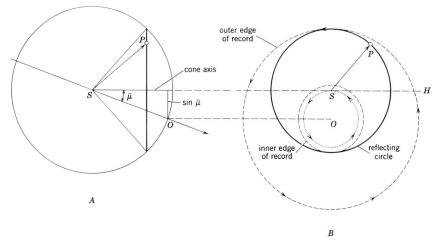

Fig. 3.

Fig. 4.
Mechanical aid for indexing cone-axis photographs.
(After Fisher.[20])

As S rotates about O, the reflecting circle is carried with it, and when the circle touches a reciprocal-lattice point P, a reflection SP is produced along a generator of the Laue cone. On the cone-axis photograph this produces a spot on the circle at P. As the precession motion proceeds, the center of the circle rotates about O, but the azimuth SH is maintained horizontal. In this motion, whenever a point P cuts the circle, a corresponding spot occurs at the corresponding point of the cone-axis ring.

A convenient aid in indexing a cone-axis photograph is a universal drafting machine by means of which a piece of tracing sheet can be translated parallel to itself over the plane of the drawing board, as shown in Fig. 4. To use this apparatus for indexing cone-axis photographs, the

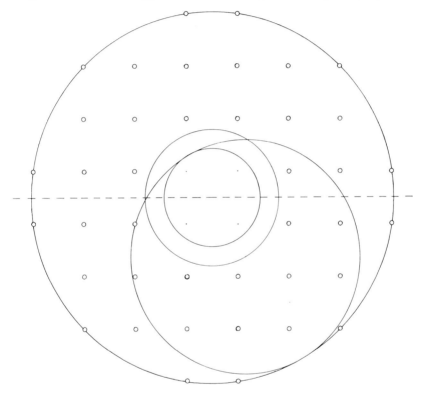

Fig. 5.
Example of plot used in the indexing of a cone-axis photograph. The first level of the reciprocal lattice of sphalerite, ZnS. The circles correspond with those shown in Fig. 3. The point P in reflecting position is $1\bar{3}1$.
(After Fisher.[20])

reciprocal lattice is first plotted on drawing paper to some convenient scale, and then fixed to the drafting table so that the row of points parallel to the dial axis is horizontal. A circle of radius $\sin \bar{\mu}$ is drawn on it, with the origin as center. Along this circle the center S of the Laue cone will be caused to migrate as in Fig. 3B. Next, on a separate sheet of tracing material, a circle is drawn to represent the reflecting circle. Its center is S and its radius is $\sin \bar{\nu}$ on the same scale as the reciprocal lattice. This sheet is stuck by means of Scotch tape to the ruler of the drafting

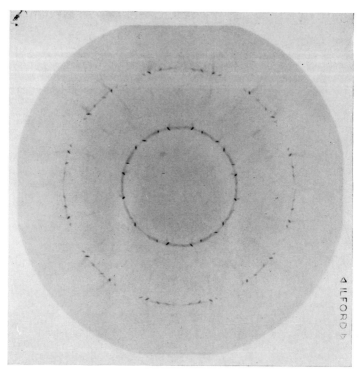

Fig. 6 *A*. Comparison of cone-axis photograph with predicted arrangement of reflections. Cone-axis photograph of sphalerite, ZnS. (Precessing axis: a_1; dial axis: a_2; $\bar{\mu} = 20°$; Mo$K\alpha$, 35 kV, 15 mA, 2 hours.)

machine, which then permits the circle to be moved by pure translation over the surface of the reciprocal-lattice level. Specifically, it is moved so that its center *S* migrates around the circle of radius sin $\bar{\mu}$ on the drawing of the reciprocal lattice. During this migration the circle encounters numerous reciprocal-lattice points. Whenever this occurs, a mark is made on the migrating circle at the place where the reciprocal-lattice point is encountered. When *S* has been allowed to migrate around *O* for a full cycle, the drawing is complete. The result is a drawing of the spot locations of one cone-axis ring, drawn on a scale such that its distance from the crystal is cos $\bar{\nu}$. To make it coincide with the corresponding ring on the cone-axis photograph, its scale must be changed by a factor $(\cos \bar{\mu})/s$. Whether the scale is changed or not, the arrangement of spots about the circle as drawn corresponds with the arrangement of spots on the cone-axis ring.

An example of the use of this technique is shown in Fig. 5. The results for two of the rings are shown in Fig. 6.

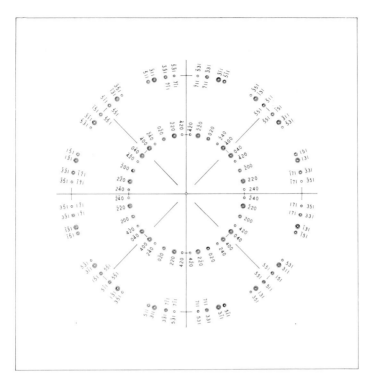

Fig. 6 *B*. Location and indexing of reflections in cone-axis photograph of sphalerite using Figs. 4 and 5. (After Fisher.[20])

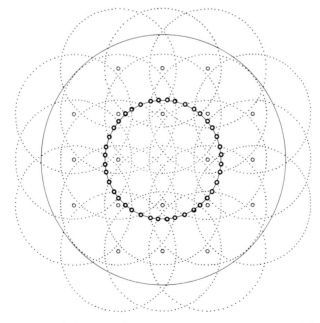

Fig. 7. Alternative indexing procedure for cone-axis photographs applied to the zero level of sphalerite. (After Fisher.[20])

Alternative indexing procedure

In Fig. 3B, the cone-axis ring of radius sin $\bar{\nu}$ is translated so that its center S follows the dotted circle of radius sin $\bar{\mu}$. An equivalent scheme is to fix the cone-axis ring and translate the reciprocal lattice so that its origin follows a circle of radius sin $\bar{\mu}$. If this is done, each reciprocal-lattice point migrates in a circle of radius sin $\bar{\mu}$. This presents an alternative method, due to Fisher[20], for indexing cone-axis photographs. The points of the reciprocal lattice are plotted, and a circle of radius

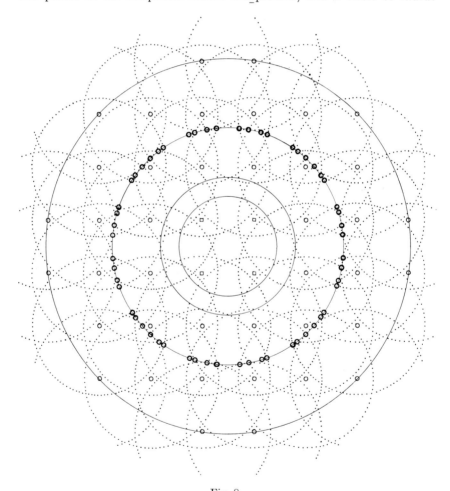

Fig. 8.
Alternative indexing procedure for cone-axis photographs applied to the first level of sphalerite.

(After Fisher.[20])

sin $\bar{\nu}$ drawn with the origin of the reciprocal lattice as center. About every reciprocal-lattice point a circle of radius sin $\bar{\mu}$ is drawn. In general, such circles intersect the cone-axis ring in two points, which are the locations of reflections. Examples of this kind of indexing are shown in Figs. 7 and 8.

Record produced by a single reciprocal-lattice point

In any diffraction method every point of the reciprocal lattice goes through the sphere of reflection twice, once on entering and once on leaving the sphere. In each method two diffraction spots correspond to each

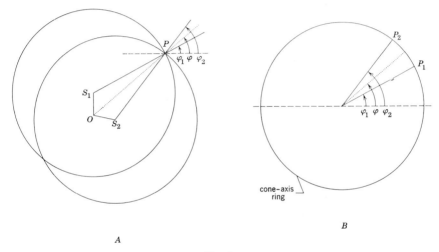

A

B

Fig. 9.

Relations between the direction φ of a point P in the reciprocal lattice and the positions φ_1 and φ_2 of its reflections in the cone-axis ring.

reciprocal-lattice point. In the rotating-crystal method the spots are symmetrical with respect to the axis of the film parallel to the rotation axis. In the Weissenberg method the spots are centrosymmetrical in a point on the center line. In the precession method the spots coincide.

In the cone-axis photograph, these two points record separately and in a novel manner. The reason is suggested by Fig. 9*A*, which is based on the geometry discussed in Chapter 7. Bearing in mind that the reflecting circle is caused to migrate by translation over the level of the reciprocal lattice, it follows that to find out where the two spots are located on the cone-axis ring, the two centers S_1 and S_2 of Fig. 9*A* must be brought together by translation. As a result, P_1 and P_2 are located as in Fig. 9*B*. In a cone-axis photograph, then, spots occur in pairs that are separated by an arc which may appear, offhand, to have arbitrary location and magnitude.

The connecting arc can be readily related to the geometry of the reciprocal lattice and to the geometry of diffraction, as follows. The location of point P of the reciprocal lattice may be described by spherical coordinate σ (its origin distance), φ (its longitude) and ρ (its co-latitude). If in Fig. 9B the view is from the direction of positive ζ, then φ is positive in the direction shown in Fig. 9A. It can be seen that

$$\varphi = \frac{\varphi_1 + \varphi_2}{2}. \tag{10}$$

Thus the mean azimuth angle of a paired couple of points on a cone-axis photograph is the φ coordinate of the reciprocal-lattice point producing it.

The length of the arc connecting P_1 and P_2 is $\varphi_1 - \varphi_2$, and is thus the same as 2ψ of Fig. 4, Chapter 7. The value of ψ was given by (3) of Chapter 7, so that the length of the arc connecting P_1 and P_2 in Fig. 9B is

$$\varphi_1 - \varphi_2 = 2\psi = 2 \cos^{-1} \frac{\xi^2 + \sin^2 \bar{\nu} - \sin^2 \bar{\mu}}{2 \, \xi \sin \bar{\nu}}. \tag{11}$$

Symmetry of cone-axis photographs

Relation between symmetries of level and ring. The last section provides a background for understanding the symmetry displayed by a ring of a cone-axis photograph. The symmetry of a level of the reciprocal lattice must be one of the 10 plane point-groups listed in Table 2 of Chapter 6. Each such symmetry can be referred to an n-fold axis and a possible mirror.

If the reciprocal lattice is symmetrical with respect to an n-fold axis in the precessing axis, then equivalent points P are related by an n-fold axis; as a consequence of this, vectors to these points from the origin have equal lengths σ, equal co-latitudes ρ, and their φ's are related by

$$\varphi_B = \varphi_A + \frac{2\pi}{n}. \tag{12}$$

In the cone-axis photograph according to (10) the paired spots therefore repeat around the circle at intervals of $2\pi/n$, as suggested by Fig. 10A.

Theorem: If the qth level of the reciprocal lattice is symmetrical with respect to an n-fold axis, so is the qth ring of the cone-axis photograph.

If two points P_A and P_B are related in the reciprocal lattice by a mirror containing the precessing axis and at azimuth φ_m, then they can be described by vectors whose magnitudes are both σ, whose co-latitudes are both ρ, and whose angles φ are related to that of the mirror by

$$\frac{\varphi_A + \varphi_B}{2} = \varphi_m. \tag{13}$$

In the cone-axis photograph the spot pairs are therefore related according to (13), as suggested by Fig. 10B.

Theorem: If the q*th level of the reciprocal lattice is symmetrical with respect to a mirror at azimuth* φ_m, *so is the* q*th ring of the cone-axis photograph.*

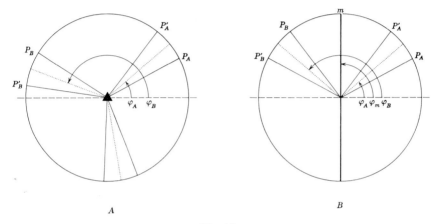

Fig. 10.
Relation between the symmetry of points in the reciprocal lattice and the symmetry of their reflections in the cone-axis ring.

Symmetry of the zero-level ring.   The zero-level ring may contain additional symmetry beyond that of the upper levels.   Friedel's law requires it to be centrosymmetrical, so that it contains a 2-fold axis whether the upper levels do or not.   Furthermore, it may contain additional symmetry elements not in the upper levels, because all axes and planes of the point group intersect at level zero.   The zero ring of the cone-axis photograph may have greater symmetry, therefore, than the upper-level rings.

Some cone-axis photographs displaying different symmetries are seen in Fig. 11.

General-radiation streaks

Most cone-axis photographs, even if made with filtered radiation, contain general-radiation streaks which have a curious distribution con-

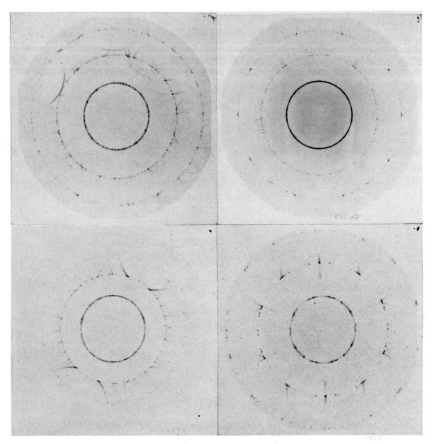

Fig. 11.
Some cone-axis photographs displaying different symmetries.
$(\bar{\mu} = 20°)$

Arrangement of symmetries;

Page 164

| 1 | roemerite | m | $S_2C_4(CN)_4$ |
| 2 | sucrose | $2mm$ | marcasite |

Page 165

3	ilmenite	$3m$	coquimbite
4	pentaerythritol	$4mm$	garnet
6	apatite	$6mm$	BeO

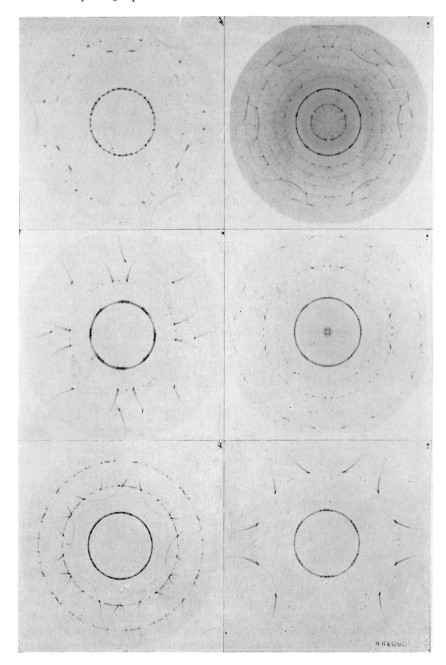

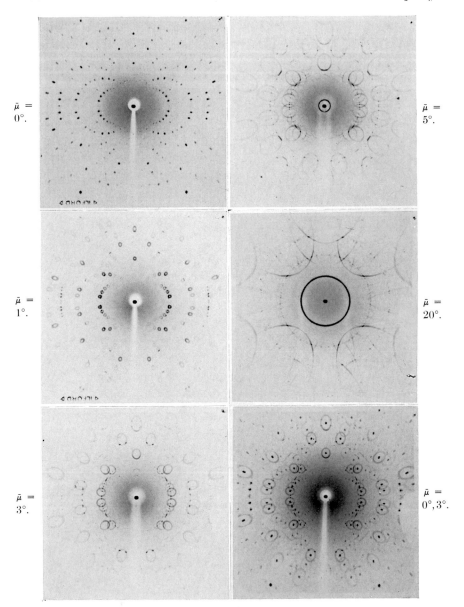

$\bar{\mu} = 0°.$

$\bar{\mu} = 5°.$

$\bar{\mu} = 1°.$

$\bar{\mu} = 20°.$

$\bar{\mu} = 3°.$

$\bar{\mu} = 0°, 3°.$

Fig. 12.
The relation between a Laue photograph and cone-axis photographs.   (Monticellite,
CaMgSiO₄, c axis; MoK, 35 kV, 18 mA, 20 minutes.)

forming to the symmetry. Fisher[20] noticed that this distribution bears an interesting relation to a Laue photograph. Why this should be so can be demonstrated with the aid of the reciprocal lattice.

It was pointed out in Chapter 8 that the reciprocal lattice for characteristic radiation is a lattice array of points at vector distances λ/d_{hkl} from the origin; but for general radiation λ is continuously variable, so each point is replaced by a ray whose course is a straight line from the origin through the point of the lattice array. This ray does not start at the origin, but rather at a distance from the origin depending on λ_{min}, the shortest wavelength in the general radiation; this in turn depends on the potential V across the x-ray tube in a manner which can be written

$$\lambda_{min} V = \frac{hc}{e} \tag{14}$$

$$= 12.39, \text{ if } \lambda \text{ is expressed in Å and } V \text{ in kilovolts.}$$

Thus the general-radiation streak starts at

$$\sigma_{min} = \frac{\lambda_{min}}{d_{hkl}} = \frac{\lambda_{min} V}{d_{hkl} V} \tag{15}$$

$$= \frac{12.39}{d_{hkl} V}, \text{ if the voltage is expressed in kilovolts.}$$

For present purposes, then, the reciprocal lattice corresponds to rays parallel to d_{hkl} which begin as indicated by (15), and each incidentally contains the reciprocal-lattice point due to the characteristic radiation. For convenience, let the component of the reciprocal lattice due to general radiation be called the *burr*. The burr can be described as a collection of line segments along lines radiating from the origin, but not including the origin.

With this background the Laue photograph is explained as follows: For the Bernal explanation of diffraction, the center of the burr is placed where the x-ray beam leaves the sphere of reflection. Many of its rays pierce the sphere. In general each such ray must enter the sphere at the origin, so the point of piercing is produced as the ray leaves the sphere. Whenever a ray does this a diffracted ray is generated, originating at the center of the sphere and extending through the point of the sphere's surface which has been pierced. The Laue photograph is a record of these diffracted rays as received on a photographic film placed normal to the direct x-ray beam. An example of a Laue photograph is shown in Fig. 12, as part of a series to be treated presently.

A well-known characteristic of a Laue photograph is that the spots occur along loci which are conic sections. The reciprocal-lattice explana-

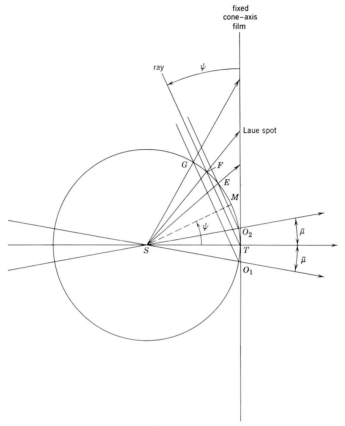

Fig. 13.

tion of this is simple. With each rational direction [*uvw*] in the direct lattice, there is associated in the reciprocal lattice a stack of planes (*uvw*)*. For the general-radiation streaks, only the zero level of this stack is significant, for the rays of the burr are coplanar only in a zero level. Those which are coplanar correspond to direct-lattice planes whose spacings are perpendicular to the original translation; these are the planes of the zone [*uvw*]. Wherever a possible zero-level plane cuts the sphere, a small-circle intersection is produced. Rays from the center of the sphere to the points of a small circle delimit a circular cone, which intersects the plane of the photographic film in a conic section. All such conic sections contain the origin, and are symmetrical in a ray from the origin. All this follows simply from the diffraction by a burr.

    If the crystal is caused to precess, the burr precesses also, with its center at the point where the x-ray beam leaves the sphere. Each ray of the burr which intersects the sphere gives rise to a reflection which becomes a general-radiation trail on the film. It is convenient to study what occurs on the cone-axis film by regarding the film in Fig. 11, Chapter 3, as fixed and placed vertically, with s taken arbitrarily as unity. Accordingly, in Fig. 13 the film, its normal ST, and the sphere are fixed, while the x-ray beam SO precesses, making a constant angle $\bar{\mu}$ with ST; this carries the origin O about a circle of radius $\sin \bar{\mu}$. Consider a particular ray which makes an angle ψ with the plane of the photograph. Since this ray is along a line containing the origin, it sweeps out a cylinder with a circular base inclined at an angle ψ to its axis. The geometry of the cylinder, the sphere, and their intersections are related by symmetry plane SM perpendicular to the cylinder and halfway between intersections, so that circle GE is the mirror image of circle O_1O_2; in fact the polar zones GFE and O_1TO_2 are duplicates, so both subtend from the center S cones of half opening angles $\bar{\mu}$. The intersection of the cone GSE with the film is a conic section with the Laue spot at one focus. If ψ is small, this general radiation trail is an ellipse.

Figure 12 traces the relation between a Laue photograph of a crystal and the general-radiation streaks of a cone-axis photograph.

Orientation errors

When the axis of the Laue cone is perfectly oriented along the precessing axis, the resulting cone-axis photograph consists of spots distributed on circles concentric with the point where the precessing axis intersects the film. If there is a small angular error between the translation and the precessing axis, the circles broaden into nearly circular bands. Examples are shown in Fig. 14.

The origin of this effect is illustrated in Fig. 15. The plane of the photograph is parallel to the correctly oriented zero level in Fig. 15A. The actual zero level, misoriented by angle ϵ, is shown dashed. This determines an abnormally large circular intersection on the upper half cycle, and an abnormally small circular intersection on the lower half cycle. Both circles project to the zero-level location (to which the film is parallel) as near-circular ellipses. These appear more or less as shown in Fig. 15B. Actually, however, the centers of all ideally located circles of Fig. 15B coincide, so that the set of four appear as shown in Fig. 15C. These comprise a set of nearly circular ellipses with centers displaced in the direction of the error, and constituting a band.

The general features of this situation correspond to the features of the orientation errors discussed in Chapter 8. The direction of the error

$\epsilon = 0°$.

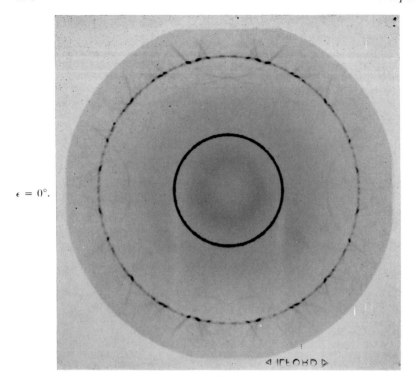

Fig. 14.
Cone-axis photographs illustrating the result of orientation errors.   (Berthierite, $FeSb_2S_4$, c axis, $\bar{\mu} = 20°$, Mo$K\alpha$, 35 kV, 5 mA, 18 hours.)

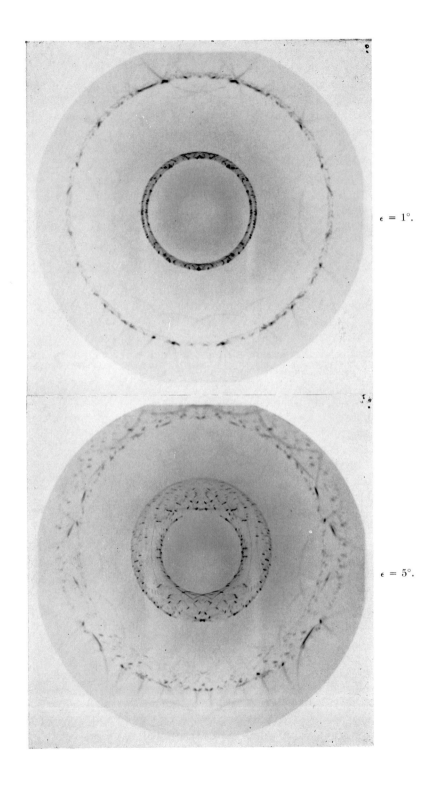

$\epsilon = 1°.$

$\epsilon = 5°.$

is the direction in which the band has been displaced from the center of the film, marked out, if necessary, by a record of the direct beam when $\bar{\mu} = 0$; the magnitude of the error can be interpreted by measuring the nearer and farther limits of the band and applying (22) of Chapter 8. Unfortunately, Fig. 6 of Chapter 8 cannot be used directly because it is drawn from $M = 6$ cm, whereas s for cone-axis photographs is usually smaller. A simple trick permits that chart to be used, however; it is based upon the fact that the crystal-to-precession-film distance is $M \cos \bar{\mu}$. If the distance s of the cone-axis film is set at half this, then Fig. 6, Chapter 8, can be used by doubling the observed displacements.

Fractional-cycle cone-axis photographs

Cone-axis photographs are ordinarily made by permitting the precession motion to go through its complete cycle many times. A useful variation is to equip the drive shaft of the precession apparatus with a switch which reverses the motor direction (as in the standard Weissenberg apparatus) after the drive shaft goes through a fraction of a cycle. In this way fractional-cycle precession may be produced. While there is no normal need for this in making ordinary precession photographs, it is sometimes useful for cone-axis photographs.

In making the ordinary cone-axis photograph, a rational direction is set parallel to the precessing axis, and this geometry holds the cone angle constant only for the Laue cones corresponding to this specific axis, as noted in Chapter 2. If there is an error in orienting the rational direction to the precessing axis, the Laue cones change in size during the precession cycle and the spots are distributed over a band, as already noted. When, with increasing orientation error, the bands become wide enough to cause neighboring rings to overlap, the cone-axis photograph ceases to give desired information and becomes useless.

On the other hand, if the precession is limited to a small fraction of a cycle, the Laue cones do not change substantially in angle, and so they record on the cone-axis photograph in such a way as to be recognizable as the intersections of a nest of circular cones with a plane. Each ring becomes an ellipse whose major axis marks the direction of the error. An example is shown in Fig. 16. Such a fractional-cycle cone-axis photograph evidently permits determining a large error.

In extension of this application, consider such a photograph for a crystal whose orientation is entirely unknown. Each diffracted beam is the common generator of several Laue cones satisfying the Laue condition. Each produces a cone-axis spot which is a common member of several cone-axis rings which may be ellipses, parabolas, or hyperbolas. The densest rings correspond to the most populated planes of the recipro-

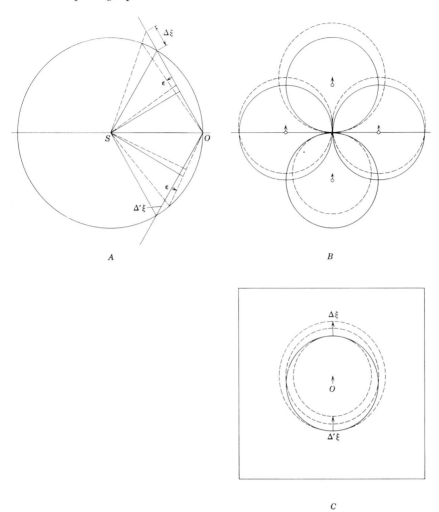

Fig. 15.
The broadening of cone-axis rings due to an orientation error ϵ.

174

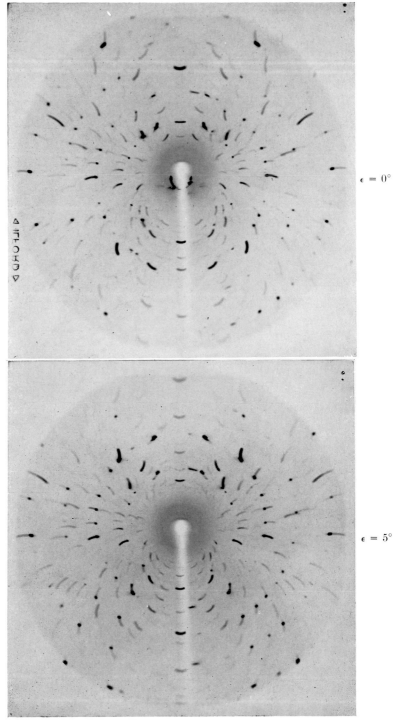

$\epsilon = 0°$

$\epsilon = 5°$

Fig. 16. Fractional-cycle cone-axis photographs. (Wollastonite, $CaSiO_3$, c axis, $\bar{\mu} = 5°$; $MoK\alpha$, 35 kV, 15 mA, 45 minutes.)

cal lattice, which, in turn, correspond to the largest reciprocal spacings, and so to the smallest direct-lattice translations. Dense rings therefore correspond to possible cell axes. The directions and angles that these axes make with the precessing axis can be determined, and accordingly any can be set parallel to the precessing axis. In this way a crystal of unknown orientation can be oriented.

10

Intensity determination

While the determination of the cell of a crystal is based upon the geometry of the location of the diffraction spots, an investigation of the arrangement of atoms in the cell requires a knowledge of the intensities of the beams which produced the spots. More exactly, the integrated power in each beam, as the crystal passes through the Bragg reflection condition, is required. The precession method provides a convenient way of making these determinations for a number of reasons:

1. Attaching an index to each spot is so easy as to be trivial;
2. All reflections can be recorded with a single setting of the crystal;
3. No corrections need be made for the elongation or contraction of upper-level spots as in the Weissenberg method;
4. Integrating cassettes, which permit easy measurements of true integrated power of each reflection, are available.

A general discussion of intensity determination is given elsewhere.[†] Here a few features that specifically affect the precession method are noted.

Planning the photographs required

In Chapter 5 the photographs needed for symmetry and cell determinations were considered. The requirements are somewhat different when the object of making the photographs is to provide material for the measurement of intensities. Furthermore, the requirements differ according as the data are to be used for two-dimensional or three-dimensional investigations.

[†] M. J. Buerger. *Crystal-structure analysis.* (John Wiley and Sons, New York, 1960) Chapter 6.

Data for two-dimensional investigations. Every possible zero-level photograph provides data for a Fourier synthesis projected in the direction of the rational crystallographic axis normal to that level. If the Fourier coefficients used are $|F_{hkl}|^2$, the Fourier synthesis is a Patterson projection; if the coefficients are F_{hkl}, the Fourier synthesis is an electron-density projection. Ordinarily, data from two such zero-level photographs, each parallel to a face of the reciprocal cell, are sufficient to permit study of the crystal by the method of two-dimensional projections. In this case the projection directions are along two direct-cell axes, one normal to each reciprocal-cell face. If the relation of the two projections is considered in advance, the crystal can be so mounted that both photographs can be made with the same mounting of the crystal by merely changing dial settings.

Sometimes an additional projection is desired in a direction intermediate between two crystallographic axes. This can be obtained from another zero-level photograph made with the same crystal mounting but a new dial setting. In a succeeding section some reciprocity relations useful in planning projections are discussed.

Since the data for several projections can be made with different dial settings for the same crystal mounting, the experimental conditions are essentially the same for the several photographs. Thus, if identical exposure and development procedures are observed, the intensity data derived from such a set of photographs are automatically on the same scale.

Data for three-dimensional investigations. The precession method is one of the most convenient to use for gathering intensity data for a three-dimensional study, because the entire reciprocal lattice within recording range can be surveyed with a single mounting of the crystal. Since this implies that no essential change in the experimental arrangement occurs during the making of this set of photographs, all intensity data are automatically on the same scale providing exposure and development procedures are uniform.

In order to obtain all reflections with a single mounting of the crystal it is necessary that a translation of the reciprocal lattice should be set parallel to the dial axis. The indexing procedure is much simplified if this translation is an edge of the reciprocal cell.

If the crystal has a unique axis of high Friedel symmetry, this should be set along the dial axis. Thus, for tetragonal crystals the 4-fold axis of the Friedel symmetry, for hexagonal crystals the 3-fold or 6-fold axis, and for monoclinic crystals the 2-fold axis should be set along the dial axis.

By setting the axis of highest Friedel symmetry along the dial axis, the reciprocal lattice can be surveyed with the minimum number of photographs.[24]   Reference to Fig. 9 of Chapter 3 shows that the reciprocal lattice can be explored to a level of $\zeta_{\text{lim}} = 0.35$ for each dial setting. Taking into account that Friedel's law requires the distribution of $|F_{hkl}|^2$ to be centrosymmetrical, a single dial setting permits collecting intensity data from the region shown shaded in Fig. 1.   Figure 2 shows how, by changing dial settings, the volume explored in Fig. 1 can be caused to cover the entire reciprocal lattice with no more than three or four dial settings even with an unsymmetrical crystal.

To make use of this method of surveying the reciprocal lattice, the indices of reciprocal-lattice points on levels not parallel to a face of the cell must be understood.   This is noted in the next section.

Some reciprocity relations.   Any given reciprocal-lattice plane is a member of a stack of equally spaced parallel planes.   All the points of the reciprocal lattice are confined to the planes of the stack.   The individual planes of the stack are usually referred to as the levels of the reciprocal lattice.   The zero level is unique in that it contains the origin at the point where the x-ray beam leaves the sphere of reflection.   Other levels are commonly called "upper levels" or "n levels."   The numerical value of n increases away from the origin.   For the purposes of the precession method n is taken as positive in the direction generally toward the center of the sphere of reflection, and negative in the opposite direction.   This is because, with this convention of numbering the levels of the reciprocal lattice, the level number n is the same as the order of diffraction n of the corresponding Laue cone; that is, the nth cone corresponds with the nth level of the reciprocal lattice.

The spacing of a stack of planes in the reciprocal lattice is indicated by the general designation d^*.   This spacing is parallel to the rational translation t in the direct lattice, so the translation is also normal to the stack of reciprocal-lattice planes.   The relation between spacing and translation is

$$\lambda \frac{1}{d^*} = t. \tag{1}$$

The constant λ must be used in this application of the reciprocal lattice because d^* is expressed in λ units.   A more symmetrical and specific form of (1) is

$$t_{uvw} \left(\frac{1}{\lambda} d^*_{uvw} \right) = 1. \tag{2}$$

This relation provides that normal to the rational direction $[uvw]$ in the direct lattice there occurs a stack of rational planes $(uvw)^*$ in the reciprocal lattice.   The most useful directions $[uvw]$ for the precession method are those of the crystallographic axes, but in some instances other

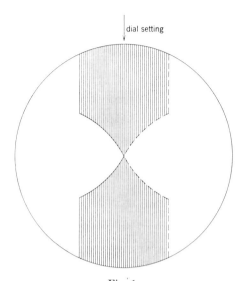

Fig. 1.
Range of the reciprocal lattice recordable with one dial setting, as seen looking along the dial axis.

(After Buerger.[44])

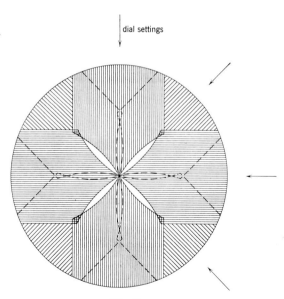

Fig. 2.
Recording the entire reciprocal lattice of an unsymmetrical crystal by using four dial settings, but only one mounting.

(After Buerger.[44])

translations within the unit cell are required.   These are listed in Table 1, together with some useful features in the reciprocal lattice associated with them.

Table 1
Some simple directions in the direct lattice and related features in the reciprocal lattice

Direct-lattice direction		Reciprocal lattice	
		Perpendicular planes	Indices of points in the nth-level plane
Cell edges	[100]	(100)*	$n\ k\ l$
	[010]	(010)*	$h\ n\ l$
	[001]	(001)*	$h\ k\ n$
Face diagonals	[110]	(110)*	$h\ k\ l$ $\quad h + k = n$
	[1$\bar{1}$0]	(1$\bar{1}$0)*	$h\ k\ l$ $\quad h - k = n$
	[101]	(101)*	$h\ k\ l$ $\quad h + l = n$
	[10$\bar{1}$]	(10$\bar{1}$)*	$h\ k\ l$ $\quad h - l = n$
	[011]	(011)*	$h\ k\ l$ $\quad k + l = n$
	[01$\bar{1}$]	(01$\bar{1}$)*	$h\ k\ l$ $\quad k - l = n$
Body diagonals of cell	[111]	(111)*	$h\ k\ l$ $\quad h + k + l = n$
	[$\bar{1}$11]	($\bar{1}$11)*	$h\ k\ l$ $\quad -h + k + l = n$
	[1$\bar{1}$1]	(1$\bar{1}$1)*	$h\ k\ l$ $\quad h - k + l = n$
	[11$\bar{1}$]	(11$\bar{1}$)*	$h\ k\ l$ $\quad h + k - l = n$

Precautions

Background. Any measurement of intensities by a photographic method involves the measurement of the background upon which the spot stands, and subtraction of this background from the intensity measured at the spot.   To reduce this correction the background should be as small as possible.   It is assumed, of course, that, to reduce air scatter, the direct beam is caught by a lead disk as far from the film as possible without interfering with the recording of reflections with small values of 2θ. To further reduce the background due to residual air scatter, as well as scattering by the specimen mount, and incoherent scattering by the specimen, the film should be exposed as little as possible to this unwanted scattering.   For intensity measurements, then, it is well to use a special set of layer-line screens with very narrow annular openings, say 2 mm.

General radiation. In addition to the desired characteristic α radiation, the x-ray tube produces β and general radiation.   The distribution of intensity against wavelength without and with a filter is shown in Fig. 3.   This is also the distribution of intensities associated with

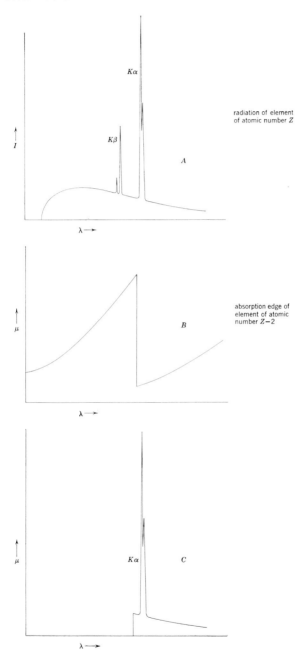

Fig. 3.

A. Distribution of intensity *I* versus wavelength λ in an x-ray beam.

B. The absorption μ of a filter used for reducing the characteristic β radiation of Fig. 3*A*, versus wavelength λ.

C. The distribution of intensity with wavelength in a filtered x-ray beam.

any point in the reciprocal lattice.   A ray in which the intensity distribution is like that of Fig. 3*C* (when using a filter) extends from the origin to every point in the reciprocal lattice.   The chief consequence of this distribution is that each spot on the film has a general-radiation trail on the side opposite the origin.   If the trail is associated with a spot *hkl*, it unfortunately produces a background for all other spots *nh nk nl* on the same ray from the origin.   This is only serious if *hkl* is a strong reflection, but the effect should always be allowed for.

Harmonics.   If Bragg's law is written

$$\sin \theta = \frac{\lambda}{2d_{hkl}}$$

$$= \tfrac{1}{2}\lambda\sigma_{hkl} \tag{3}$$

it can be seen that if λ is halved and the indices *hkl* doubled, sin θ is the same, which implies that the same diffraction spot would receive both reflections.   Now Fig. 3*A* shows that under normal operating conditions the x-ray beam contains, in addition to the desired characteristic wavelength λ, a general radiation component which is intense in the region $\lambda/2$.   If 2*h* 2*k* 2*l* is a strong reflection, it contributes to the spot *hkl* if no precautions are taken.   Use of a filter to reduce β also reduces the $\lambda/2$ contribution, as shown in Fig. 4*C*.   The submultiple wavelength can be absolutely suppressed by using a voltage across the x-ray tube which according to (14) of Chapter 9, will not excite this wavelength.   If Mo radiation is used, $\lambda/2$ is not excited if the voltage does not exceed 35 kv.

Doublets.   If, for any of the reasons mentioned in Chapter 7, the generalized de Jong-Bouman condition is not satisfied, some or all spots *hkl* become doublets.   Photographs containing such spots should not be used for intensity determinations.

The plateau method

The integrated power represented by a spot on a photographic film is not, in general, easy to determine.   The density at each point in the spot is proportional to the exposure of that point (for densities not exceeding a certain value, in the neighborhood of 1.4).[†]   Measuring the integrated power of a spot calls for integrating the density of the spot, which cannot generally be simply accomplished.   The plateau method, however, provides a straightforward approach to measurement of integrated power.

[†] See M. J. Buerger.   *Crystal-structure analysis.*   (John Wiley and Sons, New York, 1960) 80–81.

The principle of the plateau is illustrated in Figs. 4 and 5. The distribution of power in a reflection is shown in Fig. 4. If this distribution curve is repeated at regular small intervals (Fig. 5A), the sum of the

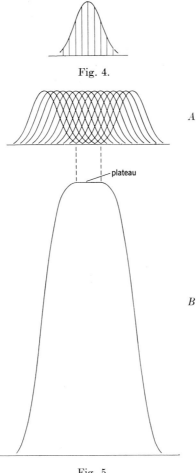

Fig. 4.

Fig. 5.
Principle of the plateau effect.
(After Buerger.[44])

ordinates (Fig. 5B) attains a constant value or plateau in the neighborhood of the center. This is because the sum represents an equal sampling of Fig. 4. The density of the plateau region is thus a measure of the integrated power of the reflection.

There are several methods of producing the plateau effect in a precession photograph, which are now noted.

Plateau from natural convergence. Under certain circumstances a plateau occurs automatically in the photographic record. Basically this calls for a rather large uniform source of radiation on the target of the x-ray tube, and a target-to-crystal distance so short that rays from the target converge to a point on the crystal at a considerable angle, as suggested by Fig. 6. This requires that the pinholes do not reduce this convergence. The ray from each point in the target produces an intensity distribution from the crystal like that of Fig. 5*A*, and the collection of the rays produces a set of distributions like Fig. 5*B*. The weak feature of this method is the likelihood that the illumination of the focal spot of the target is not uniform.

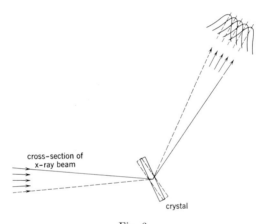

Fig. 6.
Plateau effect from the natural convergence of an x-ray beam with a large aperture.

The convergence of rays shown in Fig. 6 was a characteristic of the author's first Mark II precession apparatus. It was recognized from the earliest use that this instrument gave a natural plateau effect. Present-day commercial instruments have a long pinhole system that limits convergence so much that a plateau is not ordinarily produced.

Plateau from a focusing monochromator. Azároff[35] obtained convergence and a resulting plateau by the use of a bent-crystal monochromator used in connection with a precession camera. The geometry of producing convergent radiation at the crystal is shown in Fig. 7, the actual apparatus in Fig. 8, and a photograph produced by it in Fig. 9. As noted in the foregoing section, the success in producing a true plateau with convergent radiation depends on having a uniformly radiating area on the target. This is not often realized in commercial x-ray tubes. In addition, the monochromator produces partial polarization of the x-radiation which must be taken into account in computing the polarization fac-

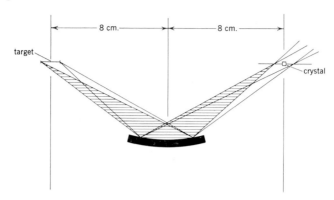

Fig. 7.
Action of a focusing monochromator.
(After Azároff,[35] modified.)

Fig. 8.
Focusing monochromator used with precession instrument.
(After Azároff.[35])

tor for the reflection. Azároff has provided the background[34] for doing this, and high-speed computers make such correction practical.

Plateau from an integrating cassette. The plateau can be produced by translating the cassette by a small amount during each precession cycle,[31] so that each x-ray spot is recorded a number of times with a small displacement between each recording. This must be done in such a way that the spot is uniformly spread over a small area. Thus the summation illustrated diagrammatically in one dimension in Fig. 5 must actually occur in two dimensions. Nordman et al.[31] accomplished this by translating the cassette in two directions parallel with the plane of the film by means of cams. These are rotated by a train of gears (Fig. 10), which are driven by the rotation of the arc producing the precession motion. This mechanism causes each point on the film to migrate in a path described as a "saw-tooth Lissajous" figure. The path covers an area of 2 x 2 mm, and the scan is complete in 3 hr. 44 min.

In another design (Fig. 11) recently made available commercially, an escapement operates a cam which shifts the cassette horizontally by $\frac{1}{12}$ mm once during each precession cycle. At the end of 12 such shifts, another escapement shifts the cassette vertically by $\frac{1}{12}$ mm. In this way the film assumes 144 locations uniformly distributed over a 1-mm square; this constitutes one integrating cycle. The position of the cassette in the cycle is indicated at all times on a dial. For a 60-cycle motor, each precession cycle is completed in 1 min., and each integrating cycle in 144 min = 2 hr 24 min. An example of a precession photograph taken without and with integration is given in Fig. 12.

The integrating cassette provides a way of permitting measurements of the integrated power of each reflection which is independent of the uniformity of the x-ray source. This is accomplished at the cost of lengthening the exposure time. When an integrating cassette is used the time of exposure should always be arranged to comprise an integral number of integrating cycles; otherwise the part of the integrated spot expected to be a density plateau will actually receive too little or too great a contribution from certain parts of the density distribution.

Density measurement

X-ray photographs enjoy the advantage that, up to a certain density limit, the density is directly proportional to the exposure which produced it. (A general discussion of this is given elsewhere.[†]) Measurement of the densities of the plateaus of the various spots, corrected for the densities of the various background effects noted earlier in this chapter,

[†] M. J. Buerger. *Crystal-structure analysis.* (John Wiley and Sons, New York, 1960) Chapter 6.

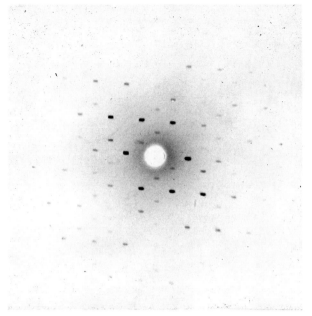

A

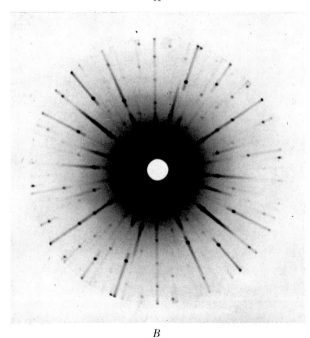

B

Fig. 9.

A. Precession photograph made with apparatus of Figs. 7 and 8. (Fairfieldite, *a* axis, $\bar{\mu} = 21°$; Ag$K\alpha$, 35 kV, 15 mA, 10 hours.)

B. Comparable photograph made in the usual way.   (After Azároff.[35])

Fig. 10. Integrating mechanism for precession camera. (After Nordman et al.[31])

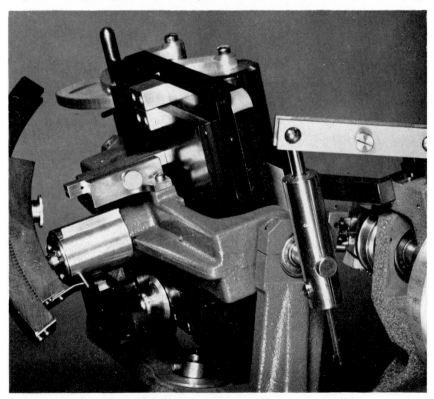

Fig. 11. Integrating mechanism for precession instrument. (Courtesy of Charles Supper Co.)

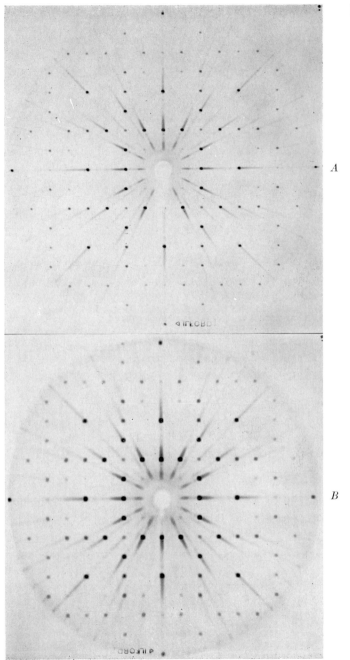

Fig. 12.

A. Ordinary precession photograph. (Garnet, a axis, zero level. $\bar{\mu} = 30°$; $MoK\alpha$, 35 kV, 17 mA, 8 hours.)

B. Precession photograph made with 8 cycles of the integrating mechanism of Fig. 11. (Same data as 12A, except 13 mA, $19\frac{1}{5}$ hours.)

gives a set of numbers proportional to the integrated powers of the reflections. When these are corrected for such factors as Lorentz, polarization, and absorption (discussed in Chapters 11 and 12), the investigator has a series of numbers proportional to $|F_{hkl}|^2$.

A great advantage of the photographic method is that, if proper density-measuring apparatus is available, it is probably faster than any other method, for example, the diffractometer method. To take advantage of the speed of the method, the densities should be measured with a densitometer designed for the purpose. In the author's experience complicated apparatus should be avoided because, in the long run, operating such apparatus consumes more time than any other method. The least desirable density-measuring apparatus is the kind that scans the photograph and presents a graphical record.

An acceptable design is based upon a split optical field in one half of which the spot is seen, in the other half a comparison density. Another acceptable design is based upon sending a tiny beam through the plateau and measuring its transmission with a photocell. In both designs the key to rapid work is that the photographic film is moved *by hand* to place the spot in the right location for examination.

If a densitometer is not available, the next best procedure is to prepare a series of spots for comparison. Since, for x-ray photography, the density is proportional to the exposure up to a certain density limit, a density scale with a uniform interval is prepared by making a series of uniformly increasing exposures. Before starting to make the scale, preliminary experiments should be made to find the exposure time which gives rise to a just-visible blackening. If the exposure time required to produce this density is t, then the series

$$t, 2t, 3t, \cdots, nt$$

produces a scale of n uniformly increasing densities. Some investigators prefer the series

$$t, a^2t, a^3t, a^4t, \cdots, a^nt,$$

or, alternatively, the series

$$t, 2^{1/2}t, 2^{2/2}t, 2^{3/2}t, \cdots, 2^{n/2}t.$$

11

The Lorentz factor

When a crystal is manipulated in an x-ray beam so that various planes are brought through the Bragg condition for reflection, there is, in general, a difference in the velocities with which the planes pass through this condition and therefore a difference in the time they have to reflect. The integrated power of the reflection is proportional to this time-of-reflection opportunity. In crystal-structure analysis the quantity $|F_{hkl}|$ is required for each reflection, so that a correction must be made for this time-of-reflection factor for each reflection. This factor is called the *Lorentz factor*, abbreviated L; the integrated power is corrected for this factor by multiplying it by $1/L$, the Lorentz-factor correction.

Since the Lorentz factor is proportional to the time during which the plane is in reflecting condition, it is inversely proportional to the velocity of its passage through this condition. This can be expressed in reciprocal-lattice terms as the velocity with which the reciprocal-lattice point passes through the sphere. In general, a point passes through the sphere obliquely. If the velocity of the point is resolved into components radial and tangential with respect to the sphere, it can be seen that only the radial component contributes to the passage of the point through the sphere. Thus the Lorentz factor is inversely proportional to the radial component of the velocity of the point through the sphere:

$$L \sim \frac{1}{v_r}. \tag{1}$$

Lorentz factor for motion of pure precession[2, 44]

To demonstrate in a simple way how the Lorentz factor arises in the precession method, it is convenient to discuss it first for a motion of the crystal which may be termed that of pure precession. In a preliminary way this can be defined as a motion which causes the condition for reflection to pass around the reciprocal-lattice plane at a uniform rate. Due to the restriction of the suspension, the motions of the commercial instruments currently available depart somewhat from this ideal motion and an appropriate correction must be made, as described later.

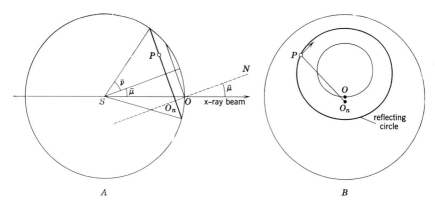

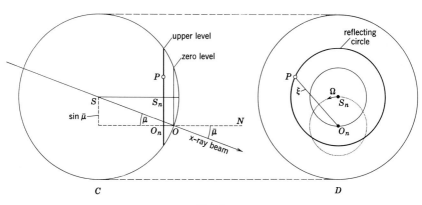

Fig. 1.

Velocity of a point through the sphere. In the precession method the reciprocal-lattice plane is tipped by angle $\bar{\mu}$ from a position normal to the x-ray beam, as shown in Fig. $1A$. The inclination causes the reciprocal-lattice plane to intersect the sphere of reflection in a circle, the *reflecting circle*. In the motion of precession the x-ray beam and its enveloping sphere are fixed, while the normal to the reciprocal lattice precesses about the x-ray beam. The relative motion of reciprocal-lattice plane and sphere remain the same if the reciprocal lattice is regarded as fixed while the x-ray beam is caused to precess about the normal to the plane, Fig. 1C. This view is convenient for some of the discussion that follows. Under these circumstances the center of the sphere rotates in a circle of radius sin $\bar{\mu}$ about the normal to the reciprocal-lattice plane.

If this view is adopted, then in the process of precession the reflecting circle sweeps around the reciprocal-lattice plane at a uniform angular rate, Fig. 1D. The center of the circle S_n rotates about the origin O_n with the angular velocity of precession Ω. The linear velocity with which the point P, at distance ξ from the origin, passes through the circle is

$$v = \Omega \xi. \tag{2}$$

The velocity required by (1) for evaluation of the Lorentz factor is the radial component of this velocity which is directed toward the center of the sphere. Let the angle between the velocity vector v and radius SP be designated δ, Fig. 2A. Then the required radial component of v is

$$v_r = v \cos \delta \tag{3}$$

$$= \Omega \xi \cos \delta. \tag{4}$$

The last term can be evaluated by geometrical means in easy stages, or it can be evaluated with the aid of vector algebra, or by using spherical-trigonometric relations. All three methods are given below.

Geometrical evaluation. Figure 2B shows that, since $SP = 1$, the value of $\cos \delta$ is the projection of SP on the velocity vector v, specifically

$$\cos \delta = q. \tag{5}$$

The radial component in (4) thus becomes

$$v_r = \Omega \xi q. \tag{6}$$

The last two terms are line segments lying in the plane of the reciprocal-lattice level. The product ξq determines twice the area of triangle $O_n S_n P$ in Fig. 2B. Figure 2C shows that another measure of this area is wR_0, where R_0 is the radius of the zero-level circle, so that this area is

$$\xi q = wR_0. \tag{7}$$

The length w is related to other well-known features by

$$\sin \Upsilon = \frac{w}{S_n P}, \tag{8}$$

and $S_n P$ is seen in Fig. 2C to be the radius R_n of the upper-level circle. Thus (8) has the value

$$\sin \Upsilon = \frac{w}{R_n}. \tag{9}$$

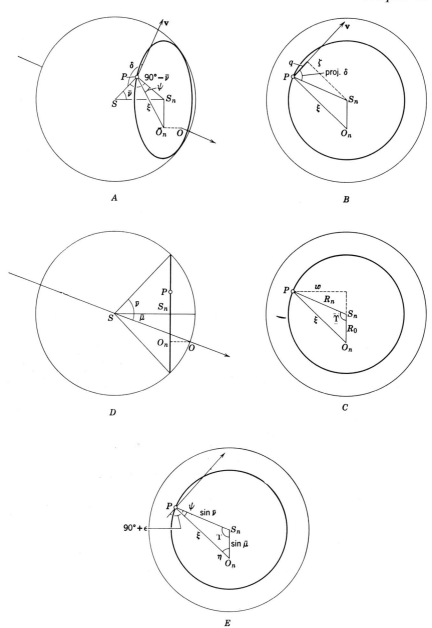

Fig. 2.
Some views of the sphere of reflection and an upper-level plane of the reciprocal lattice. (*D* corresponds with Fig. 1*C* while *B*, *C*, and *E* correspond with Fig. 1*D*; *A* is a view intermediate between *D* and *B*.)

If the value of w in (9) is substituted into (7) and the result combined with (6), it is seen that the radial component of the velocity can be expressed by

$$v_r = \Omega(\sin \Upsilon) R_n R_0. \tag{10}$$

But Fig. 2D shows that

$$R_n = \sin \bar{\nu} \tag{11}$$

and

$$R_0 = \sin \bar{\mu}, \tag{12}$$

so a suitable expression for v_r is

$$v_r = \Omega \sin \Upsilon \sin \bar{\nu} \sin \bar{\mu}. \tag{13}$$

Alternative evaluation. A more direct derivation of v_r makes use of the fact that the radial component of the velocity, on the left of (3),

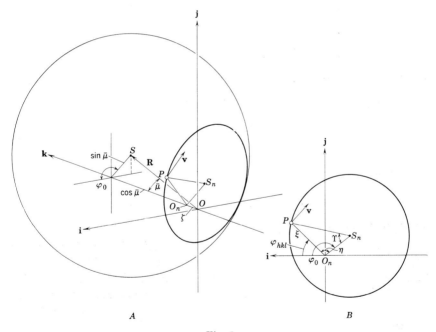

Fig. 3.

is the projection of the velocity of the point P on the vector $\mathbf{R}$, which gives the position of the center of the sphere. While the relations involved are outlined in Figs. 1C and D, they are given in more detail in Fig. 3. The value of the radial component of $\mathbf{v}$ is

$$v_r = \mathbf{v} \cdot \mathbf{R}. \tag{14}$$

Here the magnitude of $\mathbf{R}$ is unity. Figure 3A shows that $\mathbf{R}$, expressed as components on **i**, **j**, and **k**, is

$$\mathbf{R} = (\sin \bar{\mu} \cos \varphi_0)\mathbf{i} + (\sin \bar{\mu} \sin \varphi_0)\mathbf{j} + (\cos \bar{\mu})\mathbf{k}. \qquad (15)$$

The velocity vector **v** is in the plane of **i** and **j**. A view of this plane, looking in the direction of **k**, is given in Fig. 3B. It is evident that **v**, expressed as components on **i** and **j**, is

$$\mathbf{v} = -(\xi\Omega \sin \varphi_{hkl})\mathbf{i} + (\xi\Omega \cos \varphi_{hkl})\mathbf{k}. \qquad (16)$$

The evaluation of (14) is

$$
\begin{aligned}
v_r &= \mathbf{v} \cdot \mathbf{R} \\
&= -\xi\Omega \sin \varphi_{hkl} \sin \bar{\mu} \cos \varphi_0 + \xi\Omega \cos \varphi_{hkl} \sin \bar{\mu} \sin \varphi_0 \\
&= \xi\Omega \sin \bar{\mu} \, (\cos \varphi_{hkl} \sin \varphi_0 - \sin \varphi_{hkl} \cos \varphi_0) \\
&= \xi\Omega \sin \bar{\mu} \sin (\varphi_0 - \varphi_{hkl}) \\
&= \xi\Omega \sin \bar{\mu} \sin \eta,
\end{aligned} \qquad (17)
$$

where $\quad \eta = \varphi_0 - \varphi_{hkl}.$ $\qquad (18)$

In Fig. 2E, the law of sines applied to triangle $O_n S_n P$ provides

$$\frac{\sin \Upsilon}{\xi} = \frac{\sin \eta}{\sin \bar{\nu}}, \qquad (19)$$

so that in (17) $\sin \Upsilon \sin \bar{\nu}$ can be substituted for $\xi \sin \eta$, giving

$$v_r = \Omega \sin \Upsilon \sin \bar{\nu} \sin \bar{\mu}, \qquad (20)$$

which is the same as (13).

Trigonometric evaluation. A third derivation makes use of trigonometry and is straightforward, though somewhat blind. In Fig. 2A, the plane angles and dihedral angles meeting at P have the following characteristics. Angle ψ lies in the plane of the reciprocal-lattice level, and angle $PSS_n = \bar{\nu}$ lies in an orthogonal plane. The angles $\pi/2 - \bar{\nu}$ and $\pi/2 + \psi$ are orthogonal components of δ so they are related by

$$
\begin{aligned}
\cos \delta &= \cos \left(\frac{\pi}{2} - \bar{\nu}\right) \cos \left(\frac{\pi}{2} + \psi\right) \\
&= \sin \bar{\nu} \sin \psi.
\end{aligned} \qquad (21)
$$

In Fig. 2E the law of sines provides

$$\frac{\xi}{\sin \Upsilon} = \frac{\sin \bar{\mu}}{\sin \psi}. \qquad (22)$$

The radial component of the velocity as formulated by (4) can now be evaluated by substituting from (21) and (22):

$$(4): \qquad v_r = \Omega \xi \cos \delta$$

$$= \Omega \, \frac{\sin \Upsilon \sin \bar{\mu}}{\sin \psi} \cdot \sin \bar{\nu} \sin \psi$$

$$= \Omega \sin \Upsilon \sin \bar{\mu} \sin \bar{\nu}. \tag{23}$$

This is the same as (13).

According to (1), the Lorentz factor for this single passage of the point through the sphere is

$$L \sim \frac{1}{\Omega \sin \Upsilon \sin \bar{\nu} \sin \bar{\mu}}, \tag{24}$$

or

$$L \sim \frac{1}{\Omega \xi \sin \bar{\mu} \sin \eta}. \tag{25}$$

Since the point passes through the sphere twice, each time contributing to the same spot, the Lorentz factor for the spot is actually twice this amount.

Evaluation of η. The angle η can be evaluated in terms of other measurable quantities by applying the generalized Pythagorean theorem to the triangle $O_n S_n P$ in Fig. 2C:

$$R_n{}^2 = R_0{}^2 + \xi^2 - 2R_0 \xi \cos (R_0 \wedge \xi). \tag{26}$$

The elements of the triangle can be evaluated from Figs. 2C and 2E. After appropriate substitution (26) becomes

$$\sin^2 \bar{\nu} = \sin^2 \bar{\mu} + \xi^2 - 2\xi \sin \bar{\mu} \cos \eta, \tag{27}$$

from which the value of η is given by

$$\cos \eta = \frac{\sin^2 \bar{\mu} + \xi^2 - \sin^2 \bar{\nu}}{2\xi \sin \bar{\mu}}. \tag{28}$$

Practical application. The Lorentz factor for pure precession motion is radially symmetrical for each level and varies from level to level. It is usual to combine the Lorentz with the polarization factor, which also has radial symmetry. The combined factor Lp is commonly tabulated in the form of its correction, $1/Lp$. A graph of the correction for the zero level, due to Evans, Tilden, and Adams,[8] is shown in Fig. 4.

The Lorentz factor for pure precession motion is useful with instruments having a Mark III suspension, discussed at the close of this chapter. If this form of the factor is used for Mark II instruments, there is an error which has small values for small precession angles, reaching a maximum of 15% for $\bar{\mu} = 30°$, as indicated in Fig. 8.

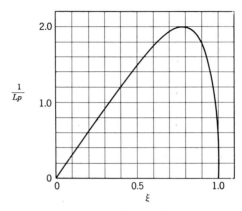

Fig. 4.
Graph of the Lorentz-polarization correction, $1/Lp$, as a function of ξ for pure preces-
sion motion for the zero level, $\bar{\mu} = 30°$.
(After Evans, Tilden, and Adams.[8])

Lorentz factor for the Mark II suspension

Although uniform precession motion is supplied to the normal to the
reciprocal-lattice plane of the Mark II precession instrument, which is in
common use, the nature of the suspension causes the reflecting circle to
sweep around the plane with an angular velocity that varies somewhat
during the cycle. This causes the Lorentz factor for this suspension to
depart from that produced by ideal precession motion. To understand
the departure, the velocity of the reflecting circle must be found as a
function of its location in the cycle. This problem was solved by Waser,[13]
who associated a coordinate system with the reciprocal lattice and investigated how it is related to a fixed coordinate system. Waser's method is
essentially as follows.

Coordinate systems. Let two Cartesian coordinate systems be
chosen with origins coinciding in the unmoved point of the suspension.
A fixed coordinate system is represented by unprimed labels; another
coordinate system associated with the reciprocal lattice is represented
by primed letters. It is convenient[†] to choose directions in these systems as shown in Fig. 5A and defined as in Table 2.

[†] In the treatment given here Waser's coordinates have been transformed as follows:

$$x_W \to x \qquad i_W \to i$$
$$y_W \to -z \qquad j_W \to -k$$
$$z_W \to y \qquad k_W \to j$$

This choice of symbols causes $+z$ to correspond with $+\zeta$ which is positive in the
direction of increasing order of the Laue cones.

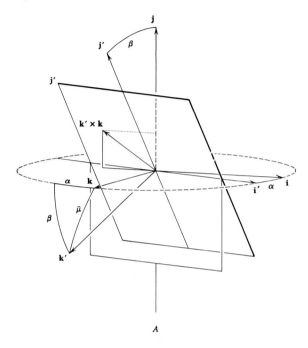

A

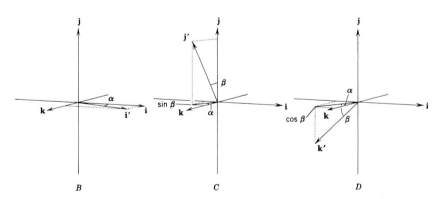

B   C   D

Fig. 5.
The relation of the film coordinate system **i′j′k′** to the fixed coordinate system **ijk**.
A. General view.
B. Components of **i′**.
C. Components of **j′**.
D. Components of **k′**.

Table 2

	Coordinates	Unit vectors	
In the	x'	$\mathbf{i}'$	In the zero level, parallel to the dial axis
reciprocal	y'	$\mathbf{j}'$	In the zero level, perpendicular to the dial axis
lattice	z'	$\mathbf{k}'$	Perpendicular to the zero level
	x	$\mathbf{i}$	Normal to $\mathbf{j}$ and $\mathbf{k}$
Fixed	y	$\mathbf{j}$	Along the vertical axis of the suspension
	z	$\mathbf{k}$	Along the x-ray beam, positive direction toward x-ray source

In order to transform from one coordinate system to the other, either the general form of the transformation from one Cartesian coordinate system to another may be used, or transformation can be found more informally by expressing each primed unit vector as the sum of its components on the unprimed axis. With the aid of Figs. 5*B*, *C*, and *D*, these are evidently

$$\mathbf{i}' = \quad \mathbf{i}\cos\alpha \qquad\qquad + \mathbf{k}\sin\alpha$$

$$\mathbf{j}' = -\mathbf{i}\sin\alpha\sin\beta + \mathbf{j}\cos\beta + \mathbf{k}\cos\alpha\sin\beta \qquad (29)$$

$$\mathbf{k}' = -\mathbf{i}\sin\alpha\cos\beta - \mathbf{j}\sin\beta + \mathbf{k}\cos\alpha\cos\beta.$$

In Figs. 5*A* and 5*D* it is shown that the orthogonal components of $\bar{\mu}$ are α and β. Spherical trigonometry supplied the relation between these:

$$\cos\bar{\mu} = \cos\alpha\cos\beta. \qquad (30)$$

Alternatively it is supplied by forming the scalar product

$$\mathbf{k}\cdot\mathbf{k}' = \mathbf{k}(-\mathbf{i}\sin\alpha\cos\beta - \mathbf{j}\sin\beta + \mathbf{k}\cos\alpha\cos\beta)$$

$$= \cos\alpha\cos\beta. \qquad (31)$$

But Figs. *A* and 5*D* show that

$$\mathbf{k}\cdot\mathbf{k}' = |\mathbf{k}|\,|\mathbf{k}'|\cos\bar{\mu} = \cos\bar{\mu}. \qquad (32)$$

Comparison of (31) and (32) yields (30).

Behavior of angles with time. The vector $\mathbf{k}'$ makes the constant precession angle $\bar{\mu}$ with $\mathbf{k}$, and rotates about it with constant angular velocity Ω. Since $\mathbf{k}' \wedge \mathbf{k} = \bar{\mu}$, the vector product $\mathbf{k}' \times \mathbf{k}$ has the magnitude $\sin\bar{\mu}$. This vector lies in the **ij** plane and also rotates with constant angular velocity Ω. If the time origin is taken when this vector is along $+\mathbf{j}$, and if the rotation is counterclockwise as seen in Fig. 5*A*, then the motion of this vector is described by

$$\mathbf{k}' \times \mathbf{k} = \sin \bar{\mu}(-\mathbf{i} \sin \Omega t + \mathbf{j} \cos \Omega t). \tag{33}$$

But forming the vector product $\mathbf{k}' \times \mathbf{k}$ from (29) gives

$$\mathbf{k}' \times \mathbf{k} = \qquad -\mathbf{i} \sin \beta \; + \mathbf{j} \sin \alpha \cos \beta. \tag{34}$$

By comparing (33) and (34) it is evident that

$$\sin \beta = \sin \bar{\mu} \sin \Omega t, \tag{35}$$

and $\qquad \sin \alpha \cos \beta = \sin \bar{\mu} \cos \Omega t. \tag{36}$

Relation (35) gives rise to

$$\cos \beta = (1 - \sin^2 \beta)^{1/2}$$
$$= (1 - \sin^2 \bar{\mu} \sin^2 \Omega t)^{1/2}, \tag{37}$$

while (36) with (37) gives

$$\sin \alpha = \sin \bar{\mu} \cos \Omega t (\cos \beta)^{-1}$$
$$= \sin \bar{\mu} \cos \Omega t (1 - \sin^2 \bar{\mu} \sin^2 \Omega t)^{-1/2}. \tag{38}$$

Finally (30) gives

$$\cos \alpha = \cos \bar{\mu}(\cos \beta)^{-1}$$
$$= \cos \bar{\mu}(1 - \sin^2 \bar{\mu} \sin^2 \Omega t)^{-1/2}. \tag{39}$$

The behaviors of α and β with time are thus

(35): $\qquad \sin \beta = \sin \bar{\mu} \sin \Omega t,$

(37): $\qquad \cos \beta = (1 - \sin^2 \bar{\mu} \sin^2 \Omega t)^{1/2}$

(38): $\qquad \sin \alpha = \sin \bar{\mu} \cos \Omega t (1 - \sin^2 \bar{\mu} \sin^2 \Omega t)^{-1/2},$

(39): $\qquad \cos \alpha = \cos \bar{\mu}(1 - \sin^2 \bar{\mu} \sin^2 \Omega t)^{-1/2},$

$$\cot \alpha = \cot \bar{\mu}(\cos \Omega t)^{-1}. \tag{40}$$

Motion of the sphere of reflection. With this background the relative motions of the sphere of reflection and the reciprocal lattice can be studied. The sphere is fixed with respect to the fixed coordinate system, with its center located at

$$x_0 = 0,$$
$$y_0 = 0, \tag{41}$$
$$z_0 = 1.$$

But with respect to the reciprocal lattice and its primed coordinate systems the sphere is in motion. The motion of its center can be represented by expressing the coordinates of (41) in terms of primed coordinates with the aid of (29).   This gives

$$x_0' = \sin \alpha,$$

$$y_0' = \cos \alpha \sin \beta, \tag{42}$$

$$z_0' = \cos \alpha \cos \beta = \cos \bar{\mu}.$$

The motion of the sphere can be more readily visualized if, instead of referring it to Cartesian coordinates $x'y'z'$, it is referred to the cylindrical

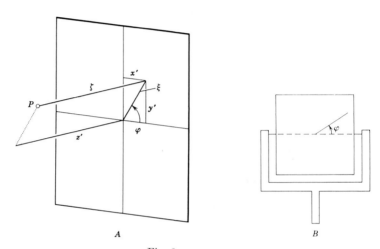

A   B

Fig. 6.
Relation of the Cartesian coordinates $x'y'z'$ to the cylindrical coordinates φ, ξ, ζ.

coordinates ξ, ζ, φ used for the reciprocal lattice.   The relation between these is illustrated in Fig. 6, and is described by

$$x' = \xi \cos \varphi,$$

$$y' = \xi \sin \varphi, \tag{43}$$

$$z' = \zeta.$$

The reverse transformation can be seen from Fig. 6 to be

$$\xi = (x'^2 + y'^2)^{\frac{1}{2}},$$

$$\zeta = z', \tag{44}$$

$$\varphi = \tan^{-1} \frac{y'}{x'}.$$

The motion of the center of the sphere in these terms is found by substituting from (42) into (44), giving

$$\xi_0 = (x_0'^2 + y_0'^2)^{1/2}$$
$$= (\sin^2 \alpha + \cos^2 \alpha \sin^2 \beta)^{1/2}$$
$$= (\sin^2 \alpha + \cos^2 \alpha [1 - \cos^2 \beta])^{1/2}$$
$$= (\sin^2 \alpha + \cos^2 \alpha - \cos^2 \alpha \cos^2 \beta)^{1/2}$$
$$= (1 - \cos^2 \alpha \cos^2 \beta)^{1/2}$$
$$= (1 - \cos^2 \bar{\mu})^{1/2}$$
$$= \sin \bar{\mu}, \tag{45}$$

$$\zeta_0 = z_0' = \cos \bar{\mu}, \tag{46}$$

$$\varphi_0 = \tan^{-1} \frac{y_0'}{x_0'} = \tan^{-1} \frac{\cos \alpha \sin \beta}{\sin \alpha} = \tan^{-1} \cot \alpha \sin \beta$$
$$= \tan^{-1} (\cot \bar{\mu} [\cos \Omega t]^{-1} \sin \bar{\mu} \sin \Omega t)$$
$$= \tan^{-1} (\cos \bar{\mu} \tan \Omega t). \tag{47}$$

Relations (45) and (46) are a more formal proof than provided by the obvious geometry of Fig. 1C that the coordinates of the center of the sphere are $\xi_0 = \sin \bar{\mu}$, and $\zeta_0 = \cos \bar{\mu}$. These coordinates are independent of time, but (47) shows that the azimuth of the sphere, φ_0, is dependent on time. The center of the sphere thus moves in a circle of radius $\xi_0 = \sin \bar{\mu}$ and in a plane at level $\zeta_0 = \cos \bar{\mu}$. The angular velocity of the center of the sphere is

$$\omega = \frac{d\varphi_0}{dt} = \frac{d(\tan^{-1} [\cos \bar{\mu} \tan \Omega t])}{dt}$$

$$= \frac{1}{1 + \cos^2 \bar{\mu} \tan^2 \Omega t} (\cos \bar{\mu} \sec^2 \Omega t)\Omega$$

$$= \Omega \cos \bar{\mu} \left(\frac{\sec^2 \Omega t}{1 + \cos^2 \bar{\mu} \tan^2 \Omega t} \right). \tag{48}$$

The term in parentheses can be consolidated somewhat, as follows:

$$\frac{\sec^2 \Omega t}{1 + \cos^2 \bar{\mu} \tan^2 \Omega t} = \left(\frac{1 + \cos^2 \bar{\mu} \tan^2 \Omega t}{\sec^2 \Omega t} \right)^{-1}$$

$$= \left(\frac{1}{\sec^2 \Omega t} + \frac{\cos^2 \bar{\mu} \tan^2 \Omega t}{\sec^2 \Omega t} \right)^{-1}$$

$$= (\cos^2 \Omega t + \cos^2 \bar{\mu} \sin^2 \Omega t)^{-1}$$

$$= (\cos^2 \Omega t + [1 - \sin^2 \bar{\mu}] \sin^2 \Omega t)^{-1}$$

$$= (\cos^2 \Omega t + \sin^2 \Omega t - \sin^2 \bar{\mu} \sin^2 \Omega t)^{-1}$$

$$= (\qquad 1 \qquad - \sin^2 \bar{\mu} \sin^2 \Omega t)^{-1}. \tag{49}$$

Thus (48) can be transformed into

$$\omega = \frac{d\varphi_0}{dt} = \Omega \cos \bar{\mu} \left(\frac{1}{1 - \sin^2 \bar{\mu} \sin^2 \Omega t} \right). \tag{50}$$

Alternatively, by making use of (47), the term in parentheses in (48) can be transformed as follows:

$$\frac{\sec^2 \Omega t}{1 + \cos^2 \bar{\mu} \tan^2 \Omega t} = \frac{1 + \tan^2 \Omega t}{1 + \cos^2 \bar{\mu} \tan^2 \Omega t}$$

$$= \frac{1 + \tan^2 \varphi_0 / \cos^2 \bar{\mu}}{1 + \tan^2 \varphi_0}$$

$$= \frac{\cos^2 \bar{\mu} + \tan^2 \varphi_0}{\cos^2 \bar{\mu}(1 - \tan^2 \varphi_0)}$$

$$= \frac{\cos^2 \bar{\mu} + \tan^2 \varphi_0 + (\cos^2 \bar{\mu} \tan^2 \varphi_0 - \cos^2 \bar{\mu} \tan^2 \varphi_0)}{\cos^2 \bar{\mu} + \cos^2 \bar{\mu} \tan^2 \varphi_0}$$

$$= \frac{\cos^2 \bar{\mu} + \cos^2 \bar{\mu} \tan^2 \varphi_0}{\cos^2 \bar{\mu} + \cos^2 \bar{\mu} \tan^2 \varphi_0} + \frac{\tan^2 \varphi_0 - \cos^2 \bar{\mu} \tan^2 \varphi_0}{\cos^2 \bar{\mu} + \cos^2 \bar{\mu} \tan^2 \varphi_0}$$

$$= 1 + \frac{- \cos^2 \bar{\mu} \tan^2 \varphi_0 + \tan^2 \varphi_0}{\cos^2 \bar{\mu} + \cos^2 \bar{\mu} \tan^2 \varphi_0}$$

$$= 1 + \frac{\tan^2 \varphi_0(1 - \cos^2 \bar{\mu})}{\cos^2 \bar{\mu}(\tan^2 \varphi_0 + 1)}$$

$$= 1 + \left(\frac{\tan^2 \varphi_0}{1 + \tan^2 \varphi_0} \right) \left(\frac{1 - \cos^2 \bar{\mu}}{\cos^2 \bar{\mu}} \right)$$

$$= 1 + \sin^2 \varphi_0 \tan^2 \bar{\mu}, \tag{51}$$

so that

$$\omega = \frac{d\varphi_0}{dt} = \Omega \cos \bar{\mu}(1 + \sin^2 \varphi_0 \tan^2 \bar{\mu}). \tag{52}$$

Evidently the Mark II suspension causes the center of the sphere to travel around the reciprocal lattice with an angular velocity which varies with position φ_0. The variation of φ_0 with time is given in Fig. 7 for various precession angles, and the ratio ω/Ω of the angular velocity of the sphere to precession velocity is shown in Fig. 8.

Each spot on the precession photograph corresponds to a reciprocal-lattice point entering and leaving the sphere. Figure 9 shows that, if

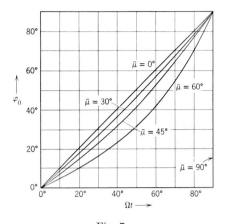

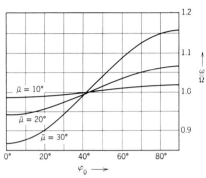

Fig. 7.
Time dependence of the angular coordinate φ_0 of the sphere of reflection in reciprocal space. (After Waser.[13])

Fig. 8.
Variation of the relative angular velocity ω/Ω with φ_0. (After Waser.[13])

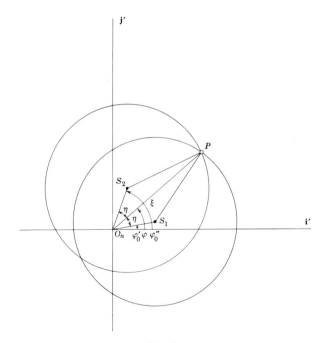

Fig. 9.
Relation of φ, φ_0' and φ_0'' to η. This diagram is similar to Fig. 9, Chapter 9.

the azimuth of point P in the reciprocal lattice is φ, the values of φ_0 involved in these penetrations are

$$\varphi_0{}' = \varphi - \eta,$$
$$\varphi_0{}'' = \varphi + \eta. \tag{53}$$

The Lorentz factor for pure precession motion for a single penetration was given by (25). The Lorentz factor for each penetration must be corrected by combining (48), (50) or (52), with (24) or (25), giving, for example,

$$L_{\text{Mark II}} \sim L_{\text{pure}} \cdot \frac{1}{1 + \tan^2 \bar{\mu} \sin^2 \varphi}. \tag{54}$$

Table 1
Lorentz-polarization corrections $1/Lp$ for the precession method[†] as a
function of the cylindrical reciprocal-lattice coordinates ξ, ζ, and $\hat{\varphi}(\bar{\mu} = 30°)$
$\zeta = -0.1340$

ξ	φ									
	0°	10°	20°	30°	40°	50°	60°	70°	80°	90°
0.5000	0	0	0	0	0	0	0	0	0	0

$\zeta = -0.10$

ξ	φ									
	0°	10°	20°	30°	40°	50°	60°	70°	80°	90°
0.2415	0	0	0	0	0	0	0	0	0	0
0.25	0.061	0.061	0.063	0.065	0.068	0.071	0.074	0.077	0.079	0.079
0.30	0.173	0.173	0.176	0.180	0.185	0.192	0.198	0.203	0.207	0.208
0.35	0.246	0.247	0.249	0.253	0.259	0.266	0.273	0.280	0.285	0.286
0.40	0.305	0.306	0.308	0.312	0.318	0.326	0.334	0.342	0.347	0.349
0.45	0.352	0.352	0.355	0.360	0.367	0.376	0.385	0.394	0.400	0.402
0.50	0.386	0.387	0.390	0.396	0.404	0.415	0.426	0.436	0.443	0.445
0.55	0.406	0.407	0.411	0.418	0.429	0.441	0.454	0.465	0.473	0.476
0.60	0.407	0.409	0.414	0.423	0.435	0.450	0.464	0.477	0.486	0.489
0.65	0.382	0.385	0.391	0.402	0.416	0.431	0.447	0.460	0.469	0.472
0.70	0.315	0.318	0.325	0.336	0.349	0.365	0.379	0.392	0.400	0.403
0.75	0.134	0.135	0.139	0.144	0.151	0.159	0.166	0.172	0.176	0.177

[†] These tables were computed on the IBM 7090 computer by Dr. Charles T. Prewitt using a program written by him for this purpose. They have been computed from the theoretical minimum value of $\zeta = \cos \bar{\mu} - 1$ to the theoretical maximum value of $\zeta = \cos \bar{\mu}$ for the front reflection region. In each case the first ξ entry is its minimum value for the recorded region of that level.

Table 1 (*Continued*)

$\zeta = -0.05$

ξ	φ									
	0°	10°	20°	30°	40°	50°	60°	70°	80°	90°
0.0989	0	0	0	0	0	0	0	0	0	0
0.10	0.017	0.017	0.018	0.018	0.019	0.020	0.021	0.022	0.022	0.022
0.15	0.146	0.146	0.145	0.145	0.145	0.146	0.147	0.149	0.150	0.151
0.20	0.234	0.233	0.231	0.228	0.225	0.223	0.222	0.222	0.223	0.223
0.25	0.312	0.310	0.307	0.302	0.297	0.293	0.290	0.289	0.289	0.289
0.30	0.384	0.382	0.377	0.371	0.365	0.359	0.356	0.354	0.354	0.353
0.35	0.451	0.449	0.443	0.436	0.429	0.423	0.419	0.418	0.417	0.417
0.40	0.512	0.510	0.505	0.497	0.490	0.484	0.481	0.480	0.480	0.480
0.45	0.568	0.566	0.560	0.553	0.547	0.542	0.540	0.541	0.542	0.543
0.50	0.616	0.615	0.610	0.604	0.599	0.596	0.597	0.599	0.601	0.602
0.55	0.656	0.655	0.651	0.647	0.644	0.645	0.648	0.653	0.657	0.659
0.60	0.685	0.684	0.682	0.680	0.681	0.685	0.692	0.700	0.706	0.709
0.65	0.699	0.699	0.699	0.701	0.706	0.715	0.726	0.737	0.745	0.749
0.70	0.695	0.696	0.698	0.704	0.714	0.728	0.743	0.758	0.768	0.772
0.75	0.665	0.667	0.672	0.683	0.697	0.716	0.735	0.753	0.765	0.769
0.80	0.597	0.600	0.608	0.622	0.641	0.663	0.685	0.704	0.717	0.722
0.85	0.464	0.467	0.476	0.492	0.511	0.533	0.554	0.571	0.583	0.587
0.90	0.075	0.075	0.077	0.081	0.085	0.089	0.093	0.096	0.099	0.099

$\zeta = 0$

ξ	φ									
	0°	10°	20°	30°	40°	50°	60°	70°	80°	90°
0	0	0	0	0	0	0	0	0	0	0
0.05	0.084	0.083	0.081	0.078	0.075	0.071	0.068	0.065	0.063	0.063
0.10	0.167	0.165	0.162	0.156	0.150	0.143	0.136	0.130	0.127	0.126
0.15	0.249	0.247	0.242	0.234	0.224	0.214	0.204	0.196	0.191	0.189
0.20	0.331	0.328	0.321	0.311	0.298	0.285	0.272	0.263	0.256	0.254
0.25	0.411	0.408	0.400	0.387	0.371	0.356	0.341	0.329	0.322	0.320
0.30	0.489	0.486	0.476	0.461	0.444	0.426	0.410	0.397	0.389	0.386
0.35	0.565	0.561	0.550	0.534	0.515	0.496	0.479	0.466	0.457	0.455
0.40	0.637	0.633	0.621	0.604	0.584	0.565	0.547	0.535	0.527	0.524
0.45	0.705	0.701	0.689	0.672	0.652	0.632	0.616	0.604	0.597	0.595
0.50	0.769	0.764	0.752	0.735	0.716	0.698	0.683	0.673	0.668	0.666
0.55	0.825	0.821	0.809	0.793	0.776	0.760	0.749	0.741	0.738	0.737
0.60	0.873	0.869	0.859	0.845	0.830	0.818	0.811	0.807	0.806	0.806
0.65	0.910	0.907	0.899	0.887	0.877	0.870	0.867	0.868	0.870	0.871
0.70	0.934	0.932	0.925	0.918	0.913	0.912	0.916	0.921	0.927	0.929
0.75	0.940	0.938	0.936	0.934	0.935	0.941	0.951	0.962	0.971	0.974
0.80	0.922	0.922	0.923	0.927	0.936	0.949	0.966	0.982	0.994	0.998
0.85	0.871	0.873	0.878	0.889	0.905	0.926	0.949	0.969	0.984	0.989
0.90	0.772	0.776	0.785	0.802	0.824	0.850	0.877	0.901	0.917	0.922
0.95	0.590	0.594	0.606	0.625	0.649	0.676	0.702	0.724	0.738	0.743
1.00	0.000	0.000	0.000	0.000	0.000	0.000	0.000	0.000	0.000	0.000

(*Continued*)

Table 1 (*Continued*)

$\zeta = 0.05$

ξ	φ									
	0°	10°	20°	30°	40°	50°	60°	70°	80°	90°
0.0781	0	0	0	0	0	0	0	0	0	0
0.10	0.097	0.097	0.097	0.097	0.097	0.097	0.098	0.099	0.100	0.100
0.15	0.222	0.220	0.216	0.210	0.204	0.197	0.191	0.187	0.184	0.183
0.20	0.329	0.327	0.320	0.309	0.297	0.284	0.272	0.262	0.256	0.254
0.25	0.429	0.426	0.417	0.403	0.385	0.367	0.350	0.336	0.326	0.323
0.30	0.525	0.521	0.510	0.492	0.471	0.448	0.427	0.409	0.398	0.394
0.35	0.617	0.612	0.599	0.579	0.554	0.528	0.503	0.483	0.471	0.466
0.40	0.705	0.700	0.685	0.663	0.636	0.607	0.580	0.559	0.545	0.540
0.45	0.790	0.784	0.768	0.744	0.715	0.685	0.657	0.635	0.621	0.617
0.50	0.869	0.864	0.847	0.821	0.791	0.761	0.734	0.713	0.700	0.695
0.55	0.943	0.937	0.920	0.895	0.865	0.835	0.810	0.791	0.779	0.775
0.60	1.010	1.004	0.987	0.962	0.934	0.907	0.885	0.868	0.859	0.856
0.65	1.067	1.062	1.046	1.023	0.998	0.975	0.957	0.945	0.938	0.936
0.70	1.113	1.108	1.094	1.074	1.054	1.036	1.024	1.017	1.015	1.014
0.75	1.145	1.141	1.129	1.114	1.099	1.089	1.084	1.083	1.085	1.086
0.80	1.158	1.155	1.147	1.137	1.130	1.128	1.131	1.138	1.144	1.146
0.85	1.146	1.144	1.141	1.139	1.141	1.148	1.160	1.174	1.184	1.188
0.90	1.101	1.101	1.103	1.109	1.121	1.139	1.160	1.180	1.195	1.200
0.95	1.010	1.013	1.021	1.035	1.056	1.082	1.111	1.136	1.154	1.161
1.00	0.849	0.853	0.866	0.886	0.914	0.946	0.978	1.006	1.025	1.031
1.05	0.545	0.549	0.562	0.582	0.607	0.634	0.660	0.682	0.696	0.701

$\zeta = 0.10$

ξ	φ									
	0°	10°	20°	30°	40°	50°	60°	70°	80°	90°
0.1428	0	0	0	0	0	0	0	0	0	0
0.15	0.069	0.069	0.071	0.073	0.075	0.078	0.081	0.083	0.085	0.086
0.20	0.244	0.243	0.241	0.237	0.233	0.230	0.229	0.228	0.228	0.228
0.25	0.380	0.378	0.371	0.361	0.349	0.337	0.327	0.320	0.315	0.313
0.30	0.504	0.500	0.490	0.474	0.455	0.435	0.417	0.403	0.394	0.391
0.35	0.619	0.614	0.601	0.580	0.556	0.529	0.505	0.485	0.472	0.468
0.40	0.728	0.722	0.706	0.682	0.653	0.621	0.591	0.567	0.551	0.546
0.45	0.831	0.825	0.807	0.780	0.746	0.711	0.677	0.650	0.632	0.626
0.50	0.930	0.923	0.903	0.873	0.837	0.799	0.763	0.735	0.716	0.710
0.55	1.022	1.015	0.994	0.962	0.924	0.885	0.849	0.820	0.802	0.796
0.60	1.108	1.100	1.079	1.046	1.008	0.969	0.934	0.907	0.890	0.884
0.65	1.185	1.178	1.156	1.124	1.087	1.050	1.018	0.994	0.980	0.975
0.70	1.252	1.245	1.224	1.194	1.160	1.127	1.099	1.080	1.069	1.065
0.75	1.306	1.299	1.280	1.253	1.224	1.197	1.176	1.163	1.156	1.154
0.80	1.344	1.338	1.322	1.300	1.277	1.258	1.246	1.240	1.238	1.237
0.85	1.361	1.357	1.344	1.329	1.314	1.305	1.303	1.305	1.308	1.310
0.90	1.351	1.349	1.341	1.334	1.330	1.332	1.340	1.351	1.361	1.364
0.95	1.306	1.305	1.305	1.306	1.314	1.328	1.348	1.367	1.382	1.387
1.00	1.213	1.214	1.220	1.232	1.252	1.278	1.307	1.334	1.353	1.360
1.05	1.048	1.052	1.065	1.086	1.115	1.150	1.185	1.216	1.238	1.245
1.10	0.759	0.764	0.779	0.803	0.835	0.870	0.903	0.932	0.951	0.957

Table 1 (*Continued*)

$\zeta = 0.15$

ξ	φ									
	0°	10°	20°	30°	40°	50°	60°	70°	80°	90°
0.1980	0	0	0	0	0	0	0	0	0	0
0.20	0.043	0.043	0.044	0.046	0.048	0.050	0.053	0.054	0.056	0.056
0.25	0.274	0.273	0.271	0.269	0.267	0.267	0.268	0.270	0.271	0.272
0.30	0.434	0.432	0.425	0.415	0.404	0.393	0.385	0.379	0.375	0.374
0.35	0.578	0.574	0.563	0.546	0.526	0.506	0.487	0.473	0.465	0.462
0.40	0.712	0.707	0.692	0.669	0.641	0.612	0.586	0.564	0.550	0.546
0.45	0.838	0.831	0.813	0.786	0.752	0.716	0.682	0.655	0.637	0.630
0.50	0.957	0.950	0.929	0.897	0.858	0.816	0.778	0.746	0.725	0.718
0.55	1.069	1.061	1.038	1.003	0.960	0.915	0.873	0.838	0.816	0.808
0.60	1.174	1.166	1.141	1.104	1.059	1.012	0.968	0.933	0.910	0.903
0.65	1.272	1.263	1.237	1.199	1.153	1.105	1.062	1.028	1.007	1.000
0.70	1.359	1.350	1.324	1.286	1.241	1.196	1.155	1.125	1.106	1.099
0.75	1.435	1.426	1.401	1.364	1.322	1.281	1.246	1.220	1.205	1.200
0.80	1.495	1.487	1.464	1.431	1.393	1.359	1.331	1.312	1.302	1.299
0.85	1.537	1.530	1.510	1.482	1.452	1.426	1.408	1.397	1.393	1.392
0.90	1.556	1.550	1.534	1.513	1.493	1.478	1.471	1.470	1.472	1.473
0.95	1.543	1.539	1.529	1.518	1.509	1.508	1.513	1.523	1.531	1.535
1.00	1.491	1.490	1.487	1.486	1.491	1.504	1.522	1.542	1.557	1.563
1.05	1.386	1.387	1.392	1.403	1.422	1.448	1.479	1.507	1.528	1.535
1.10	1.204	1.208	1.221	1.243	1.273	1.310	1.349	1.383	1.407	1.415
1.15	0.893	0.899	0.916	0.943	0.978	1.017	1.056	1.088	1.110	1.118

$\zeta = 0.20$

ξ	φ									
	0°	10°	20°	30°	40°	50°	60°	70°	80°	90°
0.2459	0	0	0	0	0	0	0	0	0	0
0.25	0.074	0.074	0.076	0.079	0.082	0.086	0.090	0.093	0.095	0.095
0.30	0.322	0.322	0.320	0.318	0.317	0.318	0.320	0.323	0.325	0.326
0.35	0.503	0.500	0.492	0.482	0.470	0.459	0.451	0.446	0.443	0.442
0.40	0.664	0.660	0.648	0.629	0.607	0.585	0.566	0.551	0.542	0.539
0.45	0.815	0.809	0.792	0.767	0.736	0.704	0.674	0.651	0.636	0.630
0.50	0.956	0.949	0.929	0.897	0.859	0.818	0.780	0.749	0.729	0.723
0.55	1.090	1.082	1.058	1.022	0.977	0.930	0.886	0.849	0.826	0.817
0.60	1.216	1.206	1.180	1.140	1.091	1.039	0.990	0.951	0.925	0.916
0.65	1.333	1.323	1.295	1.252	1.200	1.145	1.095	1.054	1.028	1.018
0.70	1.441	1.431	1.401	1.357	1.304	1.249	1.198	1.159	1.133	1.125
0.75	1.537	1.527	1.497	1.453	1.401	1.347	1.300	1.264	1.241	1.234
0.80	1.619	1.609	1.580	1.538	1.489	1.440	1.399	1.368	1.349	1.343
0.85	1.684	1.675	1.648	1.609	1.566	1.524	1.491	1.468	1.455	1.451
0.90	1.727	1.719	1.695	1.662	1.627	1.596	1.574	1.560	1.554	1.552
0.95	1.742	1.735	1.717	1.692	1.668	1.650	1.640	1.638	1.639	1.639
1.00	1.722	1.717	1.705	1.691	1.680	1.677	1.682	1.691	1.700	1.703
1.05	1.655	1.653	1.650	1.648	1.652	1.665	1.685	1.705	1.722	1.728
1.10	1.528	1.530	1.535	1.546	1.566	1.595	1.628	1.659	1.681	1.689
1.15	1.315	1.320	1.333	1.357	1.390	1.431	1.473	1.510	1.536	1.545
1.20	0.958	0.964	0.982	1.011	1.049	1.091	1.133	1.168	1.191	1.199

(*Continued*)

Table 1 (*Continued*)

$\zeta = 0.25$

ξ	φ									
	0°	10°	20°	30°	40°	50°	60°	70°	80°	90°
0.2877	0	0	0	0	0	0	0	0	0	0
0.30	0.150	0.151	0.153	0.158	0.163	0.170	0.176	0.181	0.185	0.186
0.35	0.396	0.395	0.393	0.390	0.388	0.388	0.390	0.393	0.395	0.396
0.40	0.591	0.588	0.579	0.567	0.553	0.541	0.531	0.525	0.521	0.520
0.45	0.768	0.763	0.749	0.728	0.703	0.677	0.655	0.639	0.628	0.625
0.50	0.934	0.927	0.908	0.879	0.844	0.807	0.774	0.747	0.730	0.724
0.55	1.089	1.081	1.058	1.022	0.979	0.933	0.890	0.855	0.832	0.824
0.60	1.236	1.227	1.200	1.159	1.108	1.055	1.004	0.963	0.937	0.927
0.65	1.374	1.364	1.334	1.289	1.233	1.174	1.119	1.074	1.044	1.034
0.70	1.502	1.491	1.459	1.411	1.352	1.290	1.232	1.186	1.156	1.146
0.75	1.619	1.607	1.574	1.524	1.464	1.402	1.345	1.300	1.271	1.261
0.80	1.722	1.710	1.677	1.627	1.568	1.508	1.455	1.414	1.388	1.379
0.85	1.808	1.797	1.764	1.717	1.662	1.607	1.560	1.526	1.505	1.498
0.90	1.873	1.863	1.833	1.790	1.741	1.695	1.658	1.632	1.617	1.613
0.95	1.912	1.903	1.877	1.841	1.802	1.768	1.743	1.728	1.721	1.719
1.00	1.918	1.911	1.891	1.864	1.838	1.818	1.808	1.806	1.807	1.808
1.05	1.882	1.878	1.865	1.850	1.839	1.837	1.842	1.853	1.863	1.867
1.10	1.793	1.791	1.788	1.787	1.793	1.808	1.831	1.854	1.873	1.879
1.15	1.633	1.634	1.641	1.655	1.678	1.711	1.747	1.782	1.806	1.815
1.20	1.373	1.378	1.394	1.420	1.457	1.502	1.548	1.588	1.615	1.625
1.25	0.939	0.946	0.965	0.996	1.035	1.078	1.121	1.156	1.180	1.188

$\zeta = 0.30$

ξ	φ									
	0°	10°	20°	30°	40°	50°	60°	70°	80°	90°
0.3245	0	0	0	0	0	0	0	0	0	0
0.35	0.252	0.253	0.255	0.259	'0.265	0.273	0.281	0.288	0.292	0.294
0.40	0.496	0.494	0.490	0.485	0.481	0.479	0.479	0.480	0.482	0.483
0.45	0.703	0.699	0.688	0.673	0.655	0.639	0.626	0.617	0.613	0.611
0.50	0.894	0.888	0.871	0.846	0.816	0.786	0.759	0.739	0.727	0.722
0.55	1.072	1.064	1.042	1.009	0.968	0.926	0.887	0.856	0.836	0.830
0.60	1.240	1.231	1.204	1.164	1.114	1.062	1.012	0.972	0.947	0.938
0.65	1.399	1.388	1.358	1.311	1.254	1.194	1.137	1.090	1.060	1.049
0.70	1.547	1.535	1.502	1.451	1.388	1.322	1.260	1.210	1.177	1.165
0.75	1.684	1.671	1.636	1.582	1.516	1.447	1.382	1.331	1.298	1.286
0.80	1.807	1.794	1.757	1.702	1.635	1.566	1.503	1.453	1.422	1.411
0.85	1.913	1.901	1.864	1.809	1.744	1.678	1.620	1.575	1.547	1.538
0.90	2.000	1.987	1.952	1.900	1.840	1.781	1.730	1.693	1.671	1.663
0.95	2.061	2.049	2.017	1.970	1.918	1.869	1.830	1.803	1.788	1.784
1.00	2.090	2.080	2.052	2.014	1.973	1.938	1.913	1.899	1.893	1.891
1.05	2.079	2.071	2.050	2.023	1.997	1.979	1.971	1.971	1.974	1.975
1.10	2.018	2.013	2.001	1.988	1.980	1.980	1.990	2.004	2.017	2.022
1.15	1.894	1.893	1.891	1.894	1.904	1.925	1.952	1.980	2.001	2.009
1.20	1.687	1.690	1.699	1.717	1.746	1.784	1.826	1.865	1.892	1.902
1.25	1.362	1.368	1.386	1.417	1.458	1.507	1.556	1.598	1.627	1.638
1.30	0.805	0.811	0.830	0.859	0.896	0.936	0.975	1.007	1.029	1.036

Table 1 (*Continued*)

$\zeta = 0.35$

ξ	φ									
	0°	10°	20°	30°	40°	50°	60°	70°	80°	90°
0.3566	0	0	0	0	0	0	0	0	0	0
0.40	0.378	0.378	0.379	0.381	0.385	0.392	0.399	0.406	0.411	0.413
0.45	0.623	0.620	0.614	0.605	0.596	0.589	0.586	0.584	0.585	0.585
0.50	0.840	0.835	0.821	0.801	0.778	0.756	0.738	0.725	0.718	0.715
0.55	1.042	1.035	1.015	0.985	0.949	0.912	0.879	0.854	0.838	0.833
0.60	1.232	1.223	1.198	1.158	1.111	1.061	1.016	0.979	0.955	0.947
0.65	1.411	1.401	1.370	1.324	1.267	1.207	1.150	1.104	1.074	1.064
0.70	1.579	1.568	1.533	1.481	1.416	1.348	1.283	1.231	1.197	1.185
0.75	1.736	1.723	1.686	1.628	1.559	1.485	1.416	1.359	1.323	1.310
0.80	1.878	1.865	1.825	1.765	1.693	1.616	1.546	1.489	1.453	1.440
0.85	2.004	1.990	1.950	1.889	1.817	1.741	1.673	1.620	1.586	1.574
0.90	2.110	2.096	2.057	1.997	1.927	1.857	1.795	1.747	1.718	1.708
0.95	2.191	2.178	2.140	2.085	2.021	1.959	1.907	1.869	1.846	1.839
1.00	2.241	2.228	2.195	2.146	2.093	2.043	2.004	1.979	1.965	1.960
1.05	2.251	2.241	2.213	2.175	2.135	2.102	2.080	2.068	2.064	2.063
1.10	2.214	2.206	2.187	2.162	2.139	2.125	2.121	2.125	2.132	2.134
1.15	2.117	2.113	2.103	2.094	2.091	2.098	2.114	2.134	2.150	2.156
1.20	1.945	1.945	1.947	1.955	1.973	2.000	2.034	2.068	2.092	2.102
1.25	1.676	1.680	1.693	1.717	1.753	1.797	1.845	1.888	1.918	1.928
1.30	1.260	1.267	1.288	1.322	1.366	1.417	1.468	1.511	1.540	1.550
1.35	0.437	0.442	0.454	0.472	0.495	0.519	0.542	0.561	0.573	0.578

$\zeta = 0.40$

ξ	φ									
	0°	10°	20°	30°	40°	50°	60°	70°	80°	90°
0.3847	0	0	0	0	0	0	0	0	0	0
0.40	0.222	0.224	0.227	0.234	0.242	0.251	0.260	0.268	0.273	0.275
0.45	0.529	0.528	0.526	0.524	0.524	0.526	0.530	0.535	0.539	0.541
0.50	0.777	0.773	0.763	0.748	0.733	0.719	0.710	0.704	0.702	0.701
0.55	1.003	0.997	0.979	0.953	0.923	0.893	0.867	0.848	0.837	0.833
0.60	1.215	1.207	1.182	1.146	1.102	1.057	1.016	0.984	0.963	0.956
0.65	1.415	1.405	1.375	1.329	1.274	1.215	1.161	1.117	1.089	1.079
0.70	1.603	1.591	1.556	1.503	1.438	1.369	1.304	1.251	1.217	1.205
0.75	1.778	1.765	1.726	1.667	1.595	1.518	1.446	1.387	1.348	1.335
0.80	1.940	1.925	1.884	1.821	1.743	1.662	1.586	1.524	1.484	1.470
0.85	2.084	2.069	2.026	1.961	1.881	1.798	1.722	1.662	1.623	1.609
0.90	2.209	2.193	2.150	2.084	2.006	1.926	1.854	1.798	1.762	1.750
0.95	2.307	2.292	2.250	2.187	2.114	2.040	1.977	1.929	1.899	1.889
1.00	2.375	2.361	2.322	2.265	2.200	2.137	2.086	2.049	2.028	2.021
1.05	2.404	2.392	2.358	2.310	2.257	2.210	2.174	2.152	2.141	2.138
1.10	2.386	2.376	2.350	2.314	2.278	2.249	2.233	2.227	2.226	2.227
1.15	2.310	2.304	2.287	2.266	2.250	2.243	2.247	2.258	2.269	2.273
1.20	2.164	2.161	2.156	2.153	2.158	2.174	2.199	2.226	2.246	2.254
1.25	1.930	1.932	1.939	1.954	1.980	2.017	2.059	2.099	2.127	2.137
1.30	1.579	1.585	1.602	1.633	1.675	1.726	1.778	1.824	1.856	1.867
1.35	1.029	1.037	1.058	1.092	1.136	1.184	1.230	1.270	1.295	1.305

(*Continued*)

Table 1 (*Continued*)

$\zeta = 0.45$

ξ	φ									
	0°	10°	20°	30°	40°	50°	60°	70°	80°	90°
0.4094	0	0	0	0	0	0	0	0	0	0
0.45	0.422	0.422	0.424	0.428	0.434	0.443	0.453	0.462	0.468	0.471
0.50	0.706	0.704	0.697	0.689	0.681	0.676	0.674	0.675	0.677	0.678
0.55	0.959	0.953	0.938	0.917	0.892	0.870	0.852	0.839	0.832	0.830
0.60	1.193	1.185	1.162	1.129	1.089	1.049	1.014	0.987	0.971	0.965
0.65	1.413	1.403	1.374	1.330	1.276	1.221	1.170	1.130	1.104	1.095
0.70	1.620	1.608	1.574	1.521	1.456	1.387	1.323	1.271	1.238	1.226
0.75	1.814	1.801	1.761	1.701	1.627	1.548	1.474	1.414	1.375	1.361
0.80	1.994	1.979	1.936	1.870	1.789	1.704	1.623	1.558	1.516	1.501
0.85	2.156	2.140	2.094	2.025	1.941	1.852	1.769	1.703	1.660	1.645
0.90	2.297	2.281	2.234	2.163	2.078	1.990	1.909	1.846	1.805	1.791
0.95	2.412	2.396	2.350	2.281	2.199	2.115	2.041	1.984	1.949	1.937
1.00	2.496	2.481	2.437	2.372	2.297	2.223	2.160	2.114	2.086	2.077
1.05	2.541	2.527	2.487	2.430	2.367	2.307	2.259	2.227	2.209	2.203
1.10	2.539	2.527	2.494	2.448	2.400	2.359	2.330	2.314	2.307	2.305
1.15	2.479	2.470	2.447	2.416	2.387	2.368	2.360	2.362	2.366	2.369
1.20	2.351	2.346	2.334	2.321	2.314	2.318	2.333	2.352	2.368	2.375
1.25	2.141	2.141	2.141	2.147	2.163	2.190	2.225	2.260	2.286	2.295
1.30	1.828	1.832	1.845	1.869	1.905	1.951	2.001	2.046	2.078	2.089
1.35	1.370	1.377	1.398	1.434	1.480	1.534	1.588	1.633	1.664	1.675
1.40	0.545	0.550	0.564	0.587	0.614	0.644	0.673	0.696	0.711	0.716

$\zeta = 0.50$

ξ	φ									
	0°	10°	20°	30°	40°	50°	60°	70°	80°	90°
0.4306	0	0	0	0	0	0	0	0	0	0
0.45	0.293	0.294	0.299	0.306	0.316	0.327	0.338	0.348	0.354	0.357
0.50	0.631	0.630	0.627	0.625	0.624	0.626	0.631	0.637	0.642	0.644
0.55	0.911	0.906	0.894	0.878	0.860	0.845	0.834	0.827	0.825	0.824
0.60	1.167	1.160	1.140	1.109	1.075	1.040	1.011	0.990	0.977	0.973
0.65	1.408	1.398	1.370	1.328	1.278	1.226	1.179	1.143	1.120	1.112
0.70	1.634	1.622	1.588	1.535	1.472	1.405	1.342	1.292	1.260	1.249
0.75	1.846	1.833	1.793	1.732	1.657	1.577	1.503	1.442	1.403	1.389
0.80	2.043	2.028	1.983	1.915	1.832	1.744	1.660	1.593	1.548	1.533
0.85	2.221	2.205	2.157	2.085	1.996	1.902	1.814	1.743	1.697	1.681
0.90	2.378	2.361	2.312	2.236	2.146	2.050	1.963	1.893	1.848	1.833
0.95	2.508	2.491	2.441	2.366	2.277	2.185	2.103	2.038	1.997	1.983
1.00	2.606	2.589	2.541	2.470	2.386	2.302	2.229	2.174	2.140	2.129
1.05	2.664	2.648	2.604	2.539	2.466	2.395	2.336	2.295	2.270	2.263
1.10	2.674	2.660	2.622	2.568	2.509	2.456	2.416	2.390	2.377	2.374
1.15	2.627	2.616	2.587	2.547	2.507	2.475	2.456	2.449	2.449	2.449
1.20	2.512	2.505	2.486	2.464	2.446	2.439	2.443	2.455	2.467	2.471
1.25	2.318	2.315	2.309	2.307	2.313	2.330	2.357	2.386	2.408	2.417
1.30	2.029	2.031	2.039	2.056	2.084	2.124	2.169	2.211	2.241	2.252
1.35	1.618	1.624	1.643	1.676	1.720	1.773	1.828	1.876	1.909	1.920
1.40	0.998	1.005	1.027	1.061	1.104	1.152	1.198	1.236	1.262	1.271

Table 1 (*Continued*)

$\zeta = 0.55$

ξ	φ									
	0°	10°	20°	30°	40°	50°	60°	70°	80°	90°
0.4488	0	0	0	0	0	0	0	0	0	0
0.45	0.074	0.075	0.077	0.080	0.084	0.089	0.093	0.096	0.098	0.099
0.50	0.552	0.552	0.553	0.556	0.561	0.569	0.579	0.589	0.596	0.599
0.55	0.863	0.859	0.850	0.838	0.827	0.818	0.814	0.813	0.814	0.815
0.60	1.142	1.136	1.117	1.091	1.061	1.032	1.009	0.993	0.984	0.981
0.65	1.403	1.393	1.366	1.326	1.279	1.231	1.189	1.157	1.136	1.130
0.70	1.647	1.636	1.602	1.550	1.487	1.422	1.362	1.315	1.284	1.274
0.75	1.877	1.863	1.823	1.761	1.686	1.606	1.532	1.472	1.432	1.419
0.80	2.090	2.074	2.028	1.959	1.874	1.783	1.698	1.628	1.583	1.567
0.85	2.283	2.266	2.217	2.141	2.049	1.951	1.860	1.785	1.736	1.720
0.90	2.454	2.436	2.384	2.305	2.209	2.109	2.015	1.940	1.891	1.875
0.95	2.597	2.579	2.526	2.446	2.351	2.252	2.161	2.090	2.045	2.029
1.00	2.706	2.688	2.637	2.559	2.468	2.376	2.294	2.231	2.192	2.179
1.05	2.775	2.758	2.709	2.638	2.556	2.475	2.407	2.357	2.327	2.317
1.10	2.794	2.779	2.736	2.674	2.606	2.543	2.492	2.458	2.440	2.434
1.15	2.755	2.743	2.708	2.660	2.610	2.568	2.539	2.524	2.518	2.517
1.20	2.649	2.640	2.616	2.585	2.557	2.540	2.535	2.539	2.546	2.550
1.25	2.464	2.460	2.449	2.438	2.435	2.443	2.462	2.485	2.504	2.511
1.30	2.191	2.191	2.194	2.203	2.224	2.256	2.296	2.334	2.363	2.373
1.35	1.809	1.813	1.829	1.856	1.897	1.946	2.000	2.047	2.080	2.092
1.40	1.269	1.276	1.299	1.335	1.382	1.435	1.488	1.533	1.563	1.573

$\zeta = 0.60$

ξ	φ									
	0°	10°	20°	30°	40°	50°	60°	70°	80°	90°
0.4639	0	0	0	0	0	0	0	0	0	0
0.50	0.472	0.473	0.476	0.482	0.492	0.504	0.517	0.529	0.537	0.540
0.55	0.817	0.815	0.809	0.801	0.795	0.793	0.794	0.798	0.801	0.803
0.60	1.119	1.114	1.097	1.074	1.049	1.026	1.008	0.996	0.991	0.989
0.65	1.400	1.391	1.365	1.327	1.283	1.239	1.201	1.172	1.155	1.149
0.70	1.662	1.650	1.617	1.566	1.505	1.442	1.384	1.339	1.310	1.301
0.75	1.908	1.894	1.853	1.791	1.716	1.637	1.563	1.503	1.464	1.451
0.80	2.135	2.119	2.073	2.002	1.915	1.823	1.736	1.666	1.620	1.604
0.85	2.343	2.325	2.274	2.197	2.101	2.000	1.905	1.828	1.777	1.760
0.90	2.526	2.507	2.453	2.371	2.271	2.165	2.067	1.987	1.936	1.918
0.95	2.680	2.660	2.605	2.521	2.420	2.315	2.218	2.141	2.092	2.075
1.00	2.798	2.779	2.724	2.642	2.544	2.445	2.355	2.286	2.243	2.228
1.05	2.874	2.856	2.804	2.727	2.637	2.549	2.472	2.415	2.380	2.368
1.10	2.899	2.882	2.836	2.768	2.692	2.619	2.560	2.519	2.495	2.488
1.15	2.865	2.851	2.812	2.757	2.699	2.648	2.610	2.588	2.577	2.574
1.20	2.763	2.752	2.724	2.686	2.650	2.623	2.610	2.607	2.610	2.612
1.25	2.584	2.577	2.562	2.544	2.532	2.532	2.543	2.561	2.576	2.583
1.30	2.318	2.317	2.315	2.318	2.332	2.357	2.391	2.425	2.451	2.461
1.35	1.953	1.957	1.969	1.991	2.026	2.072	2.122	2.168	2.200	2.212
1.40	1.457	1.464	1.485	1.521	1.568	1.622	1.677	1.724	1.756	1.767
1.45	0.668	0.673	0.690	0.717	0.750	0.785	0.819	0.847	0.865	0.871

(Continued)

Table 1 (*Continued*)

$\zeta = 0.65$

ξ	φ									
	0°	10°	20°	30°	40°	50°	60°	70°	80°	90°
0.4764	0	0	0	0	0	0	0	0	0	0
0.50	0.389	0.391	0.396	0.405	0.416	0.430	0.444	0.456	0.465	0.468
0.55	0.776	0.775	0.771	0.768	0.767	0.769	0.775	0.782	0.788	0.790
0.60	1.102	1.097	1.082	1.062	1.041	1.023	1.010	1.002	0.999	0.998
0.65	1.401	1.392	1.368	1.332	1.290	1.250	1.216	1.190	1.176	1.171
0.70	1.680	1.668	1.635	1.585	1.526	1.464	1.409	1.366	1.339	1.330
0.75	1.941	1.927	1.886	1.824	1.748	1.669	1.596	1.537	1.499	1.486
0.80	2.182	2.166	2.119	2.047	1.958	1.864	1.777	1.705	1.659	1.643
0.85	2.401	2.383	2.331	2.251	2.153	2.049	1.951	1.872	1.820	1.802
0.90	2.595	2.575	2.520	2.435	2.331	2.221	2.118	2.035	1.981	1.962
0.95	2.757	2.737	2.679	2.592	2.486	2.375	2.273	2.192	2.139	2.121
1.00	2.882	2.862	2.804	2.718	2.615	2.509	2.413	2.338	2.291	2.275
1.05	2.962	2.943	2.888	2.806	2.710	2.615	2.531	2.467	2.429	2.416
1.10	2.990	2.972	2.922	2.849	2.766	2.686	2.619	2.572	2.544	2.535
1.15	2.956	2.941	2.899	2.839	2.773	2.714	2.669	2.640	2.626	2.622
1.20	2.855	2.843	2.811	2.767	2.723	2.689	2.669	2.661	2.660	2.661
1.25	2.676	2.669	2.649	2.625	2.607	2.599	2.604	2.617	2.629	2.634
1.30	2.414	2.412	2.406	2.404	2.411	2.430	2.458	2.489	2.513	2.522
1.35	2.059	2.061	2.070	2.088	2.118	2.159	2.206	2.249	2.281	2.292
1.40	1.589	1.595	1.615	1.648	1.693	1.746	1.801	1.849	1.882	1.893
1.45	0.913	0.920	0.941	0.973	1.014	1.058	1.102	1.138	1.161	1.170

$\zeta = 0.70$

ξ	φ									
	0°	10°	20°	30°	40°	50°	60°	70°	80°	90°
0.4861	0	0	0	0	0	0	0	0	0	0
0.50	0.304	0.306	0.312	0.321	0.333	0.347	0.360	0.371	0.379	0.381
0.55	0.743	0.743	0.741	0.741	0.743	0.750	0.759	0.769	0.777	0.779
0.60	1.092	1.087	1.074	1.057	1.039	1.025	1.016	1.011	1.010	1.010
0.65	1.409	1.400	1.377	1.342	1.303	1.266	1.234	1.212	1.199	1.195
0.70	1.703	1.692	1.659	1.609	1.551	1.491	1.437	1.396	1.371	1.362
0.75	1.978	1.963	1.922	1.860	1.784	1.705	1.632	1.573	1.536	1.523
0.80	2.231	2.214	2.166	2.093	2.003	1.908	1.819	1.747	1.700	1.683
0.85	2.460	2.441	2.388	2.306	2.206	2.099	1.999	1.917	1.863	1.845
0.90	2.661	2.641	2.584	2.496	2.389	2.275	2.169	2.083	2.026	2.007
0.95	2.829	2.808	2.749	2.658	2.549	2.433	2.326	2.241	2.186	2.167
1.00	2.957	2.936	2.877	2.787	2.679	2.568	2.467	2.387	2.337	2.319
1.05	3.038	3.018	2.961	2.875	2.775	2.673	2.584	2.515	2.473	2.459
1.10	3.065	3.046	2.994	2.917	2.828	2.742	2.670	2.617	2.586	2.576
1.15	3.029	3.013	2.968	2.903	2.832	2.767	2.716	2.683	2.665	2.659
1.20	2.924	2.911	2.876	2.828	2.779	2.738	2.712	2.700	2.696	2.695
1.25	2.743	2.734	2.712	2.683	2.659	2.646	2.645	2.654	2.664	2.668
1.30	2.480	2.476	2.468	2.461	2.463	2.477	2.501	2.528	2.550	2.558
1.35	2.130	2.131	2.137	2.151	2.176	2.213	2.257	2.298	2.328	2.339
1.40	1.676	1.681	1.699	1.729	1.772	1.823	1.877	1.925	1.957	1.969
1.45	1.057	1.065	1.086	1.120	1.164	1.212	1.260	1.299	1.326	1.335

Table 1 (*Continued*)

ζ = 0.75

ξ	φ									
	0°	10°	20°	30°	40°	50°	60°	70°	80°	90°
0.4932	0	0	0	0	0	0	0	0	0	0
0.50	0.217	0.219	0.224	0.232	0.243	0.254	0.264	0.273	0.279	0.281
0.55	0.721	0.721	0.721	0.723	0.729	0.738	0.750	0.762	0.770	0.774
0.60	1.091	1.087	1.075	1.060	1.045	1.033	1.027	1.026	1.026	1.027
0.65	1.424	1.416	1.393	1.360	1.323	1.287	1.258	1.238	1.226	1.223
0.70	1.733	1.721	1.688	1.639	1.581	1.522	1.470	1.430	1.405	1.397
0.75	2.019	2.005	1.963	1.900	1.823	1.744	1.671	1.613	1.575	1.563
0.80	2.282	2.265	2.216	2.141	2.050	1.953	1.863	1.790	1.743	1.726
0.85	2.519	2.500	2.445	2.361	2.259	2.149	2.047	1.963	1.908	1.889
0.90	2.725	2.705	2.646	2.556	2.446	2.329	2.219	2.130	2.072	2.052
0.95	2.896	2.874	2.813	2.720	2.607	2.488	2.377	2.288	2.230	2.211
1.00	3.024	3.002	2.941	2.848	2.737	2.621	2.516	2.432	2.379	2.361
1.05	3.103	3.082	3.023	2.934	2.829	2.723	2.629	2.557	2.512	2.497
1.10	3.125	3.105	3.051	2.970	2.878	2.787	2.710	2.654	2.620	2.609
1.15	3.083	3.066	3.019	2.951	2.876	2.806	2.750	2.713	2.693	2.686
1.20	2.970	2.957	2.920	2.869	2.815	2.770	2.740	2.724	2.718	2.716
1.25	2.783	2.774	2.749	2.717	2.689	2.671	2.667	2.673	2.680	2.684
1.30	2.516	2.512	2.501	2.491	2.489	2.499	2.519	2.544	2.564	2.572
1.35	2.167	2.167	2.171	2.182	2.204	2.238	2.278	2.318	2.346	2.357
1.40	1.723	1.728	1.744	1.772	1.812	1.861	1.914	1.960	1.992	2.004
1.45	1.139	1.147	1.168	1.202	1.246	1.296	1.345	1.386	1.413	1.423

ζ = 0.80

ξ	φ									
	0°	10°	20°	30°	40°	50°	60°	70°	80°	90°
0.4978	0	0	0	0	0	0	0	0	0	0
0.50	0.127	0.128	0.132	0.137	0.144	0.151	0.157	0.163	0.166	0.168
0.55	0.713	0.713	0.714	0.718	0.726	0.737	0.750	0.763	0.773	0.776
0.60	1.102	1.098	1.087	1.073	1.060	1.050	1.046	1.046	1.048	1.049
0.65	1.450	1.442	1.419	1.386	1.350	1.315	1.288	1.269	1.258	1.255
0.70	1.771	1.759	1.725	1.676	1.617	1.559	1.507	1.467	1.443	1.435
0.75	2.066	2.051	2.009	1.945	1.867	1.787	1.713	1.655	1.617	1.604
0.80	2.336	2.319	2.269	2.193	2.100	2.001	1.909	1.835	1.787	1.770
0.85	2.578	2.558	2.502	2.417	2.312	2.200	2.095	2.009	1.954	1.934
0.90	2.786	2.765	2.705	2.613	2.500	2.380	2.268	2.176	2.117	2.096
0.95	2.956	2.934	2.871	2.776	2.660	2.537	2.424	2.332	2.273	2.252
1.00	3.081	3.059	2.996	2.901	2.786	2.667	2.559	2.473	2.418	2.399
1.05	3.153	3.132	3.071	2.980	2.873	2.763	2.666	2.591	2.545	2.529
1.10	3.167	3.147	3.091	3.009	2.913	2.820	2.740	2.681	2.645	2.634
1.15	3.115	3.098	3.049	2.908	2.902	2.829	2.771	2.731	2.709	2.702
1.20	2.993	2.979	2.941	2.887	2.831	2.784	2.751	2.732	2.725	2.723
1.25	2.796	2.787	2.761	2.727	2.696	2.676	2.669	2.673	2.679	2.682
1.30	2.524	2.519	2.507	2.495	2.490	2.497	2.515	2.538	2.557	2.564
1.35	2.172	2.173	2.175	2.184	2.203	2.235	2.273	2.311	2.338	2.348
1.40	1.735	1.739	1.754	1.780	1.818	1.866	1.916	1.961	1.993	2.004
1.45	1.173	1.180	1.201	1.235	1.278	1.328	1.377	1.418	1.446	1.455

(Continued)

Table 1 (*Continued*)

$\zeta = 0.85$

ξ	φ									
	0°	10°	20°	30°	40°	50°	60°	70°	80°	90°
0.4999	0	0	0	0	0	0	0	0	0	0
0.50	0.032	0.032	0.033	0.034	0.036	0.038	0.040	0.041	0.042	0.042
0.55	0.722	0.722	0.724	0.728	0.737	0.749	0.764	0.778	0.788	0.791
0.60	1.127	1.123	1.112	1.098	1.085	1.077	1.073	1.074	1.077	1.078
0.65	1.478	1.478	1.455	1.422	1.385	1.351	1.323	1.304	1.294	1.291
0.70	1.816	1.804	1.770	1.720	1.660	1.601	1.548	1.508	1.484	1.476
0.75	2.119	2.104	2.060	1.995	1.916	1.834	1.758	1.699	1.661	1.648
0.80	2.393	2.375	2.324	2.246	2.151	2.051	1.957	1.881	1.832	1.815
0.85	2.636	2.616	2.559	2.471	2.364	2.250	2.143	2.055	1.998	1.978
0.90	2.843	2.822	2.760	2.666	2.551	2.428	2.313	2.220	2.159	2.138
0.95	3.008	2.986	2.922	2.825	2.706	2.582	2.465	2.372	2.311	2.290
1.00	3.125	3.103	3.039	2.942	2.826	2.705	2.594	2.506	2.450	2.431
1.05	3.188	3.166	3.105	3.013	2.903	2.792	2.693	2.617	2.569	2.553
1.10	3.190	3.170	3.113	3.030	2.933	2.838	2.756	2.696	2.660	2.648
1.15	3.125	3.108	3.059	2.988	2.909	2.835	2.776	2.735	2.712	2.705
1.20	2.990	2.976	2.937	2.883	2.827	2.778	2.744	2.724	2.716	2.714
1.25	2.782	2.773	2.746	2.712	2.680	2.659	2.651	2.654	2.659	2.662
1.30	2.502	2.497	2.484	2.472	2.466	2.472	2.489	2.510	2.528	2.535
1.35	2.148	2.147	2.149	2.157	2.175	2.205	2.242	2.279	2.305	2.315
1.40	1.713	1.718	1.731	1.756	1.793	1.839	1.888	1.932	1.963	1.974
1.45	1.167	1.174	1.194	1.226	1.269	1.317	1.365	1.406	1.433	1.443

$\zeta = 0.8660$

ξ	φ									
	0°	10°	20°	30°	40°	50°	60°	70°	80°	90°
0.5000	0	0	0	0	0	0	0	0	0	0
0.55	0.728	0.729	0.731	0.735	0.744	0.756	0.771	0.785	0.795	0.799
0.60	1.138	1.134	1.123	1.109	1.096	1.087	1.084	1.085	1.087	1.088
0.65	1.501	1.492	1.469	1.436	1.398	1.364	1.336	1.317	1.307	1.304
0.70	1.833	1.821	1.786	1.735	1.675	1.615	1.562	1.522	1.497	1.489
0.75	2.137	2.122	2.078	2.012	1.932	1.849	1.773	1.713	1.675	1.662
0.80	2.412	2.394	2.342	2.264	2.168	2.067	1.972	1.896	1.846	1.829
0.85	2.654	2.634	2.577	2.489	2.380	2.265	2.157	2.069	2.012	1.992
0.90	2.860	2.838	2.777	2.682	2.566	2.443	2.327	2.233	2.172	2.150
0.95	3.023	3.001	2.936	2.839	2.720	2.594	2.477	2.383	2.322	2.301
1.00	3.137	3.114	3.050	2.953	2.836	2.715	2.603	2.515	2.459	2.440
1.05	3.196	3.174	3.112	3.020	2.910	2.799	2.699	2.623	2.575	2.559
1.10	3.193	3.173	3.116	3.032	2.936	2.840	2.759	2.698	2.662	2.650
1.15	3.123	3.106	3.057	2.986	2.907	2.833	2.774	2.733	2.710	2.703
1.20	2.984	2.969	2.931	2.877	2.820	2.772	2.737	2.718	2.710	2.708
1.25	2.772	2.762	2.736	2.702	2.670	2.649	2.641	2.643	2.649	2.652
1.30	2.489	2.484	2.472	2.459	2.453	2.459	2.475	2.497	2.515	2.522
1.35	2.133	2.133	2.135	2.143	2.161	2.190	2.227	2.263	2.290	2.300
1.40	1.700	1.704	1.718	1.743	1.779	1.825	1.873	1.917	1.947	1.958
1.45	1.157	1.164	1.184	1.216	1.258	1.306	1.354	1.394	1.421	1.431
1.50	0.000	0.000	0.000	0.000	0.000	0.000	0.000	0.000	0.000	0.000

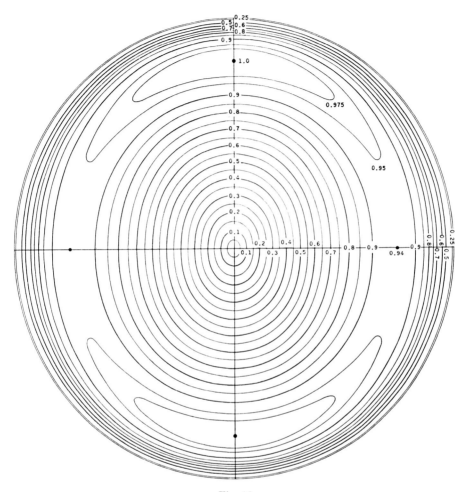

Fig. 10.

Chart showing the variation of the Lorentz-polarization correction $1/Lp$, over the zero level for $\bar{\mu} = 30°$. (After Waser[13].)

The Lorentz factor for the two penetrations corresponding to a single recorded spot on a precession photograph is therefore

$$L \sim \frac{1}{\Omega\xi \sin \bar{\mu} \sin \eta} \left[\frac{1}{1 + \tan^2 \bar{\mu} \sin^2 (\varphi+\eta)} + \frac{1}{1 + \tan^2 \bar{\mu} \sin^2 (\varphi-\eta)} \right],$$

(55)

where η is given by (28).

Practical application. Values of the combined Lorentz-polarization correction $1/Lp$ for the precession method, as a function of the cylindrical

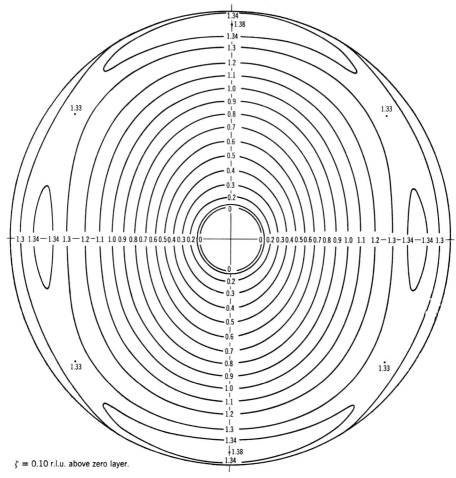

Fig. 11.
Chart showing the variation of the Lorentz-polarization correction $1/Lp$, over an upper level for $\bar{\mu} = 30°$, $\zeta = 0.10$ reciprocal-lattice units.
(After Grenville-Wells and Abrahams.[18])

reciprocal-lattice coordinates ξ, ζ, and φ for $\bar{\mu} = 30°$, are listed in Table 1. A tabulation is also available[39] for ξ as a function of $1/Lp$, ζ, and φ, which is convenient for the construction of graphs of the function $1/Lp$ mapped on a level of the reciprocal lattice. Such maps for the zero level have been published by Waser,[13] and for upper levels in steps of $\zeta = 0.05$ by Grenville-Wells and Abrahams.[18] Examples are shown in Figs. 10 and 11. Plastic overlays of these maps are available.[†]

[†] Produced by Nelson P. Nies, U. S. Borax Res. Corp., 412 Crescent Way, Anaheim, California.

The Mark III suspension

It has already been pointed out that for spots having the same ξ value the Mark II suspension causes a variation of average Lorentz factor up to a maximum of about 15% for precession angles as large as $\bar{\mu} = 30°$.

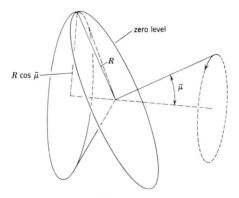

Fig. 12.
The motion of pure precession illustrated as the rolling (with slippage) of a disk over the surface of a cone.

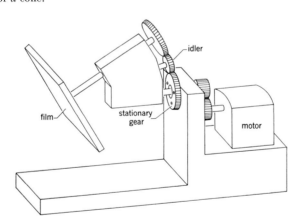

Fig. 13.
A mechanism for producing pure precession motion.

It has also been noted that charts which take account of the variation are also available. But it is also possible to devise suspensions which automatically provide the reciprocal lattice with pure precession motion.

In pure precession motion the reflecting circle travels around the reciprocal-lattice level at a uniform angular rate. This is assured if the reciprocal lattice is caused to move as if its zero level were rolling

uniformly around the surface of a cone. In this motion, illustrated in
Fig. 12, if the radius of the circle shown as the zero level is R, then the
radius of the cone making contact with it is $R \cos \bar{\mu}$. The circumference
of the circle is $2\pi R$, while that of the cone is $2\pi R \cos \bar{\mu}$. If a line in the
reciprocal lattice is to remain in the same location at each cycle, there
must occur a linear slippage between circle and cone amounting to
$2\pi R - 2\pi R \cos \bar{\mu} = 2\pi R(1 - \cos \bar{\mu})$ per cycle, or an angular slippage of
$2\pi(1 - \cos \bar{\mu})$ per cycle. This must occur in a direction opposite to that
of the precession. Mechanically this could occur if the cone and disk of
Figure 12 were gears with equal numbers of teeth.

There are several practical ways of achieving this motion. One is
shown in Fig. 13. Models constructed on this plan function quite well.

12

Absorption

The crystal specimen absorbs both the direct beam and the diffracted beam so that the diffracted beam is, in general, reduced in intensity. The amount of reduction depends on the length of the path traversed; this is a function of the shape of the crystal as well as the attitude of the set of planes responsible for the reflection.

It is worth making an estimate of the absorption to be expected for a particular specimen before the experimental work begins. For rough work the absorption can often be ignored. For example, it is usual to ignore it for small crystals of organic compounds because the absorption differs little from reflection to reflection. For the same reason, it can also be neglected for rough work on tiny inorganic crystals when using the relatively penetrating Mo or Ag radiations. On the other hand, neglect of corrections of reflected intensities for their difference in absorption when proceeding with a refinement gives rise to an effect similar to anisotropy in temperature factors[†] so that the refinement ordinarily imputes a false anisotropic temperature factor to the atoms of the crystal. Generally speaking, therefore, present-day refinement techniques call for correction of the intensities of the various reflections for absorption. Except for certain simple shapes this procedure is too tedious to carry out by hand calculation, but the availability of modern high-speed computers makes the procedure possible even for complicated shapes. Some of the basic features underlying the correction for the precession method are outlined in this chapter.

Basic absorption theory

The theory of absorption is treated elsewhere.[§] Some of the basic features are as follows.

[†] See M. J. Buerger. *Crystal-structure analysis.* (John Wiley and Sons, New York, 1960) 608–609.

[§] For example, a survey is given in M. J. Buerger. *Crystal-structure analysis.* (John Wiley and Sons, New York, 1960) 204–231.

A beam whose initial intensity is I_0, after being transmitted by matter through a path of length x, is reduced to an intensity

$$I = I_0 \, e^{-\mu x}, \tag{1}$$

where μ (not to be confused with the precession angle $\bar{\mu}$) is a constant, characteristic of the substance, and known as the *linear-absorption coefficient*.

In actual experimental procedure it is usual to have a uniform beam incident upon a body of matter which may have an irregular shape. It is convenient to treat the absorption by the body in terms of its transmission. For this purpose a *transmission factor*, T, is defined as the ratio of the intensity actually transmitted by the body to the intensity which would be transmitted if there were no absorption. This requires integrating quantities like (1) over the volumes of the body, specifically

$$T = \frac{\int_V I_0 \, e^{-\mu x} \, dV}{\int_V I_0 \, dV}$$

$$= \frac{1}{V} \int_V e^{-\mu x} \, dV. \tag{2}$$

In diffraction experiments, the path x consists of two parts. The first comprises the distance x_1 of the incident ray from the exterior of the crystal to some element of volume dV_j. The second comprises the distance x_2 of the diffracted ray, from the diffracting volume to the crystal surface. The form of (1) for diffraction is therefore specifically

$$T = \frac{1}{V} \int e^{-\mu(x_1 + x_2)} \, dV. \tag{3}$$

The integration indicated by (3) is tedious to carry out by hand computation except for special shapes. For the precession method two shapes are easy to treat: a sphere completely bathed in the x-ray beam, and an extended plate (larger than the x-ray beam) parallel to the reciprocal-lattice plane being photographed. These are the simplest cases of two different relations between specimen and beam. The sphere is an example of a small specimen completely immersed in the uniform part of an x-ray beam, while the plate is an example of a specimen which extends across the entire beam and includes portions having different intensities. This distinction calls for a brief discussion of intensity distribution in the direct beam.

Intensity distribution in the direct beam

Whenever radiation is limited by apertures to define a beam, variations in intensity occur in its cross-section, especially near the edges. It is important to understand how this occurs in the x-ray beam issuing from a pinhole system.

Figure 1*A* illustrates the way the front and back apertures limit the rays running from target region to crystal region. First, suppose that the target area is uniformly illuminated and indefinitely large. The views through the pinhole system toward the target from different points in the plane of the crystal are shown in Fig. 1*C*. At the center of the cross-section the front aperture appears centered in the back aperture.

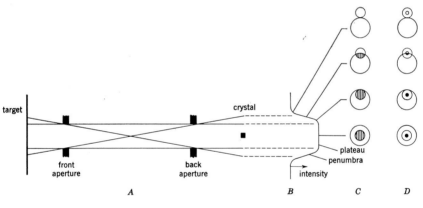

Fig. 1.

At a position near the center the entire front aperture, although uncentered, is also seen within the back aperture. From both of these positions an equal area of the uniformly illuminated target can be seen from the plane of the crystal. This condition terminates at the point from which the rim of the front aperture is seen to just touch the rim of the back aperture. At points farther from the center than this, the rim of the back aperture partially occludes the opening of the front aperture, and so reduces the target area visible. At some point still farther from the center none of the front aperture can be seen within the back aperture, so none of the target can be seen through the aperture system. For this simple case the intensity of the beam is proportional to the area of the target visible through the two apertures, so the intensity varies along the cross-section as shown in Fig. 1*B*. The cross-section contains a uniform central *plateau region* surrounded by a rapidly declining *penumbra region*.

Usually the target does not contain a large uniformly illuminated area.

If the illuminated area of the target subtends less than the front aperture as seen from the crystal, there is still a plateau in the cross-section throughout the region in the plane of the crystal where the whole illuminated area of the target can be seen, as suggested by Fig. 1*D*. If the illuminated area is non-uniform, the chief consequence is to round off the sharp edges of the plateau and penumbra.

The size of the plateau can be computed from the geometry of the pinhole system and its relation to the target. This should be done for the particular experimental conditions and the results checked by means of a short exposure on a photographic film. Ordinarily the plateau is found to be about as large as the back aperture provided a large front aperture is used. When the method calls for a crystal completely bathed in a direct beam, it is assumed that the crystal is immersed only in this uniform plateau region of the beam. If the crystal protrudes beyond this, the absorption correction is vitiated because the integration in (3) is based upon a uniform I_0 for integration over all paths.

Correction for absorption by hand calculation

Only in a few cases are the calculations required for corrections for absorption sufficiently simple to permit easy hand computation. When they are, the symmetry of the crystal shape and beam have at least cylindrical symmetry about the axis of the x-ray beam. Three such cases are treated in this section.

Correction for absorption by a spherical specimen. Because of the high symmetry of a spherical specimen completely immersed in a uniform beam of radiation, the transmission factor is a function of the Bragg angle θ. The transmission for spherical specimens has been computed and tabulated by Evans and Ekstein[†] and by Bond.[§] To use these tables one needs to measure the radius R of the sphere, and, from a knowledge of the density, composition of the crystal, and a table of mass-absorption coefficients, must calculate its linear-absorption coefficient μ. The required transmission factor is then found listed under μR for various glancing angles θ.

Correction for absorption by a plate parallel to the reciprocal-lattice plane. Because of high symmetry it is easy to evaluate the transmission of a specimen in the form of a flat plate parallel to the reciprocal-lattice plane being photographed and which intercepts the entire x-ray

---

[†] H. T. Evans, Jr., and Miriam G. Ekstein. *Tables for absorption factors for spherical crystals.* Acta Cryst. **5** (1952) 540–542.

[§] W. L. Bond[39], pages 39–300, 302–305. In these tables, Bond's $A = T$, and Bond's $A^* = 1/T$.

beam. Figure 2 shows the geometry of the Laue cones, rational axis, and plate. The x-ray beam always enters the plate at angle $\bar{\mu}$ to the normal and always leaves the plate at angle $\bar{\nu}$ to the normal. If A is the cross-sectional area of the beam, then the volume of the crystal intercepting the beam is a circular cylinder the area of whose base is

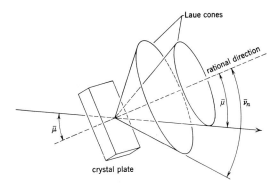

Fig. 2.

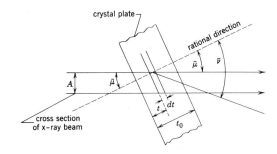

Fig. 3.

$A/\cos \bar{\mu}$, Fig. 3. The integration (3) must be carried out over paths $x_1 + x_2$ for the volume of the crystal which intercepts the beam. If this volume is divided into elementary slabs of thickness dt, the integration is given by (3), in which

$$V = (A \sec \bar{\mu})t_0$$

$$dV = (A \sec \bar{\mu})\, dt$$

$$e^{-\mu(x_1+x_2)} = e^{-\mu(t \sec \bar{\mu}+[t_0-t]\sec \bar{\nu})}$$

$$= e^{-\mu t_0 \sec \bar{\nu}}\, e^{-\mu(\sec \bar{\mu}-\sec \bar{\nu})t}.$$

When these are substituted into (3), it becomes

$$(3): \quad T = \frac{1}{V} \int e^{-\mu(x_1 + x_2)} \, dV$$

$$T = \frac{1}{A t_0 \sec \bar{\mu}} \int e^{-\mu t_0 \sec \bar{\nu}} e^{-\mu(\sec \bar{\mu} - \sec \bar{\nu})t} A \sec \bar{\mu} \, dt$$

$$= \frac{e^{-\mu t_0 \sec \bar{\nu}}}{t_0} \left[\frac{1}{-\mu(\sec \bar{\mu} - \sec \bar{\nu})} e^{-\mu(\sec \bar{\mu} - \sec \bar{\nu})t} \right]_{t=0}^{t=t_0}$$

$$= \frac{e^{-\mu t_0 \sec \bar{\nu}}}{-\mu t_0(\sec \bar{\mu} - \sec \bar{\nu})} \left(e^{-\mu(\sec \bar{\mu} - \sec \bar{\nu})t_0} - 1 \right)$$

$$= \frac{e^{-\mu t_0 \sec \bar{\mu}} - e^{-\mu t_0 \sec \bar{\nu}}}{-\mu t_0(\sec \bar{\mu} - \sec \bar{\nu})}. \tag{4}$$

The result is the same for all reflections on the same level, so that the correction varies only from level to level, and is expressed in (4) as a function of the Laue-cone angle $\bar{\nu}$.

For the zero level, $\bar{\mu} = \bar{\nu}$, and direct integration of (3) gives

$$T = \frac{1}{t_0} \int e^{-\mu t_0 \sec \bar{\mu}} \, dt = e^{-\mu t_0 \sec \bar{\mu}}. \tag{5}$$

Correction for absorption by a cylinder perpendicular to the reciprocal-lattice plane. A cylindrical specimen perpendicular to the reciprocal-lattice plane, and confined to the uniform section of the beam, also has cylindrical symmetry. It is easy to make an approximate correction for absorption by such a specimen for zero-level reflection by using existing tables.

Claassen[†] (and later Bradley[§] and Bond[‡]) derived tables for correcting absorption in rod-shaped powder samples. Buerger and Niizeki[¶] showed how this can be adapted to the correction of absorption in rod-shaped single crystals when using the equi-inclination method. While the precession method does not ordinarily employ equi-inclination geometry, its

---

[†] A. Claassen. *The calculation of absorption in x-ray powder photographs and the scattering power of tungsten.* **Phil. Mag.** (7) 9 (1930) 57–65.

[§] A. J. Bradley. *The absorption factor for the powder and rotating-crystal methods of x-ray analysis.* Proc. Phys. Soc. (London) **47** (1935) 879–899.

[‡] W. L. Bond,[39] pages 292–299. In these tables, Bond's $A = T$, and Bond's $A^* = 1/T$.

[¶] M. J. Buerger and N. Niizeki. *The correction for absorption for rod-shaped single crystals.* Am. Mineralogist **43** (1958) 726–731.

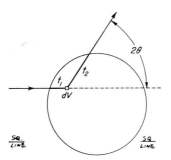

Fig. 4.
(After Buerger and Niizeki.[†])

zero-level recording does have a similar geometry, so Claassen's results can be utilized for zero-level precession photographs.

The adaptation is illustrated in Figs. 4 and 5. Claassen graphically integrated (3), specifically

$$(3): \qquad T = \frac{1}{V} \int e^{-\mu(x_1 + x_2)}\, dV$$

over the volume of a cylinder of radius R and tabulated the transmission factor against μR and θ. The corresponding integration for the zero-

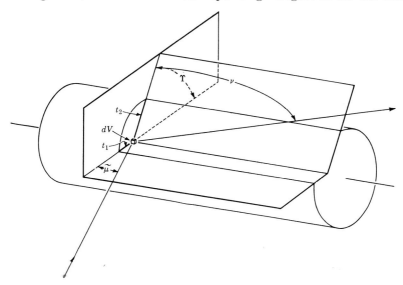

Fig. 5.
(After Buerger and Niizeki.[†])

† M. J. Buerger and N. Niizeki. *The correction for absorption for rod-shaped single crystals.* Am. Mineralogist **43** (1958) 726–731.

level precession photographs is suggested by Fig. 6, and is seen to be

$$T = \frac{1}{V} \int e^{-\mu(x_1 \sec \bar{\mu} + x_2 \sec \bar{\mu})} \, dV$$

$$= \frac{1}{V} \int e^{-\mu \sec \bar{\mu} (x_1 + x_2)} \, dV. \tag{6}$$

This differs from (3) only in that, for μ, there is substituted $\mu \sec \bar{\mu}$ (or that, for R, there is substituted $R \sec \bar{\mu}$). Thus, to correct the zero level for absorption in this case, the value of $\mu R \sec \bar{\mu}$ is computed and this is regarded as μR for purposes of using Claassen's tables. The transmission factors are then looked up under the appropriate values of θ for the reflections.

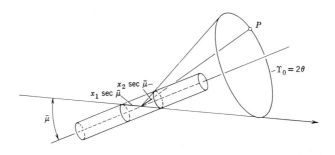

Fig. 6.

Correction for absorption in more complicated cases

Nature of the problem. When the shape of the specimen is not cylindrically symmetrical with respect to the axis of the Laue cones, the correction for absorption is more complicated and is too tedious to be easily handled by hand computation. Part of the difficulty is due to the fact that each spot on the precession photograph is composed of two contributions, one made when the reciprocal-lattice point enters the sphere of reflection and one when it leaves the sphere. Unless special symmetry conditions occur, therefore, each calculation must be made for two different geometrical settings of the shape of the crystal with respect to the geometry of the diffraction. The following general discussion is due to Burbank and Knox.[52]

The *LpT* correction. Let T' be the transmission factor when the reciprocal-lattice point enters the sphere, and let T'' be the transmission factor when the reciprocal-lattice point leaves the sphere. Then the effect of these transmission factors on the intensity I of the beam is indicated by

$$IT' + IT'' = I(T'+T'').$$ (7)

This has the same form as the effect of the Lorentz and polarization factors:

$$L'pI + L''pI = Ip(L'+L'').$$ (8)

Thus, the effect of Lorentz, polarization, and transmission factors on the intensity can be lumped together to give

$$L'pT'I + L''pT''I = [(L'T'+L''T'')p]I,$$ (9)

where the term in brackets on the right is the combined LpT factor for the spot. The correction for this combined factor is

$$\frac{1}{LpT} = \frac{1}{p(L'T'+L''T'')}.$$ (10)

This assumes that the crystal is immersed in a uniform beam of radiation.

In the event that the crystal is elongated parallel to the dial axis so that it projects through the beam, the volume of the crystal in the beam is proportional to sec α, an angle which will be defined later. In this event (7) and (9) must be multiplied by sec α, and the correction corresponding to (10) becomes

$$\frac{1}{LpT} = \frac{1}{p(L'T' \sec \alpha' + L''T'' \sec \alpha'')}.$$ (11)

Angular variables. An analysis of the angular variables which must be treated in discussing the general case of absorption in the precession method is due to Burbank and Knox.[52] The geometry of the direct and diffracted beams is illustrated in Fig. 7. The angle α is the angle that the direct beam makes with the normal to the dial axis, at the time of diffraction, so it is the same as angle α of the last chapter. At the same time the diffracted beam is characterized by angles a, the projection onto a horizontal plane of the angle between the diffracted beam and a plane normal to the dial axis, and b, the projection onto the plane normal to the dial axis of the angle between direct and diffracted beams.

If the specimen has a noncircular cross-section, an additional angle is needed to define the azimuth of the specimen on the dial axis. A common case would be a prismatic specimen of uniform cross-section parallel to the dial axis. Let the angle between a reference azimuth in the cross-section of the crystal and the x-ray beam, with $\bar{\mu}$ set at 0°, be designated δ. This is the dial angle required to bring the reference azimuth parallel to the x-ray beam. With a selected precession angle $\bar{\mu}$, when the crystal is in reflecting position the reference direction has been rotated by an angle β about the dial axis. The projection on the cross-sectional plane of the angle between the incident beam and reference direction is $\delta + \beta$. The projection on the same plane of the angle between the reflected beam and the reference direction is $180° - (\delta + \beta) - b$.

Evaluation of diffraction angles. The angles α, β, a, and b must be evaluated in terms of the coordinate system used in the last chapter. The coordinate systems were illustrated in Chapter 11, Figures 5A and 6, and angles α and β as used there have the same meanings here; specifically,

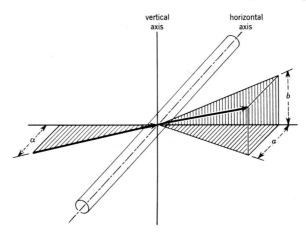

Fig. 7.
Definitions of the angles α, a, and b.
(After Burbank and Knox.[52])

rotation of the crystal about the vertical axis is α, and about the dial axis is β. The cylindrical reciprocal-lattice coordinates are

$$x' = \xi \cos \varphi,$$

Ch. 11 (43):
$$y' = \xi \sin \varphi,$$ (12)

$$z' = \zeta.$$

Reflections occur as the reciprocal-lattice point enters and leaves the sphere when the coordinates of the center of the sphere are

Ch. 11 (53):
$$\varphi_0' = \varphi - \eta,$$ (13)
$$\varphi_0'' = \varphi + \eta.$$

If the following relations are combined

Ch. 11 (42): $$x_0' = \sin \alpha,$$

(12): $$x' = \xi \cos \varphi,$$ (14)

Ch. 11 (45): $$\xi_0 = \sin \bar{\mu},$$

there can be deduced

$$\sin \alpha = \sin \bar{\mu} \cos \varphi_0. \qquad (15)$$

Also, rearrangement of (30), Chapter 11, gives

$$\cos \beta = \frac{\cos \bar{\mu}}{\cos \alpha}. \qquad (16)$$

The angles a and b may be evaluated with the aid of Fig. 8, in which the origin is at O, the center of the sphere of reflection at S, and the

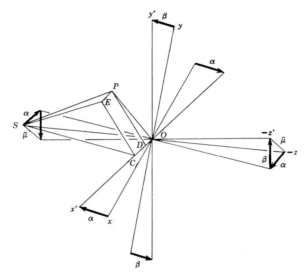

Fig. 8.
Geometry for derivation of a and b in terms of ξ, ζ, φ.
(After Burbank and Knox.[52])

reciprocal-lattice point at P. The line SC is perpendicular to the x' axis at C. In right triangle SCO,

$$SO = 1,$$

$$SC = \cos \alpha, \qquad (17)$$

$$CO = \sin \alpha.$$

The line PD is perpendicular to the x' axis at D. The x' coordinate of P is

$$DO = \xi \cos \varphi. \qquad (18)$$

The length of CD is

$$CD = CO - DO$$

$$= \sin \alpha - \xi \cos \varphi. \qquad (19)$$

$PDCE$ is a rectangle. Triangle ESC lies in a plane perpendicular to the x' axis. Then

$$a = \angle PSE,$$

$$b = \angle ESC. \tag{20}$$

In right triangle SEP,

$$SP = 1,$$

$$EP = CD = \sin \alpha - \xi \cos \varphi,$$

$$SE = \cos a. \tag{21}$$

Also,

$$\sin a = EP$$

$$= \sin \alpha - \xi \cos \varphi. \tag{22}$$

In triangle ESC,

$$EC = PD = (y'^2 + z'^2)^{\frac{1}{2}}, \tag{23}$$

and this can be transformed by (12) into

$$EC = (\xi^2 \sin^2 \varphi + \zeta^2)^{\frac{1}{2}}. \tag{24}$$

If the law of cosines is applied to triangle ESC there results

$$(EC)^2 = (SE)^2 + (SC)^2 - 2(SE)(SC) \cos (ESC). \tag{25}$$

The values of these terms can be substituted from (24), (21), (17), and (20) to give

$$\xi^2 \sin^2 \varphi + \zeta^2 = \cos^2 a + \cos^2 \alpha - 2 \cos a \cos \alpha \cos b, \tag{26}$$

which, by rearrangement, provides

$$\cos b = \frac{\cos^2 a + \cos^2 \alpha - \xi^2 \sin^2 \varphi - \zeta^2}{2 \cos a \cos \alpha}. \tag{27}$$

The assembled information about these angles is

(15): $\quad \sin \alpha = \sin \bar{\mu} \cos \varphi_0,$

(16): $\quad \cos \beta = \dfrac{\cos \bar{\mu}}{\cos \alpha},$

(22): $\quad \sin a = \sin \alpha - \xi \cos \varphi,$

(27): $\quad \cos b = \dfrac{\cos^2 a + \cos^2 \alpha - \xi^2 \sin^2 \varphi - \zeta^2}{2 \cos a \cos \alpha}.$

For cylindrical specimens parallel to the dial axis, only the magnitude of α, a, and b must be known. For noncylindrical specimens it is necessary to know the magnitude of α and a, and both the magnitudes and signs of α and a. Equation (16) must be supplemented by

$$\beta \text{ is } (+) \quad \text{when} \quad 0° < \varphi_0 < 180°, \tag{28}$$

and (27) must be supplemented by

$$\beta \text{ is } (+) \quad \text{when} \quad \sin \varphi > \zeta \tan \beta. \tag{29}$$

Practical applications. The discussion just given, due to Burbank and Knox,[52] sets a frame for determining the corrections for absorption in a specific case. Ordinarily the work may be expected to be too tedious to be handled by hand computation, and the integration (3) over a specific shape must be handled by high-speed computation as it must be when applied to any other x-ray diffraction method. In certain symmetrical cases, symmetry conditions arise between the angles α, β, a, and b for various reflections, and Burbank and Knox[52] have discussed these conditions for a prism of uniform cross-sections extending across the entire beam. More generally, programs are available for computing the transmission factor for any shape, and these must be combined with the results of the discussion of the foregoing sections in order to derive appropriate transmission factors.

Surface-reflection fields

When a crystal that has extreme absorption is investigated by any diffraction method, some effects occur which can be readily understood by considering the distribution of reflections from the surfaces of a crystal. The distributions of these reflections are called *surface-reflection fields*. They were first studied for precession photographs by Takéuchi,[36] and later by Buerger[44] and by Wuensch.[50]

Fields for a single plane. Surface-reflection fields can be best approached by considering the effect on the reflections of a crystal of a single plane surface parallel to the dial axis. A general view of the geometry involved is shown in Fig. 9. The reflections from the crystal all travel along the generators of the Laue cone. Some of the rays must be transmitted through the body of the crystal to reach the photographic film. These are called *transmitted reflections*. Others, called *surface reflections*, may reach the film without being transmitted through the body of the crystal.

The distribution of surface-reflections corresponding to a plane parallel to the dial axis and on the upper part of the crystal can be derived as

shown in Fig. 10.   This diagram illustrates three stages of the precession
cycle.   At the left are vertical sections through the centers of the zero-
level Laue cones; on the right are diagrams of the resulting photographs.
In Fig. 10*C*, the Laue cone is in the same position as shown in Fig. 9,
i.e., at the top of the precession cycle; in Fig. 10*B* the Laue cone is on
the extreme right in Fig. 9, while Fig. 10*A* shows a condition in which
the precession cycle has brought the crystal plane parallel with the x-ray
beam.   Surface reflections can only occur for those generators of the

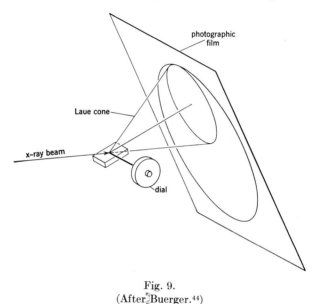

Fig. 9.
(After Buerger.[44])

Laue cone which are located above the crystal-surface plane.   They
record only in that part of the photograph in which its intersection with
the Laue cone is drawn heavy.   At the various stages of the precession
cycle this arc assumes the positions shown on the right of Fig. 10.   Reflections produced along the generators of the cone which lie below the
crystal surface or its extension, as shown in Fig. 10*A*, are not surface
reflections, but transmitted reflections.

If the arcs of surface reflection like those shown in Fig. 10 are sketched
for a series of nearby stages of the precession cycle, a collection of arcs
like those shown at the left of Fig. 11 is produced.   These arcs outline
the fields shown at the right of Fig. 11.   In the doubly shaded field,
surface reflections are produced for both left and right sides of the precession cycle.   The height *C* of the cusp of this field above the origin
can be used to compute the slope δ of the surface plane with respect to
the axis of the rational direction corresponding to the axis of the Laue

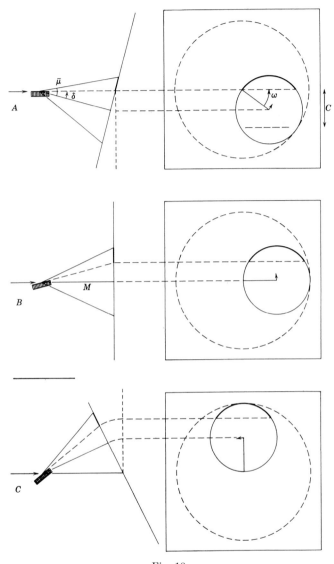

Fig. 10.
(After Buerger.[44])

cone. Figure 14 shows that

$$\cos \bar{\mu} = \frac{ST}{M},$$ (30)

$$\tan \delta = \frac{\frac{1}{2}C}{ST}.$$ (31)

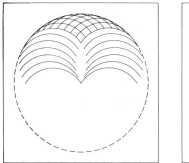
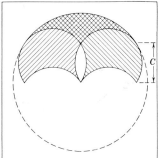

Fig. 11.

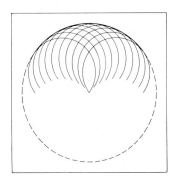
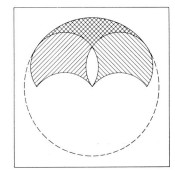

Fig. 12.

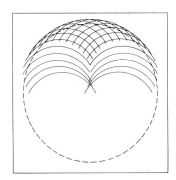
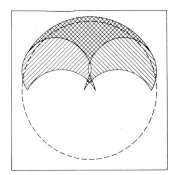

Fig. 13.

Figs. 11–13.
(After Buerger.[44])

If these are combined it is seen that δ can be computed from

$$\tan \delta = \frac{C}{2M \cos \bar{\mu}}.$$ (32)

When δ is negative, the arcs of Fig. 10 are greater than a semicircle. Yet Fig. 12 shows that a similar distribution of surface-reflection fields results. Figure 13 shows the distribution of surface-reflection fields for upper levels.

Fields for crystal habits. The results of the foregoing discussion can be applied to finding the surface-reflection fields for crystal habits. Some simple examples are discussed briefly below.

For a single surface plane parallel to the precessing axis, the arcs of Fig. 10 become semicircles. For this case, the doubly shaded field of Fig. 11 extends downward to cover the entire surface-reflection field of the crystal plane, as shown in Fig. 15. This result can be utilized to derive the surface-reflection fields for any collection of planes parallel to the Laue-cone axis. The surface-reflection field for each plane of the habit is like Fig. 15, except that it is rotated by the amount which the crystal plane is rotated away from parallelism with the dial axis. The com-

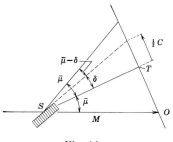

Fig. 14.

bined surface-reflection fields are found by superposing the individual fields of the several planes of the habit. Figures 16–19 give some fields derived by Takéuchi.[36] These are for a pair of pinacoids (Fig. 16), a trigonal prism (Fig. 17), a tetragonal prism (Fig. 18), and a prism of orthorhombic or monoclinic symmetry (Fig. 19). In these illustrations the lines of dots are rows of reciprocal-lattice points.

Application to absorption. Surface-reflection fields provide a qualitative guide to regions of the photographic film within which the reflections recorded have suffered various degrees of absorption. The doubly shaded regions of Figs. 16–19 are fields in which the reflections have suffered little absorption. The unshaded regions are fields in which the reflections have suffered extreme absorption, since within these fields all reflections are transmitted reflections.

Background patterns. Surface-reflection fields are often seen outlined on x-ray photographs as *background patterns*. The darkened background is due to exposure to soft, incoherently scattered radiation. The patterns produced in this way are especially intense when the radiation

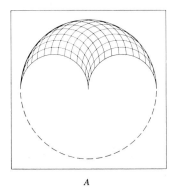
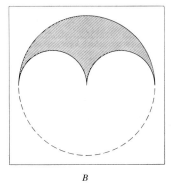

A   B

Fig. 15.
(After Buerger.[44])

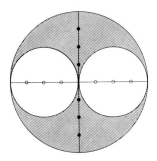
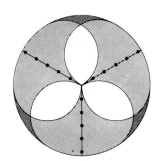

Fig. 16.   Fig. 17.

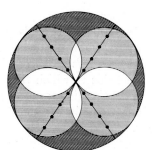
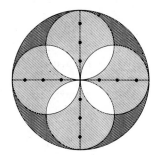

Fig. 18.   Fig. 19.
Figs. 16–19.
(After Takéuchi.[36])

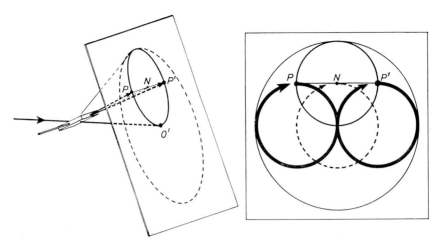

Fig. 20.

A. Location of beams diffracted along the plane of a thin plate for an instantaneous position of the zero-level Laue cone.

B. Locus of reflections diffracted along the plane of a thin plate, zero level.

(After Wuensch.[50])

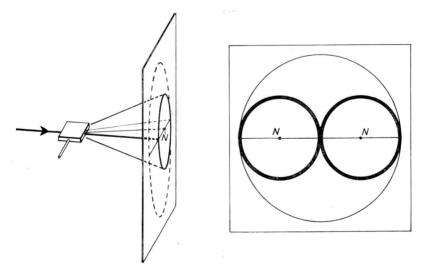

Fig. 21.

A. Position of the Laue cone for which the incident beam lies in the plane of the plate.

B. Locus of reflections arising as the incident beam lies in the plane of the plate, zero level.

(After Wuensch.[50])

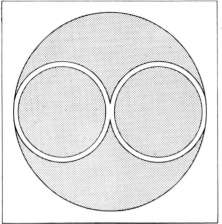

Fig. 22.
Predicted locus of attenuated reflections for a zero-level precession photograph of a thin plate; $\bar{\mu} = 25°$.
(After Wuensch.[50])

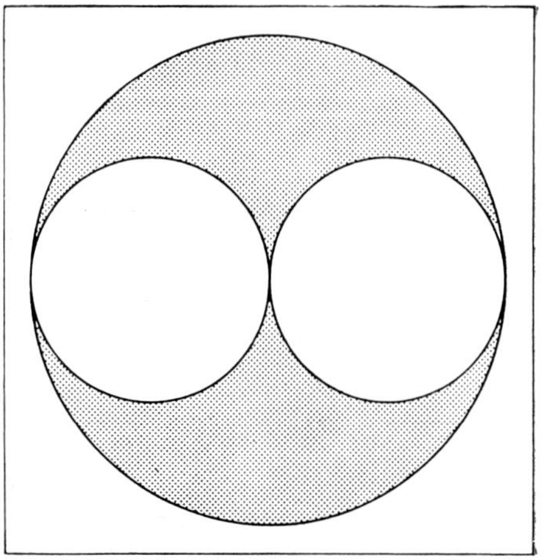

Fig. 23.
Background pattern for a thick plate, as derived by Takéuchi;[31] $\bar{\mu} = 25°$.
(After Wuensch.[50])

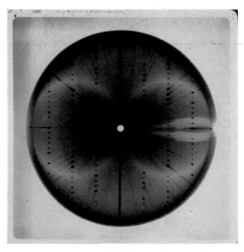

Fig. 24.
Precession photograph from a thin plate .007-mm thick by .67-mm mean diameter (mcgovernite, [11·0] axis, zero level, $\bar{\mu} = 25°$; Cu$K\alpha$, 35 kV, 15 mA, 160 hours.)
(After Wuensch.[50])

employed has a wavelength just shorter than the absorption edge of an element in the composition of the crystal producing the diffraction. The scattered radiation that arises in this way is absorbed by the crystal, so that only the radiation scattered in the hemisphere over each face can reach the photographic film. The part that passes the layer-line screen

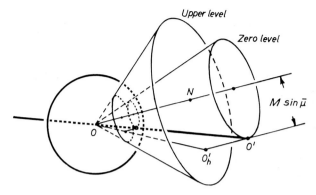

Fig. 25.

Location of cone axis and Laue cone relative to the film origin in the recording of upper levels.

(After Wuensch.[50])

has the geometry of a surface reflection, and records as a darkened background in the surface-reflection field of the face.

The Wells effect. Surface-reflection fields constitute a generalization of a complete-absorption locus discovered by Wells[†] in Weissenberg photographs. This effect has been investigated in detail for precession photographs by Wuensch.[50]

When the habit of a crystal is such that it is indefinitely extended parallel to a line or to a plane, substantially complete absorption occurs when either the incident or diffracted beam is parallel to the extension. As a result, regions corresponding to such suppressed reflections lack diffraction spots. This is the *Wells effect*. These regions appear white in background patterns.

Figure 20 shows the derivation of the Wells region arising from complete absorption of the diffracted beam corresponding to the zero level for a thin plate; Fig. 21 shows it for complete absorption of the diffracted beam. These two loci coincide for the zero level. They are shown together in Fig. 22 compared with the surface-reflection field for a *thick* plate in Fig. 23. An actual photograph showing the effect is shown in Fig. 24.

For upper levels the effect is more complicated, and the locus of the Wells effect is different for reflected and incident beams. The derivations of these cases are shown in Figs. 25, 26, and 27. A photograph showing the effect is shown in Fig. 28, compared with the derived appearance, Fig. 29.

[†] A. F. Wells. *A note on absorption and Weissenberg photographs.* Z. Krist. **96** (1937) 451–453.

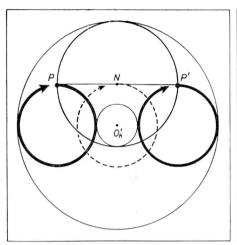

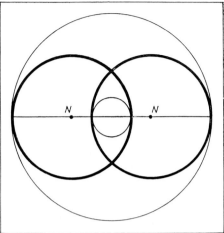

Fig. 26.
Locus of reflections diffracted along the
plane of the plate on upper levels. The
loci are of radius $M \sin \bar{\mu}$ on all levels.
(After Wuensch.[50])

Fig. 27.
Locus of reflections generated as the
incident beam lies in the plane of plate
on upper levels.
(After Wuensch.[50])

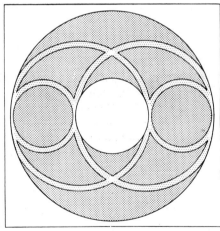

Fig. 28. Precession photograph from
a thin plate 0.007-mm thick by 0.67-mm
mean diameter (mcgovernite, [11·0] axis,
first level, $\zeta = .188$, $\bar{\mu} = 15°$; Cu$K\alpha$
35 kV, 15 mA, 200 hours.) (After
Wuensch.[50])

Fig. 29. Predicted loci of attenuated
reflections for an upper-level precession
photograph with $\zeta = 0.188$, $\bar{\mu} = 15°$.
(After Wuensch.[50])

Literature

1942

[1] M. J. Buerger. *X-ray crystallography*. (John Wiley and Sons, New York 1942) 204–211.

1944

[2] M. J. Buerger. *The photography of the reciprocal lattice*. ASXRED Monograph No. 1, 1944, 37 pages.

1945

[3] M. J. Buerger. *Soap crystals*. Am. Min. **30** (1945) 551–571.

1948

[4] George L. Clark and Hung Kao. *A versatile technique for x-ray single crystal structure analysis applied to benzaldehyde 2,4-dinitrophenylhydrazone and zinc salts of salicylic and benzoic acids*. J. Am. Chem. Soc. **70** (1948) 2151–2154.

1949

[5] William H. Barnes. *The unit cell and space group of childrenite*. Am. Min. **34** (1949) 12–18.

[6] William H. Barnes. *The unit cell and space group of probertite*. Am. Min. **34** (1949) 19–25.

[7] Douglas P. Adams and Howard T. Evans, Jr. *Developments in the useful circular nomogram*. Rev. Sci. Instr. **20** (1949) 150–155.

[8] Howard T. Evans, Jr., S. G. Tilden, and Douglas P. Adams. *New techniques applied to the Buerger precession camera for x-ray diffraction studies*. Rev. Sci. Instr. **20** (1949) 155–159.

[9] William H. Barnes. *The unit cell and space group of lindgrenite*. Am. Min. **34** (1949) 163–172.

[10] William H. Barnes. *Some comments on the Buerger precession method for the determination of unit cell constants and space groups*. Am. Min. **34** (1949) 173–180.

[11] Howard T. Evans, Jr. *Note on the accuracy of the Buerger precession camera*. Rev. Sci. Instr. **20** (1949) 751.

1951

[12] Elysiário Tavora. *A new chart for setting the Buerger precession camera*. An. Acad. Brasil. Ciencias **23** (1951) 113–118.

[13a] Jürg Waser. *The Lorentz factor for the Buerger precession method.* Rev. Sci. Instr. **22** (1951) 563–566.

[13b] Jürg Waser, *Lorentz and polarization correction for the Buerger precession method.* Rev. Sci, Instr. **22** (1951) 567–568.

[14] W. H. Barnes, Maria Przybylska, and Violet C. Shore. *Further notes on the precision of the Buerger precession instrument.* Am. Min. **36** (1951) 430–435.

[15] [Howard T. Evans, Jr.] *Manual for the use of the Buerger precession camera.* (Charles Supper Company, Newton Centre, Mass. 1951) 11 pages.

1952

[16] D. Jerome Fisher. *Lattice constants of synthetic chalcanthite by the x-ray precession technique using a single mounting of the crystal.* Am. Min. **37** (1952) 95–114.

[17] Robinson D. Burbank. *Upper level precession photography and the Lorentz-polarization correction. Part I.* Rev. Sci. Instr. **23** (1952) 321–327.

[18] H. J. Grenville-Wells and S. C. Abrahams. *Upper level precession photography and the Lorentz-polarization correction. Part II.* Rev. Sci. Instr. **23** (1952) 328–331.

[19] J. V. Smith. *Two aids for the orientation of crystals in a precession camera.* Acta Cryst. **5** (1952) 723.

[20] D. Jerome Fisher. *Cone-axis diffraction patterns.* Am. Min. **37** (1952) 1007–1035.

[21] D. Jerome Fisher. *X-ray precession techniques.* Am. Min. **37** (1952) 1036–1054.

1953

[22] D. Jerome Fisher. *Precession orientation photos.* Am. Min. **38** (1953) 399–404.

[23] M. M. Qurashi and W. H. Barnes. *A note on cone axis and upper level precession photographs.* Am. Min. **38** (1953) 552–556.

1954

[24] Leonid V. Azároff. *Crystal settings for upper level photography, precession method.* Rev. Sci. Instr. **25** (1954) 928–929.

[25] Masao Atoji and William N. Lipscomb. *Lorentz polarization factors for precession angles of 10°, 15°, and 21°.* Acta. Cryst. **7** (1954) 595–596.

[26] G. Donnay and J. D. H. Donnay. *An integrating precession technique.* Acta Cryst. **7** (1954) 619–620 (abstract).

1955

[27] Murray Vernon King. *Two charts for setting the Buerger precession camera.* Acta Cryst. **8** (1955) 53–55.

[28] Masao Atoji and William N. Lipscomb. *Lorentz polarization factors for precession angles of 10°, 15°, and 21°: correction.* Acta Cryst. **8** (1955) 364.

[29] Gabrielle Donnay and J. D. H. Donnay. *Domain of reciprocal space accessible to precession photography.* Rev. Sci. Instr. **26** (1955) 610–612.

[30] Warner E. Love and D. Sayre. *Pseudo-precession photographs from an oscillation camera.* Rev. Sci. Instr. **26** (1955) 621–622.

[31] Christer E. Nordman, A. L. Patterson, Alice S. Weldon, and Charles E. Supper. *Integrating mechanism for the Buerger precession camera.* Rev. Sci. Instr. **26** (1955) 690–692.

[32] Gabrielle Donnay, J. D. H. Donnay and Vernon J. Hurst. *Precession goniometry to identify neighboring twins.* Acta Cryst. **8** (1955) 507–509.

[33] D. Jerome Fisher. *Precession camera settings.* Acta Cryst. **8** (1955) 594.

[34] Leonid V. Azároff. *Polarization correction for crystal-monochromatized x-radiation.* Acta Cryst. **8** (1955) 701–704.

1957

[35] Leonid V. Azároff. *A new method for measuring integrated intensities photographically.* Acta Cryst. **10** (1957) 413–417.

[36] Yoshio Takéuchi. *X-ray surface reflexion fields on precession photographs.* Mineral. J. (Japan) **2** (1957) 162–168.

1958

[37] A. Jayaraman. *Reciprocal lattice photography.* Proc. Ind. Acad. Sci. **47** (1958) 142–146.

1959

[38] [Tibor Zoltai and Charles T. Prewitt.] *Manual for the Buerger precession camera.* (Otto von der Heyde, Newton Highlands, Mass. 1959) 24 pages.

[39] John S. Kasper and Kathleen Lonsdale (Editors). *International tables for x-ray crystallography,* Volume II. (The Kynoch Press, Birmingham, England, 1959):

Howard T. Evans, Jr. Section 4.5: *Buerger precession method.* 194–200;

C. E. Nordman. Table 5.2.5*H: Lorentz-polarization corrections for the precession method,* $\bar{\mu} = 30°$. 278–285;

J. Kraut. Table 5.2.5*I:* $(Lp)^{-1}$ *for zero-level precession photographs, for odd values of* $\bar{\mu}$. 286–290.

[40] Elizabeth A. Wood. *Precession photographs of reciprocal-lattice rods in* $HfFe_2$. Z. Krist. **112** (1959) 97–107.

[41] Chang Yuan-Lung. *A combination of x-ray precession camera with two-circle goniometer.* Science Record **3** (1959) 258–262.

1960

[42] A. L. Patterson and Warner E. Love. *Error analysis for the Buerger precession camera.* Am. Min. **45** (1960) 325–333.

[43] N. F. M. Henry, H. Lipson, and W. A. Wooster. *The interpretation of x-ray diffraction photographs.* (Macmillan and Co., London, 2nd Ed., 1960) 132–142.

[44] Martin J. Buerger. *Crystal-structure analysis.* (John Wiley and Sons, New York, 1960) 163–171, 226–231.

[45] E. C. T. Chao. *A device for viewing x-ray precession photographs in three dimensions.* Am. Min. **45** (1960) 890–892.

[46] Chang Yuan-Lung. *Extension of the reciprocal lattice record by composite precession photograph.* Science Record **4** (1960) 65–69.

1961

[47] F. Donald Bloss and Gerald V. Gibbs. *Nomograms for determining 2θ from precession photographs.* Am. Min. **46** (1961) 26–31.

[48] D. R. Fitzwater. *X-ray absorption factors for ellipsoidal crystals.* Acta Cryst. **14** (1961) 521–526.

[49] S. W. Kennedy and J. H. Patterson. *Absorption corrections for the precession method.* Rev. Sci. Instr. **32** (1961) 564–565.

[50] Bernhardt J. Wuensch. *The Wells effect in precession photography.* Z. Krist. **115** (1961) 359–372.

1962

[51] H. G. Smith. *Use of polaroid film in neutron and x-ray diffraction.* Rev. Sci. Instr. **33** (1962) 128–129.

[52] R. D. Burbank and Kerro Knox. *Lorentz polarization absorption corrections in the x-ray precession method.* Rev. Sci. Instr. **33** (1962) 218–222.

[53] F. Donald Bloss. *Choosing precession screen settings.* Am. Min. **47** (1962) 802–804.

1963

[54] Tibor Zoltai. *Double spots and their elimination in precession photography.* Am. Min. **48** (1963) 759–771.

[55] A. S. Parkes and R. E. Hughes. *Irradiated volume in Weissenberg and precession techniques.* Acta Cryst. **16** (1963) 1185–1187.

[56] H. G. Smith and D. L. Holcomb. *Modified polaroid film holder for x-ray and neutron diffraction.* Rev. Sci. Instr. **34** (1963) 1441.

1964

[57] M. J. Buerger and Wayne A. Dollase. *Shape of the recorded area in precession photographs and its application in orienting crystals.* Science **143** (1964) 264–265.

Appendix

Heating and cooling techniques

It is often desirable to investigate a single crystal at temperatures above or below room temperature. For example, it may be of interest to study the inversion behavior of a crystal, or the structure of the crystal beyond the inversion temperature. Such investigations call for devices and techniques that permit maintaining the crystal at a constant abnormal temperature for a considerable period and at the same time do not interfere with taking the precession photograph. They must also annul undesirable side effects; for example, they must protect the apparatus from the high temperature, or prevent the condensation of ice crystals from the moisture in the atmosphere onto the specimen. A limited number of devices for these purposes, and adapted especially for the precession method, have been described.

Heating devices

Several devices have been described for maintaining crystals at elevated temperatures while making precession photographs. One is designed for growing low-melting organic crystals in the apparatus, another for studying crystals in the 0–300°C range, several for studying crystals in the neighborhood of 1300°C, and another for studying them in the range 1000°C to 2000°C.

Crystal-growing and heating device. Katz and Kay[a] have described a device designed for growing crystals in a capillary within a cylindrical heating unit attached to the goniometer head. For this technique the crystal must melt congruently at a low temperature. The furnace has been used to investigate the high-temperature phases of organic substances up to 200°C. The technique parallels that introduced by Kaufman and Fankuchen (described later) for studying crystals frozen by low temperature from a liquid in a capillary held by the goniometer head.

In the arrangement described by Katz and Kay (Fig. 1), the capillary is suspended coaxially in a thin cylindrical glass sleeve by means of transite spacers. It is heated by a winding consisting of a few turns of No. 28B gauge nichrome wire; the turns are omitted for a short distance where the x-ray beam strikes the capillary.

Furnaces for the range 0–300°C. Morimoto and England[b] devised a furnace for studying the transitions of some sulfide minerals up to 300°C and for obtaining crystal data from the resulting polymorphic forms.

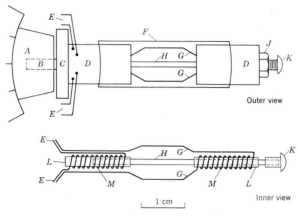

Fig. 1.
Crystal growing and heating device.
(After Katz and Kay.[a])

A. Goniometer head.	*G.* Copper wire.
B. Brass pin.	*H.* Sample.
C. Transite disk.	*J.* Nut.
D. Transite cylinder.	*K.* Bolt.
E. Lead wires.	*L.* Core.
F. Thin glass sleeve.	*M.* Resistance wire.

The device was briefly described as a small, circular, single-strip platinum furnace of the radiant type, mounted on the collimator of the precession instrument. The crystal was attached with epoxy cement to the crome-alumel thermocouple, which was fastened by a fiber pin to the goniometer head. The temperature variation noted when using a precession angle of $\bar{\mu} = 20°$ amounted to $\pm 5°C$.

A modification of Morimoto's and England's furnace was built by Wuensch,[d] who used it in studying the structure of sulfide minerals in the range 100°–300°C. Wuensch's description of the construction of the furnace and the mounting of the crystal is excellent and is quoted here with his permission:

An exploded view of the device is given in Fig. 2, and a section through the device, when in position on the precession camera, in Fig. 3. The entire device is supported on the x-ray collimator, A. A mushroom-shaped cap, B has two cylindrical portions which have been slotted to provide a firm friction fit to the other pieces of the assembly. The inner cylinder slides snugly over the x-ray collimator and is secured in proper position by means of a small ring, C, containing a recessed screw. A hollow brass cylinder, D, in which the heating element is mounted, slides snugly over the outer cylinder of the cap. This motion allows the entire heater to be retracted

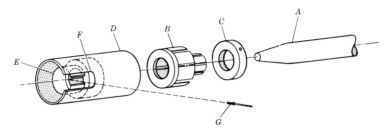

Fig. 2.
Exploded view of furnace for use with precession instrument.
(After Wuensch.[d])

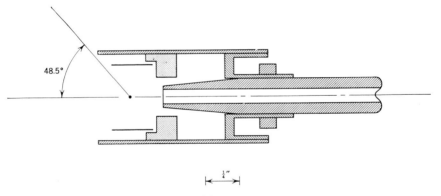

Fig. 3.
Cross-section of furnace for use with precession instrument.
(After Wuensch.[d])

towards the x-ray tube as the crystal and goniometer are mounted on the precession camera. Once the crystal is in position, the heating unit, D, is slid forward to center the crystal with respect to the heating element. The heating element, E, consists of a $\frac{3}{8}$ inch strip of 0.001 inch 90% Pt–10% Rh foil. The foil is bent into a cylindrical shape concentric with the x-ray beam. The foil is supported at the ends by two copper wires which also serve as electrical contacts. These wires are crimped onto the foil and make only a mechanical connection. The wire supports, in turn, are supported by a pyrophyllite base, F, which is attached to the brass cylinder. The leads are extended through the pyrophyllite base and out the side of the brass cylinder where electrical connections are made. The pyrophyllite base serves as both a thermal and an electrical insulator. A slight lip extends around the lower portion of the cylindrical heating element to aid in supporting the foil and in preserving its cylindrical shape as it expands at elevated temperatures. The brass cylinder is extended beyond the top of the heating foil to serve as a heat shield. The geometry is such as to permit passage of a cone of diffracted radiation of half-angle 48.5° without interference.

The fiber supporting the crystal, G, is admitted through a slot in the side of the brass cylinder, D, and passes between the two wires supporting the heating foil to intersect the x-ray beam. Normal centering of the crystal by sighting through the x-ray collimator may be performed with the heating attachment in place. Figure 3 shows that contact between the heating assembly and the x-ray collimator is limited to the very thin top of the mushroom cap, B. This prevents heating of the x-ray collimator when the heater is in operation.

Regulation of the heater is very simple. The output leads of the secondary winding of a standard variac are connected to the primary winding of a 6.3 V, 20 A transformer. The secondary winding of this transformer is connected directly to the heating unit leads.

Two problems are encountered in mounting the crystal when the device is used. First, an adhesive which will withstand the elevated temperatures must be found to secure the crystal to a supporting fiber. Second, the supporting fiber passes in close proximity to the copper leads supporting the heating element. This portion of the fiber experiences a higher temperature than the crystal itself, since it is closer to the foil than is the crystal. This problem is made worse by the fact that the mechanical connection of the wires to the foil has relatively high resistance and thus becomes considerably hotter than the foil itself. The glass used to prepare the fibers on which crystals are usually mounted may be expected to soften at about 700–800°C. A thin fiber would begin to creep and sag at a much lower temperature.

Two types of mounts which were found useful are illustrated in Fig. 4A and B. In the first type, a copper-constantan thermocouple is mounted in double-bore Alundum thermocouple tubing. The crystal is attached directly to the end of the thermocouple. The thermocouple wires are led out through a nick filed in the side of the Alundum tubing, thus leaving the end of the tubing free for mounting in a goniometer head. This type of mount has the advantage of permitting continuous determination of the temperature of the crystal. Unfortunately, it is troublesome to use: The two wires in the thermocouple expand differentially as the temperature is increased. Final orientation of the crystal must therefore be performed after the crystal is at temperature. This is undesirable if the crystal has any tendency to deteriorate upon prolonged heating.

A more satisfactory, though less elegant, mount is shown in Fig. 4B. In this arrangement a straight copper wire is soldered to the usual brass pin, and then extended to a length sufficient to almost bring it into the x-ray beam. A very short length of glass fiber is then attached to the end of the wire, and the crystal, in turn, is attached to the end of the glass fiber. The glass fiber is just long enough to prevent the copper wire from entering the x-ray beam.

The problem of a suitable adhesive has not been completely solved. The organic adhesives normally used in mounting crystals are unsuitable since they deteriorate at about 100°C. Epoxy resin was found to be suitable for use with high chalcocite, since only the modest temperature of 125°C was required. At 200°C epoxy resin begins to deteriorate by carbonizing, and the crystal eventually drops off. Okazaki[†] has used

[†] Atsushi Okazaki. *The superstructures of iron selenide* Fe_7Se_8. J. Phys. Soc. Japan **16** (1961) 1162–1170.

potter's clay as an adhesive. This material is quite sticky. The bond should actually grow stronger with time and temperature, since the clay will tend to shrink and sinter.

It should be noted that introduction of a thermocouple or polycrystalline adhesive into the x-ray beam does not cause excessive background problems. Any scattered radiation reaching the film must pass through the layer-line screen, and thus travels essentially along the Laue cone. During the precession cycle, this radiation is uniformly distributed over the film. A copper-constantan thermocouple placed in the x-ray beam was found to cause no appreciable increase of background in Mo$K\alpha$ precession photographs of over 60 hours duration.

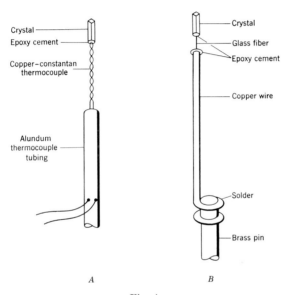

Fig. 4.
Methods of mounting a crystal when making high-temperature precession photographs.
(After Wuensch.[d])

Furnaces for temperatures up to about 1300°C. Smith and Brown[c] have described a platinum-wound resistance furnace, designed especially for the precession camera, which is capable of attaining 1300°C. This was built specifically to study the inversion between rhombic enstatite and protoenstatite in the neighborhood of 1000°C.

A longitudinal section of the furnace is shown in Fig. 5. The heating element is about 18 inches of 0.028-in. platinum wire wound around a thin-walled mullite tube having an external diameter of 0.24 in. The winding is coated with ceramic cement and the whole inserted in a larger mullite tube. The right side is partly plugged with cement to reduce air currents through the tube.   The furnace unit is mounted in an insulating cradle which is attached to the collimator post so that the furnace axis is parallel to the x-ray beam.   This assembly can be adjusted by three orthogonal translations.

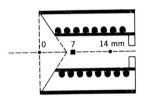

Fig. 5.   Cross-section of high-temperature furnace for use with precession instrument.   (After Smith and Brown.[c])

The crystal is placed in a cradle formed by welding together, at two points 1 mm apart, thermocouple wires of Pt-Pt, 10% Rh.   The wires pass through a two-hole ceramic tube which, in turn, is cemented to a ceramic block screwed to a standard goniometer head.   The sample enters the furnace axially at the end with a conical opening.

The furnace is heated by 115-V AC, controlled by a variable transformer of 25-A rating. The temperature gradient in the furnace is shown in Fig. 6.   This figure also shows the maximum cone angle $\bar{\nu}$ attainable as a function of the position of the crystal in the gradient.   The 7-mm position was chosen as an acceptable location by the crystal.

When the crystal is placed in the cradle formed by the thermocouple wires it is temporarily held there by a drop of water.   After adjustment,

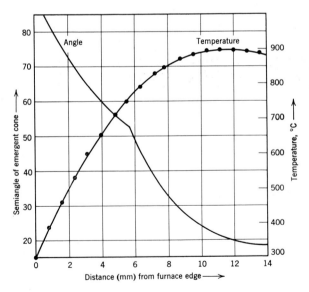

Fig. 6.
Variation of temperature and of maximum cone angle along axis of furnace shown in Fig. 5.   (After Smith and Brown.[c])

the temperature is raised without moving the crystal, which usually becomes stuck to the thermocouple. When working in the neighborhood of 1000°C platinum gradually coats the crystal, first causing platinum diffraction spots, and later rendering the crystal opaque.

A somewhat different heating device was designed by Robinson and Flörke.[e] Views of the assembly are shown in Figs. 7 and 8. The crystal is heated by passing a heavy current through a metal band which nearly

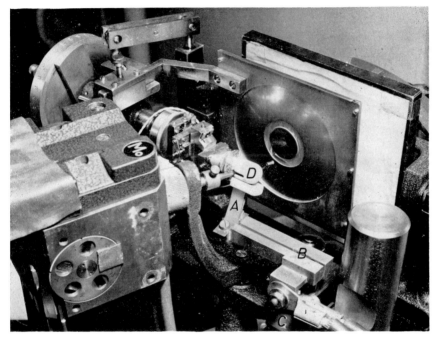

Fig. 7.
Precession instrument with heating attachment.
(After Robinson and Flörke.[e])

surrounds it. The band is made of Kanthal $A1$ strip (10 mm wide, 0.3 mm thick) or Pt, 20% Rh strip (10 mm wide, 0.1 mm thick). An edge view of the band is seen in Fig. 9; the loop shown at the top surrounds the crystal. To cause this part of the band to heat relative to the rest, it is made of a single strip while the rest is three ply. The three-ply conductor is marked A in Figs. 7 and 8. It is supported by a pair of bus bars B, which are fastened by a clamp C to the member of the precession instrument on which the dial is mounted. The heat is supplied by dissipating a maximum of 200 W (50 A at 4 V).

To permit the x-ray beam to reach the crystal while the dial support is

Fig. 8.
View of furnace mounting.
(After Robinson and Flörke.[e])

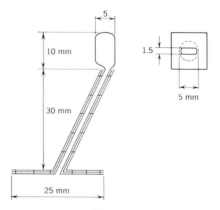

Fig. 9.
Left: Edge view of the heating band.
Right: Detail of slot in the face of the heating loop.
(After Robinson and Flörke.[e])

oscillating left and right over a range of $2\bar{\mu}$, the part of the band that loops around the crystal has a horizontal slot, shown on the right of Fig. 9. On the opposite side of the loop a circular hole 5 mm in diameter permits the beam to leave the band, and also allows the diffracted radiation to reach the film in a cone of half angle 35°.

12 mm

3

Fig. 10.
Thermocouple and crystal mount. (After Robinson and Flörke.[e])

The heating loop is surrounded by a ceramic heat shield D cut from the closed end of a sintered clay tube. This has an entrance slot and a circular exit hole to correspond with the holes in the band. Another ceramic shield, E (of dimensions 15 x 10 x 5 mm, with a longitudinal slot of 10 x 3 mm), is clamped to the conductor bands beneath the furnace shield.

The crystal is mounted on the thermocouple, which is made as shown in Fig. 10. The Pt-Pt, 10% Rh thermocouple wires, joined by a tiny solder bead, are melted into a short glass rod which is mounted on a standard goniometer head. To protect the goniometer head from the

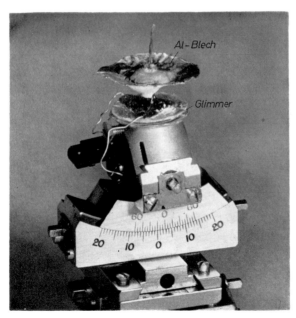

Al-Blech

Glimmer

Fig. 11.
Goniometer head with crystal holder, radiation shield and plug for thermocouple.
(After Robinson and Flörke.[e])

heat an aluminum sheet and a mica sheet are placed between it and the crystal, Fig. 11.

To use this heating device, some minor alterations must be made in the normal precession apparatus.

(*a*) The regular collimator must be replaced by a somewhat shorter one.

(*b*) The cellophane sheets of the layer-line screens must be replaced by aluminum foil.

(*c*) Since the furnace is sensitive to drafts it is advisable to cover the whole precession apparatus with a plastic tent.

The heat flow and radiation to the unprotected parts of the camera and goniometer head, even in extended service, do not result in a temperature of over 60°C, so that water cooling is unnecessary. Furthermore, the conductors have such a large cross-section that they do not become hotter than 90°C.

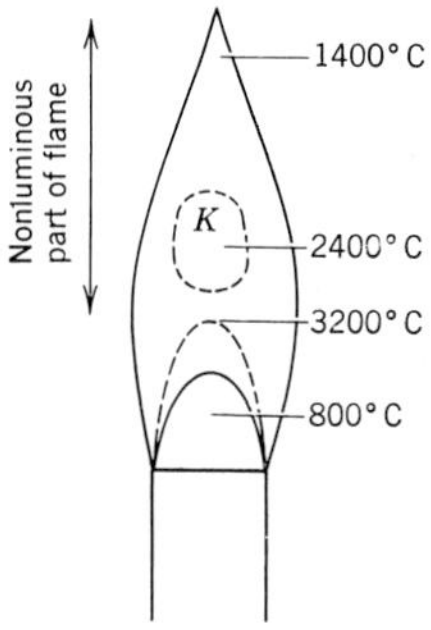

Heating devices for the range 1000°C to 2000°C. For maintaining crystals in the range 1000°C to 2000°C, Gubser, Hoffmann, and Nissen[*f*] used a small open gas flame. The temperatures potentially attainable in this way are suggested in Fig. 12. The *K* zone of Fig. 12 is well adapted to heating the crystal to high temperatures, but the heat conductivity of the thermocouple unfortunately diminishes the extreme temperatures which are otherwise available. The flame issues from an ordinary burner with a fine nozzle, and the burner mounting is independent of the precession apparatus. The gas flame is regulated as shown diagrammatically in Fig. 13. The somewhat complex flow scheme is designed to maintain the crystal at constant temperature.

Fig. 12. Temperature distribution in an oxyacetylene flame. (After Gubser, Hoffmann, and Nissen.[*f*])

Cements for attaching the crystal to the thermocouple are difficult to find. The ceramic material 250 of the Haldenwanger Co., Berlin, was found to have good properties, is useful up to 1800°C, but showed powder diffraction lines. Above 1800°C, the thermocouple must be protected by tiny sintered corundum tubes, and the cement must be replaced by pure clay. The layer-line screen of the precession apparatus must be also further protected by strips of asbestos board.

Flame heating is unsuitable for crystals that are chemically sensitive to oxidizing or reducing atmospheres, or which would react with the water formed in the flame.

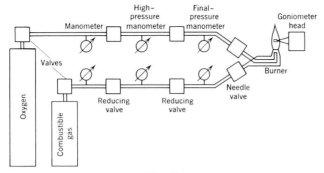

Fig. 13.
Diagram of the gas flow to the flame of the heating device.
(After Gubser, Hoffmann, and Nissen.[f])

Low-temperature techniques

Low-temperature techniques are ordinarily used to study crystals that would be liquids or gasses at room temperature. There are two general procedures. The crystal may be grown elsewhere, and then attached to the x-ray apparatus while it is maintained at subnormal temperatures, or the crystal may be grown in place on the apparatus by freezing the liquid in a capillary.

The first procedure does not appear to have been specifically used in connection with the precession apparatus, but it has been used in connection with the rotating-crystal and oscillating-crystal methods. For example, Cox[g] determined the structure of benzene by utilizing a special rotating-crystal camera which was maintained at −40°C by circulating metholated spirits (denatured alcohol) cooled by carbon dioxide snow. A simplified procedure was used by Vonnegut and Warren[h] for determining the structure of crystalline bromine using an oscillating-crystal apparatus. A crystal, obtained by condensing bromine vapor on a cold surface, was stuck to a capillary with soft Vaseline. During exposure in an oscillating-crystal camera the crystal was maintained at about −150°C by the exhaust stream of a liquid-air container. This method, shown in Fig. 14, came into general use in many later cooling devices.

With the second procedure the crystal is grown by cooling the liquid in a capillary mounted on a goniometer head, and usually manipulated by melting and freezing until a suitable single crystal results. The process is preferably followed by means of a polarizing microscope. Review articles of the technique have been presented by Fankuchen and Post[o] and by Lipscomb.[p]

In an early procedure[i] the crystal was grown in a thin-walled glass tube in a complicated "cryostat" suspended in a cylindrical camera. More

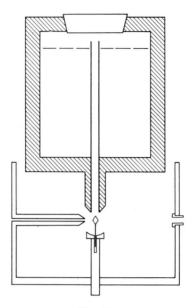

Fig. 14.
(After Vonnegut and Warren.[h])

recently Kaufman and Fankuchen[j] froze the liquid in a capillary, mounted on an ordinary goniometer head, by means of a stream of cold gas. The capillary was surrounded coaxially by an insulating device consisting of two thin cylinders of very thin polystyrene film with a $\frac{3}{4}$-cm dead air space between them. The cooling system was a jet of cold compressed gas, usually nitrogen, directed along the axis of the capillary. The gas was cooled in a heat exchanger consisting of a coil of copper tubing immersed in dry ice-solvent mixture, or liquid nitrogen. Specimen temperature down to $-60°C$ could be attained.

Abrahams, Collin, Lipscomb, and Read[k] used a similar scheme and applied it specifically to the precession instrument. In their arrangement the capillary was not surrounded by an insulating cylinder, but was mounted open in a plexiglass cup having a 120° conical depression, as shown in Fig. 15. The cooled gas was directed to the capillary by a

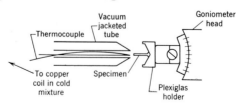

Fig. 15.
(After Abrahams, Collin, Lipscomb, and Reed.[k])

jacketed tube, and its temperature determined by means of a thermo-couple. The arrangement permitted precession angles up to $\bar{\mu} = 23°$. Temperatures down to $-120°C$ could be reached by the use of a second cooling coil immersed in liquid nitrogen. To avoid condensation of ice on the capillary the air of the room was dehumidified so that the water-vapor pressure was reduced to about 5 mm.

Post, Schwartz, and Fankuchen[l] further developed this arrangement in such a way that dehumidifying the air was unnecessary. They accom-plished this by surrounding the main cooling jet with a sheath of dry gas

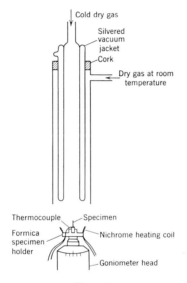

Fig. 16.
(After Post, Schwartz, and Fankuchen.[l])

at room temperature, as illustrated in Fig. 16. They attained specimen temperatures down to $-180°C$ and could work in a laboratory whose relative humidity was as high as 95%.

The Lipscomb school prefers[n] to use as a coolant nitrogen derived by controlled evaporation of liquid nitrogen. This method is said to permit runs for periods of up to 3 months without clogging. Humidity leading to icing is avoided by surrounding the entire apparatus with a poly-ethylene bag.

Literature

Heating attachments

[a] Lewis Katz and Mortimer I. Kay. *Single crystal heater and grower for the precession camera.* Rev. Sci. Instr. **28** (1957) 968–969.

[b] N. Morimoto and J. L. England. *High-temperature Buerger precession camera.* Carnegie Institution of Washington Year Book **59** (1960) 175.

[c] J. V. Smith and William L. Brown. *X-ray precession photography at temperatures up to 1300°C.* Z. für Kristallogr. **115** (1961) 93–96.

[d] Bernhardt John Wuensch. *The nature of the crystal structures of some sulfide minerals with substructures.* Ph. D. Thesis, M.I.T. 1963, 201-213.

[e] J. M. M. Robinson and O. W. Flörke. *Ein einfacher Heizaufsatz für die Präzessionskamera.* Z. für Kristallogr. **119** (1963) 257–263.

[f] R. A. Gubser, W. Hoffmann, and H. U. Nissen. *Röntgenaufnahmen mit der Buergerschen Präessionskamera bei Temperaturen zwischen 1000°C und 2000°C.* Z. für Kristallogr. **119** (1963) 264–272.

Low-temperature techniques

[g] E. G. Cox. *The crystalline structure of benzene.* Proc. Roy. Soc. **135A** (1932) 491–498.

[h] B. Vonnegut and B. E. Warren. *The structure of crystalline bromine.* J. Am. Chem. Soc. **58** (1936) 2459–2461.

[i] W. H. Keesom and K. W. Taconis. *An x-ray goniometer for the investigation of the crystal structure of solidified gases.* Physica **2** (1935) 463–471.

[j] H. S. Kaufman and I. Faukuchen. *A low temperature single crystal x-ray diffraction technique.* Rev. Sci. Instr. **20** (1949) 733–734.

[k] S. C. Abrahams, R. L. Collin, W. N. Lipscomb, and T. B. Reed. *Further techniques in single-crystal x-ray diffraction studies at low temperatures.* Rev. Sci. Instr. **21** (1950) 396–397.

[l] Benjamin Post, Robert S. Schwartz, and I. Fankuchen. *An improved device for x-ray diffraction studies at low temperatures.* Rev. Sci. Instr. **22** (1951) 218–219.

[m] Robert L. Collin and William N. Lipscomb. *The crystal structure of hydrazine.* Acta Cryst. **4** (1951) 10–14.

[n] Thomas B. Reed and William N. Lipscomb. *The crystal and molecular structure of 1,2-dichloroethane at −140°C.* Acta Cryst. **6** (1953) 45–48.

[o] Benjamin Post and Isidor Fankuchen. *Low temperature x-ray crystallography.* Anal. Chem. **25** (1953) 736–737.

[p] William N. Lipscomb. *Low temperature crystallography.* Norelco Reporter **4** (1957) 54 and 75.

Index

Abrahams, S. C., 218, 244, 258, 260
Absolute unit, 76
Absorption, 90, 221
  by an extended plate, 222
  by a sphere, 222
Absorption correction,
  by hand calculation, 224
  for a cylinder, 226
  for a plate, 224
  for a spherical specimen, 224
  in complicated cases, 228
Absorption factor, 190
  for specimen with noncircular cross-
      section, 229
  for specimen with uniform cross-
      section, 229
  theory of, 221
Accuracy of interaxial angles, 89
Adams, Douglas P., 197, 198, 243
Adhesive, 47
Adjustment,
  crystallographic, with autocollimator,
      52
  of an axis of a triclinic crystal, 125
  of crystals, 48, 53
  of zero-level plane, 128
  original, recovery of, 45
Air scatter, residual, 180
Alignment of precession instrument, 44
Allowable orientation error for screens,
      117
Ambiguities in indexing, 3
Analysis, crystal-structure, 1, 58, 76, 89
Andalusite, 67
Angle,
  between planes of two photographs, 81
  between reciprocal-lattice rows, 80
  cone, 27, 33
  diffraction, 230

Angle,
  interaxial, 76, 86
    accuracy of, 89
  Laue-cone, 226
  measurement of, 80
  reciprocal-cell, 86
Angular error, 102, 107, 122, 123, 126
Annular aperture, 28
Annular layer-line screen, 105
Annular opening, 33, 34, 67
Annulus, 22
  of layer-line screen, 56
Apatite, 144, 167
Aperture, 223
  annular, 28
  guard, 38
  second, 38
Apparatus,
  de Jong-Bouman, 7
  oscillating-crystal, 8, 257
  precession, Mark II, 184
  Supper, 25, 89
    use of, 44
  Weissenberg, 39, 172
Appearance of orientation photographs,
      114
Appropriate table, 44
Appropriate x-ray tube, 44
Araldite, 47
Arc, 30, 41, 55
  goniometer-head, 49, 52
Area, shaded, 114, 120, 127, 128, 129,
      134, 136
  displacement of, 119
  shift of, 116, 123
Arm, hacksaw-like, 30, 31, 33
Assembly, dial-axis, 39, 40
Atoji, Masao, 244

Attachment,
  autocollimator, 51
  heating, 260
Autocollimator, 33, 37, 38, 52, 57
  crystallographic adjustment with, 52
  use of, 51
Autocollimator attachment, 51
Axis,
  collimator, 55
  cone, 39
  crystal, 31
  dial, 31, 48, 49, 52, 54, 55, 83, 177,
    229
  horizontal, 6, 31, 35, 37
  of Laue cone, 150, 156, 228, 237
  of mounting pin, 54, 55
  precessing, 28, 39, 59, 60, 61, 156
  rotation, 72
    n-fold, 162
  screw, 58, 70
  symmetry, 58
  vertical, 6, 43
Azároff, Leonid V., 45, 184, 185, 186,
    187, 244
Azároff beam tunnel, 45, 46, 49

Background, 38, 39, 47, 67, 180, 182
  measurement of, 180
Background pattern, 237, 238
Back-reflection Weissenberg method, 88
Ball-and-socket joint, 37
Band, cone-axis, 172
Barnes, W. H., 89, 90, 101, 154, 155,
    243, 244
Base,
  lower, 37, 44
  upper, 37, 38, 46
Beam, direct,
  divergence of, 38
  intensity distribution in, 223
Beam stop, 48
Beam tunnel, Azároff, 45, 46, 49
Benzene, 257
BeO, 164
Berman, Harry, 50
Bernal explanation of diffraction, 167
Berthierite, 20, 111, 132, 170
Beta spots, use of, 101
Blind region, 19, 138
  central, 24, 128
  radius to edge of, 139

Blind spot, 39, 96, 140
Bloss, F. Donald, 66, 246
Bloss chart, 66
Bond, W. L., 224, 226
Bouman, J., 7
Boundary curvature method, 144, 145
Bradley, A. J., 226
Bragg condition, 14
  for reflection, 191
Bragg equation, 13
Bragg law, 182
Brass pin, 46
Broadening of cone-axis ring, 173
Brown, William L., 251, 252, 260
Buerger, M. J., 3, 12, 69, 76, 80, 176,
    179, 182, 183, 186, 221, 226, 227,
    233, 234, 235, 236, 238, 243, 245
Bulge in film, 103, 104
Burbank, R. D., 228, 229, 230, 231, 233,
    244, 246
Burr, 167

Calibration of dial readings, 50
Camera,
  cone-axis, 154
  rotating-crystal, 154, 257
Cap, lens, 49
Capillary, 46, 47, 48
Carrier, layer-line screen, 34
Cartesian coordinates, 202
Cassette, 39, 40, 41, 61, 67, 90, 104, 126
  cone-axis, 39, 57, 151, 152
  integrating, 176
  plateau from, 186
Catcher, direct beam, 105
Cell,
  reciprocal, 84
    of monoclinic crystal, 84, 85
    of triclinic crystal, 87
  theory of, 69
  unit, 1, 3, 59, 69, 76
    dimensions of, 58
Cell determination, from one setting of
    crystal, 83, 86
Cell dimensions, error in, 91
Cell edge, 83, 90
Cell of direct lattice, determination of,
    83
Center, inversion, 12, 72
Centering crystal, 48, 90
Centerline, horizontal, 41

Central blind region, 24, 128
Central plane of reciprocal lattice, 107
Chao, E. C. T., 245
Characteristic radiation, 101, 106, 107,
    127, 167, 180
Charles Supper Company, 25, 188, 244
Chart,
    Bloss, 66
    for determining orientation error, 118
    of Lorentz-polarization correction,
        217, 218
    for pure precession motion, 198
Chord, common, 128, 144
    theory of, 133
Cid-Dresdner, Hilda, 88
Circle,
    Laue, 133
    upper-level, symmetry of, 12
    zero-level, cone-axis, 153
        symmetry of, 12
Circular cone, 27
Claassen, A., 226, 227, 228
Clark, George L., 243
Coarse collimator, 38, 45, 46, 48, 49, 51
Coefficient,
    Fourier, 177
    linear-absorption, 222, 224
    mass-absorption, 224
Collimator, 39, 48, 248, 249
    coarse, 38, 45, 46, 48, 49, 51
    removable, 37
Collimator axis, 55
Collimator insert, 51
Collin, R. L., 258, 260
Common chord, 128, 144
    theory of, 133
Comparable intensities, 58
Computation,
    hand, 233
    high-speed, 186, 233
    of d^* from cone-axis data, 154
Condition,
    Bragg, 14
        for reflection, 191
    equi-inclination, 25
    de Jong-Bouman, generalized, 13, 103,
        104, 127, 182
    errors in satisfying, 92
Cone,
    circular, 27
    generator of, 11

Cone,
    Laue, 10, 11, 12, 13, 14, 15, 16, 22, 28,
        39, 56, 115, 116, 133, 136, 151, 172,
        225, 233, 234, 239, 241
    axis of, 150, 156, 228
    generator of, 14, 156, 234
    intersection of, 134, 135, 136
    invariant, 10
    order of, 151
    zero-order, 13
    upper-level, 28
    zero-order, 11
Cone angle, 27, 33
Cone axis, 39
Cone-axis band, 172
Cone-axis camera, 154
Cone-axis cassette, 39, 57, 151, 152
Cone-axis circle, zero-level, 153
Cone-axis data, computation of d^*
    from, 154
Cone-axis film, 28, 155
Cone-axis film setting, 172
Cone-axis method,
    crystal-to-film distance for, 29
    orientation error in, 169
    photograph, cone-axis
Cone-axis photograph, *see* Photograph,
    cone-axis
Cone-axis record produced by a single
    reciprocal-lattice point, 161
Cone-axis ring, 153, 155, 158, 161, 163
    broadening of, 173
    negative-order, 151
    zero-order, 151
Cone-axis setting, 57
Cone half-angle, 30
Conic section, 167, 169
Constant, proportionality, 15, 18
Convention of numbering levels, 178
Convergence, natural, plateau effect
    from, 184
Cooling technique, 247
Coordinate system, 198, 199
Coquimbite, 164
Correction,
    for absorption,
        by a cylinder, 226
        by a plate, 224
        by a spherical specimen, 224
        by hand calculation, 224
        in complicated cases, 228

Correction,
  Lorentz-factor, 191
  Lorentz-polarization, 206
    chart showing, 217, 218
  of orientation errors, 56, 120, 123
Counterbalance, 41
Cox, E. G., 257, 260
Cryostat, 257
Crystal,
  adjusting, 48, 53
  centering, 90
  hexagonal, 61, 84, 177
  isometric, 61, 71, 75, 83, 84
  monoclinic, 55, 56, 61, 84, 85, 145,
    177
    first setting of, 84, 85
    reciprocal cell of, 84, 85
  mounting, 46, 47 251
  oblique, 145
  optical properties of, 49
  orienting,
    geometrical methods of, 49
    optical methods of, 49
  orthorhombic, 52, 54, 55, 61, 70
  representative settings of, 60
  rotating, 8
  single mounting of, 177
  symmetry properties of, 60
  tetragonal, 61, 84, 177
  triclinic, 84, 87, 145
    adjustment of axis of, 125
    reciprocal cell of, 87
Crystal axis, 31
Crystal fragment, unoriented, 145
Crystal-growing device, 247
Crystal habits, surface reflection fields
    for, 237
Crystallographic adjustment with auto-
    collimator, 52
Crystallographic data, 49
Crystallography, 3
  x-ray, 76, 89
Crystal mount, 46, 255
Crystal shape, 89
Crystal size, 89
Crystal-structure analysis, 1, 58, 76, 89
Crystal symmetry, 3, 6, 150
Crystal system, 70, 71, 83
  hexagonal, 71
  isometric, 61, 71, 75, 83, 84
  monoclinic, 70

Crystal system,
  orthogonal, 83
  tetragonal, 70
  triclinic, 70
Crystal-to-film distance, 33, 34
  for the cone-axis method, 29
Crystal with 4-fold symmetry, photo-
    graph of, 6
Crystal with 6-fold symmetry, photo-
    graph of, 6
Curvature, boundary, 144
  of the recorded region, 142
Cycle,
  integrating, 185, 186
  precession, 41, 107
Cylindrical coordinates, 202

Data,
  cone-axis, computation of d^* from, 154
  crystallographic, 49
  intensity, 178
    for three-dimensional investigations,
      177
    for two-dimensional investigations,
      177
Densitometer, 190
Density,
  measurement of, 186
  photographic, 182
  scale of, 190
Determination,
  geometrical, requirements for, 58
  intensity, 176
  of cell, from one setting of crystal, 83,
    86
  of cell of direct lattice, 83
  of orientation error, 116, 144
  of reciprocal-lattice type, 75
  of setting error, 97
  of space group, 69, 76
    photographs desirable for, 58
  of translation, 150
  of unit-cell, photographs desirable for,
    58
Device,
  crystal-growing, 247
  heating, 247, 248
  measuring, 80, 81, 84
  parallelizing, 34
  Zoltai, 104

Dial, 50, 51, 52, 54
Dial axis, 31, 48, 49, 52, 54, 55, 83, 177, 229
Dial-axis assembly, 39, 40
Dial reading, 55, 86
Dial setting, 58, 177, 178, 179
  range recordable with one, 179
Diffraction,
  Bernal explanation of, 167
  by a point in an upper level, 18
  by a point in a zero level, 16
  from neighboring levels, 67
  symmetry of, 3
Diffraction angle, 230
Diffraction effect, 70, 71
  symmetry of, 12
Diffraction record, 6
Diffraction symbol, 58, 59, 70, 73, 76
Diffraction techniques, 3
Diffraction theory, 3
Diffractometer method, 190
Dimensions,
  of cell, error in, 91
  of film, 39, 41
  of unit cell, 58
  of upper arc of Supper goniometer head, 47
Direct beam, divergence of, 38
Direct-beam catcher, 105
Direct-beam stop, 38
Direction, rational, 55
Direct lattice, 77, 78
  determination of cell of, 83
Displacement, 40
  of adjacent levels of reciprocal lattice, 74
  of film, 17
  of plane-lattice levels, 75
  of the shaded area, 119
Distance,
  crystal-to-film, 33, 34
  for the cone-axis method, 29
Distortion, 92
Distribution, intensity, in the direct beam, 223
Divergence of the direct beam, 38
Dollase, Wayne A., 246
Donnay, Gabrielle, 1, 244, 245
Donnay, J. D. H., 1, 244, 245
Doubled spots, 56, 92, 93, 103, 104

Doublet, 103, 182
Doublet separation, 100
Duco, 47

Edge,
  cell, 83, 90
  reciprocal-cell, 83, 86
  unit-cell probable error of, 89
Effect,
  diffraction, 70, 71
    symmetry of, 12
  plateau,
    natural, 184
    principle of, 183
  Wells, 241
Ekstein, Miriam G., 224
Electron-density projection, 177
Element, symmetry, 12, 73
Enantiomorphic pair of space groups, 76
England, J. L., 248, 260
Equi-inclination condition, 25
Equi-inclination precession photograph, 24
Error,
  angular, 102, 107, 122, 123, 126
  in cell dimension, 91
  in satisfying the generalized de Jong-Bouman condition, 92
  large, orientation photographs for, 127
  orientation, 90, 106, 139, 140, 145, 150, 173
    allowable, for screens, 117
    correction of, 56, 120
    determination of, 116, 144
    graph for determining, 118, 138
    in cone-axis photograph, 171
    in the cone-axis method, 169
    measurement of, 114
  probable, 91
    of unit-cell edge, 89
  setting, 96, 97
    determination of, 97
    of $M\zeta$, 92
  wavelength, 91
Evans, H. T., Jr., 66, 197, 198, 224, 243, 244, 245
Evan's function, 117
Explanation, Bernal, of diffraction, 167
Extinction, systematic, 73
Extrapolating d^* against $r_n^{\,2}$, 154
Extrapolation techniques, 90

Factor,
  absorption, 190
  Lorentz, 190, 191, 229
    for Mark II suspension, 198
  magnification, 13, 33, 76, 92
  polarization, 184, 190, 191, 229
  proportionality, 17
  transmission, 222, 224, 228, 229
Fairfieldite, 187
Fankuchen, Isidor, 247, 257, 258, 259,
  260
Features in reciprocal lattice, 180
Field, surface-reflection, 233, 241
Film,
  bulge in, 103, 104
  cone-axis, 28, 155
  flat, 8, 9
  Polaroid, 106
Film dimensions, 39, 41, 56
Film displacement, 17
Film holder, 33
Film position, 28
Film scraps, 56
Film setting, 57
  cone-axis, 172
Film shrinkage, 89, 90, 91
First setting of monoclinic crystal, 84, 85
First version of Mark II precession
  instrument, 30, 31, 32
Fisher, D. Jerome, 117, 120, 126, 156,
  157, 159, 160, 244, 245
Fitzwater, D. R., 246
Flame oxyacetylene, temperature dis-
  tribution in, 256
Flame heating, 256
Flat film, 8, 9
Flörke, O. W., 253, 254, 255, 260
Fluorescent screen, 40, 45, 46
Focal spot of the x-ray tube, 45
Focusing monochromator, 185
  photograph made with, 187
  plateau from, 184
4-fold symmetry, 5
Fourier coefficients, 177
Fourier synthesis, 177
Fractional-cycle cone-axis photograph,
  172, 174
Fragment crystal, unoriented, 145
Front-reflection precession photograph,
  25

Front-reflection region, 26
Friedel, G., 71
Friedel's law, 12, 71, 163, 178
Friedel symmetry, 3, 14, 50, 58, 73, 76,
  150, 177
Frondel, Clifford, 50
Fundamental reciprocity relation, 83
Furnace,
  for temperature up to 300°C, 248
  for temperature up to 1300°C, 251
  for use with precession instrument, 249

Garnet, 164, 189
General radiation, 107, 150, 167
General-radiation record, 101
General-radiation streak, 100, 101, 107,
  127, 128, 145, 163, 167
  use of, 100
General-radiation trail, 169, 182
Generalized de Jong-Bouman condition,
  13, 103, 104, 127, 182
Generalized de Jong-Bouman principle,
  8, 9, 15, 56
Generator of the Laue cone, 11, 14, 156,
  234
Geometrical determination, require-
  ments for, 58
Geometrical features, measurable, 76
Geometrical interpretation of precession
  photographs, 69
Geometrical methods of orienting a
  crystal, 49
Geometry,
  of oscillation, 3
  of upper-level recording, 17
Gibbs, Gerald V., 246
Gimbal, 6, 30, 35, 40
Gimbal suspension, 31, 35
Glass capillary, 46
Glide plane, 58, 70
Goniometer, 48, 49, 50
  designed by C. R. Wolfe, 50
  made by LaPine, 50
  made by Nedinsco, 50
  made by Stoe, 50
  made by Techne, 50
Goniometer arc, 49, 52
Goniometer-arc setting, 57
Goniometer head, 31, 39, 46, 48, 50, 52,
  54, 67, 247, 248, 252, 255, 257,
  258

Goniometer head,
  Supper, 46
  dimensions of upper arc of, 47
Goniometer-head arc, 52
Grenville-Wells, H. J., 48, 218, 244
Group,
  points, 70, 71, 163
  space, 1, 58, 69
    determination of, 76
    enantiomorphic pair of, 76
Guard aperture, 38
Gubser, R. A., 256, 257, 260

Hacksaw-like arm, 30, 31, 33
Haldenwanger Company, 256
Half-angle, cone, 30
Hand computation, 233
Hanic, F., 41, 42
Harmonics, 182
Head, goniometer, *see* Goniometer head
Heating attachment, 253, 260
Heating device, 247, 248
  for the temperature range 1000°C to
    2000°C., 256
Heating flame, 256
Heating techniques, 247
Henry, N. F. M., 245
Hexagonal crystal, 61, 84, 177
Hexagonal-crystal system, 71
High-speed computation, 186, 233
Hoffmann, W., 256, 257, 260
Holcomb, D. L., 246
Holder,
  film, 33
  layer-line screen, 39, 46, 57
Horizontal axis, 6, 31, 35, 37
Horizontal centerline, 41
Hughes, R. E., 246
Hurst, Vernon J., 245

Ideal precession motion, 12, 14
Identity period, 11
Ilmenite, 164
Incoherently scattered radiation, 237
Incoherent scattering, 180
Indexing ambiguities, 3
Indexing cone-axis photograph, 154, 155,
    156, 157
Indexing procedure for cone-axis photo-
    graphs, 159, 160

Indices of points in the *n*th-level plane,
    180
Information, symmetry, 6
Insert, collimator, 51
Instrument, precession, *see* Precession
    instrument
Instrumental setting, 61, 67
Integrated power, 176, 182
Integrating cassette, 176
  plateau from, 186
Integrating cycle, 185, 186
Integrating mechanism, 188
  photograph made with, 189
Intensity, 69
  comparable, 58
  measurement of, 58, 180
  plateau of, 38
  reflection, 38
Intensity data, 178
  for three-dimensional investigations,
    177
  for two-dimensional investigations,
    177
Intensity determination, 176
Intensity distribution,
  in the direct beam, 223
  with wavelength, 181
Interaxial angle, 76, 86
  accuracy of, 89
Interfacial-angle table, 55
Interpretation, geometrical, of preces-
    sion photographs, 69
Intersection of Laue cone, 134, 135, 136
Invariant Laue cone, 10
Inversion center, 12, 72
Investigation,
  three-dimensional, intensity data for,
    177
  two-dimensional, intensity data for,
    177
Isolating a level, 25
Isometric crystal system, 61, 71, 75, 83,
    84
Isotypes, 1

Jayaraman, A., 245
Joint, ball-and-socket, 37
de Jong, W. F., 7
de Jong-Bouman apparatus, 7

de Jong-Bouman condition,
  generalized, 13, 103, 104, 127, 182
  errors in satisfying, 92
de Jong-Bouman method, 3, 15, 89
de Jong-Bouman principle 7, 8
  generalized, 8, 9, 15, 56

Kaliborite, 129
Kao, Hung, 243
Kasper, John S., 245
Katz, Lewis, 247, 248, 260
Kaufman, H. S., 247, 258, 260
Kay, Mortimer I., 247, 248, 260
Keesom, W. H., 260
Kennedy, S. W., 246
King, Murray Vernon, 66, 117, 244
Kiss, A., 42, 43
Knox, Kerro, 228, 229, 230, 231, 233,
  246
Kraut, J., 245

Lambda unit, 76
LaPine, goniometers made by, 50
Larsen, Esper S., 50
Lattice, *see* Direct lattice, Plane lattice,
  Reciprocal lattice
Lattice type, 72, 74, 76
Laue circle, 133
Laue cone *see* Cone, Laue
Laue-cone angle, 226
Laue photograph, 11, 12, 71, 150, 167,
  169
Laue photograph and cone-axis photo-
  graph, relation between, 166
Laue spot, 168, 169
Laue symmetry, 71
Laves' method, 126
  orientation photograph made with,
  126
Layer-line screen, *see* Screen layer-line
Lens cap, 48 49
Leveling screw, 45, 46
Levels,
  adjacent, of reciprocal lattice, dis-
    placement of, 74
  convention of numbering, 178
  isolating, 25
  negative-order, 107
  neighboring, diffraction from, 67
  of reciprocal lattice, 178
  plane-lattice, displacement of, 75

Levels,
  upper, 59, 92
  zero, 59, 78
    recorded radius of, 58
Limit of record, 18
Limit of recording,
  mechanical, 25
  outer, 24
  practical, 26
  theoretical, 26
Linear absorption coefficient, 222, 224
Line symmetry, 72
Linkwork, parallelogram, 30
Lipscomb, William N., 244, 257, 258,
  259, 260
Lipson, H., 245
Liquid nitrogen, 259
Lissajous figure, 186
Literature, 243, 260
Lonsdale, Kathleen, 245
Lorentz factor, 190, 191, 229
  for Mark II suspension, 198
  for pure precession motion, 191, 197
Lorentz-factor correction, 191
Lorentz-polarization correction, 206
  chart showing, 217, 218
  for pure precession motion, graph of,
  198
Love, Warner E., 91, 244, 245
Lower base, 37, 44
Low-temperature technique, 257, 260

Mačar, J., 42, 43
Magnification factor, 13, 33, 76, 92
Marcasite, 164
Mark I precession instrument, 4, 5, 6, 7
  photographs made by, 6
Mark II precession instrument, 9, 30, 36,
  42, 184, 197, 198
  first version, 30, 31, 32
  second version, 34, 35
  Supper, 25, 89
  use of, 44
Mark II suspension, 219
  Lorentz factor for, 198
Mark III suspension, 197, 204, 219
Mass-absorption coefficients, 224
Maximum radius of shaded area, 136
Mcgovernite, 240
Measurable geometrical features, 76

Measurement,
  of angles, 80
    and distances, device for, 80
  of background, 180
  of density, 186
  of intensities, 58, 180
  of orientation error, 114
  of row spacings, 82
  of translations in reciprocal lattice, 82
Measuring device, for precession photo-
    graphs, 76, 81, 84
Mechanical limits, 25
Mechanism,
  for producing pure precession motion,
    219
  precession, 30, 37
Meionite, 5
Melanovanadite, 155
Method,
  back-reflection Weissenberg, 88
  boundary-curvature, 145
  diffractometer, 190
  geometrical, of orienting crystals, 49
  de Jong-Bouman, 3, 15, 89
  Laves', 126
    orientation photograph made by, 126
  moving-film, 3
  optical, of orienting crystals, 49
  oscillating-crystal, 3, 6, 89
  plateau, 182
  precession, 3, 6
  rotating-crystal, 8, 161
  Weissenberg, 3, 8, 89, 161, 176
Microscope, polarizing, 50
Minimum radius of shaded area, 136
Mirror, 163
Misoriented zero-level plane, 128
Missetting $M\zeta$, precession photographs
    illustrating result of, 94
Missing reciprocal-lattice points, 77, 78
Molybdophyllite, 154
Monochromator, 184
  focusing, 185
    plateau from, 184
Monoclinic crystal, 55, 56, 61, 84, 85, 145,
    177
  first setting of, 84, 85
  reciprocal cell of, 84, 85
Monoclinic crystal system, 70
Monoclinic prism, 237
Monticellite, 95, 98, 166

Morimoto, N., 248, 260
Motion,
  oscillating-crystal, 6
  precession, 9, 16, 30, 33
    ideal, 12, 14
    pure, 219
  symmetry of, 3, 6
Motor, 41
Mount, crystal, 46, 255
Mounting single crystals, 47
Mounting the crystal, 46, 251
Moving-film methods, 3
$M\zeta$,
  errors in setting, 92
    precession photographs illustrating
      result of, 94

Natural convergence, plateau effect
    from, 184
Natural plateau effect, 184
Nedinsco, goniometers made by, 50
Negative-order cone-axis ring, 151
Negative-order level, 107
n-fold rotation axis, 162
Nies, Nelson P., 218
Niizeki, N., 226, 227
Nissen, H. U., 256, 257, 260
Nitrogen, 258
  liquid, 259
Non-recording of additional levels, 68
Nordman, Christer E., 186, 245
nth-level plane, indices of points in, 180

Oblique crystal, 145
Okazaki, Atsushi, 250
One setting of crystal, cell determination
    from, 86
Opening, annular, 33, 34, 67
Optical methods of orienting crystal, 49
Optical properties of crystal, 49
Order,
  of Laue cone, 151
  zero, 14
Ordway, Fred, 47
Orientation correction, 123
Orienting crystal,
  geometrical methods of, 49
  optical methods of, 49
Orientation error, *see* Error, orientation
Orientation photograph, *see* Photograph,
    orientation

Orienting, study preliminary to, 49
Original adjustment, recovery of, 45
Origin of reciprocal lattice, 17
Orthogonal crystal systems, 83
Orthorhombic crystal, 52, 54, 55, 61
Orthorhombic crystal system, 70
Orthorhombic prism, 237
Orthorhombic system, 83
Oscillating-crystal apparatus, 8, 257
Oscillating-crystal method, 3, 6, 89
Oscillating-crystal motion, 6
Oscillating-crystal photograph, 6, 69
Oscillation, geometry of, 3
Outer limit of recording, 24
Oxyacetylene flame, temperature distribution in, 256

Pair, enantiomorphic, of space groups, 76
Palache, Charles, 50
Parallelizing device, 34
Parallelogram, three-dimensional, 34
Parallelogram linkwork, 30
Parkes, A. S., 246
Pattern, background, 237, 238
Patterson, A. L., 91, 245
Patterson, J. H., 246
Patterson projection, 177
Pentaerythrital, 164
Penumbra region, 223
Period, identity, 11
Philips, F. C., 3
Photograph, 59
  cone-axis, 10, 11, 12, 28, 29, 39, 57, 72, 83, 150, 155, 161
    and Laue photograph, relation between, 166
    fractional-cycle, 172, 174
    indexing, 154, 155, 156, 157
      procedure for, 159, 160
    of sphalerite, 158, 159
    orientation error in, 170
    points on, 162
    ring of, 162
    symmetry of, 162, 164
  desirable for space-group determination, 58
  desirable for unit-cell determination, 58
  Laue, 11, 12, 71, 150, 167, 169

Photograph,
  made by Mark I instrument, 6
  made with focusing monochromator, 187
  made with integrating mechanism, 189
  of crystal with 4-fold symmetry, 6
  of crystal with 6-fold symmetry, 6
  orientation, 57, 81, 106, 145
    appearance of, 114
    for large errors, 127
    made by the Laves method, 126
    made with layer-line screen, 110
    made without layer-line screen, 109, 132
  oscillating-crystal, 6, 69
  precession, 13, 240
    equi-inclination, 24
    front-reflection, 25
    geometrical interpretation of, 69
    illustrating result of missetting $M\zeta$, 94
    measuring device for, 76
    planning required for, 58
    upper-level, 67, 153
      example, of 20, 21
    zero-level, 13
      example of, 20, 21
  rotating-crystal, 11, 150
    upper-level, 27, 28, 61, 67
  Weissenberg, 150, 241
    zero-level, 59, 61, 72
Photographic density, 182
Photographic film, bulge in, 103
Photographs, two, angles between planes of, 81
Photography, reciprocal-lattice, theory of, 15
Pin, mounting, 46, 54, 55
Pinacoid, 52, 54, 55, 237
Pinhole system, 34, 37, 38, 46, 49
Plane,
  central, of reciprocal lattice, 107
  glide, 58, 70
  of two photographs, angles between, 81
  reciprocal-lattice, 82, 92
    symmetry of, 6
  reflecting, 14
  shaded, 129
  spacing of a stack of, 178

Plane,
  symmetry, 55
  types of, 77
  zero-level,
    adjusted, 128
    misoriented, 128
Plane lattice, 82
Plane-lattice levels, displacement of, 75
Plane-lattice type, 75
Plane point groups, 72, 162
Planning required for precession photo-
    graphs, 58
Plate, extended, absorption by, 222
Plateau,
  from focusing monochromator, 184
  from integrating cassette, 186
  of intensity, 38
Plateau effect,
  from natural convergence, 184
  principle of, 183
Plateau method, 182
Plateau region, 223, 224
Plug, removable, 38, 46, 52
Point group, 70, 71, 163
  plane, 72, 162
Pointed rod, 38
Points,
  on a cone-axis photograph, 162
  reciprocal-lattice, missing, 77, 78
Polarization factor, 184, 190, 197, 229
Polarizing microscope, 50
Polaroid film, 106
Position, film, 28
Post, Benjamin, 257, 259, 260
Potential across x-ray tube, 167
Power, integrated, 176, 182
Practical limits of recording, 26
Precautions, 89
Precessing axis, 28, 39, 59, 60, 61, 156
Precessing motion, 9, 30, 33
Precession apparatus,
  Mark II, 184
  Supper, 89
  use of, 44
Precession cycle, 41, 107
Precession instrument,
  aligning, 44
  furnace for use with, 249
  Mark I, 4, 5, 6, 7
    photographs made by, 6

Precession instrument,
  Mark II, 9, 30, 36, 42, 197, 198
    first version, 30, 31, 32
    second version, 34, 35
Precession mechanism, 30, 37
Precession method, 3, 6
Precession motion, 16
  ideal, 12, 14
  pure, 219
Precession photograph, *see* Photograph,
    precession
Precession suspension, 10
Precession symmetry, 71
Prewitt, Charles T., 206, 245
Principle,
  de Jong-Bouman, 7, 8
  generalized, 15, 56
  of plateau effect, 183
Prism, 55
  monoclinic, 237
  orthorhombic, 237
  tetragonal, 237
  trigonal, 237
Probable error, 91
  of unit-cell edge, 89
Projection,
  electron-density, 177
  Patterson, 177
Properties of crystals,
  optical, 49
  symmetry, 60
Proportionality constant, 15, 18
Proportionality factor, 17
Przybylska, Maria, 244
Pseudo-symmetry, 12

Qurashi, M. M., 101, 154, 155, 244

Radiation,
  characteristic, 101, 106, 107, 127, 167,
    180
  general, 107, 150, 167
  incoherently scattered, 237
  unfiltered, 101, 106
Radius,
  maximum, of shaded area, 136
  minimum, of shaded area, 136
  of recorded zero level, 58
  screen, 66

Radius,
to edge of recorded region, 139, 146, 148
to edge of blind region, 139
Range recordable with one dial setting, 179
Rational direction, 55
Reading, dial, 50, 86
calibration of, 50
Reciprocal cell, 84
of monoclinic crystal, 84, 85
of triclinic crystal, 84, 87
theory of, 69
Reciprocal-cell angle, 86
Reciprocal-cell edge, 83, 86
Reciprocal lattice, 3, 77, 78
central plane of, 107
displacement of adjacent levels of, 74
features in, 180
level of, 178
measurement of translations in, 82
origin of, 17
recordable region of, 22
rhombohedral, 75
Reciprocal-lattice photography, theory of, 15
Reciprocal-lattice plane, 92
symmetry of, 6
Reciprocal-lattice points, missing, 77, 78
Reciprocal-lattice rows, angle between, 80
Reciprocal-lattice spacing, 83
Reciprocal-lattice type, determination of, 75
Reciprocal plane lattice, 82
Reciprocity relation, 177, 178, 180
fundamental, 83
Record, 6
general-radiation, 101
limits of, 18
zero-level, 59
Recordable range, 22
Recordable region of reciprocal-lattice, 22
Recorded region, 138, 142
curvature of boundary of, 142
radius to edge of, 139, 146, 148
shape of, 142
Recording,
outer limit of, 24

Recording,
practical limits of, 26
theoretical limits of, 26
upper-level, geometry of, 17
Recovery of original adjustment, 45
Reed, Thomas B., 258, 260
Reference tabulations, 50
Reflecting plane, 14
Reflection, 51, 52
Bragg condition for, 191
sphere of, 6, 7
surface, 233, 234
transmitted, 233, 234, 237
Reflection intensity, 38
Reflection region, front, 26
Region,
blind, 19, 138
central, 24, 128
radius to edge of, 139
front reflection, 26
penumbra, 223
plateau, 223, 224
recordable, of reciprocal lattice, 22
recorded, 138, 142
curvature of boundary of, 142
radius of, 139
shape of, 142
Relation,
between Laue photograph and cone-axis photograph, 166
fundamental reciprocity, 83
reciprocity, 177, 178, 180
Removable collimator, 37, 38
Representative settings of crystals, 60
Requirements for geometrical determination, 58
Residual air scatter, 180
Rhodonite, 125
Rhombohedral reciprocal lattice, 75
Ring,
cone-axis, 153, 155, 158, 161, 163
broadening of, 173
negative-order, 151
zero-order, 151
of a cone-axis photograph, 162
zero-level, symmetry of, 163
Robinson, J. M. M., 253, 254, 255, 260
Roemerite, 164
Rotating crystal, 8
Rotating-crystal camera, 154, 257
Rotating-crystal method, 8, 161

Rotating-crystal photograph, 11, 150
Rotation axis, 72
  n-fold, 162
Row, reciprocal-lattice, angle between, 80
Row spacings, measurement of, 82

$S_2C_4(CN)_4$, 164
Sayre, D., 244
Scale, density, 190
Scatter, air, residual, 180
Scattering,
  by specimen mount, 180
  incoherent, 180
  unwanted, 180
Schwartz, Robert S., 259, 260
Scraps, film, 56
Screen,
  allowable orientation error for, 117
  fluorescent, 40, 45, 46
  layer-line, 3, 25, 27, 33, 34, 38, 39, 61, 67, 127, 152, 180
    annular, 105
    annulus of, 56
    carrier, 34
    holder, 39, 46, 57
    orientation photographs made with, 110
    orientation photographs made without, 109, 132
    setting, 28, 57
    slits, widths of, 67
    special, 56, 106, 115, 116
Screen holder, layer-line, 39, 46, 57
Screen radius, 66
Screen setting, layer-line, 28, 62, 64, 66
  zero-level, 59
Screw, leveling, 45, 46
Screw axis, 58, 70
Second aperture, 38
Second version of Mark II precession instrument, 34, 35
Section, conic, 167, 169
Separation, doublet, 100
Setting,
  cone-axis, 57, 172
  dial, 58, 177, 178, 179
  film, 57
  first, 84, 85
  gonimeter-arc, 57

Setting,
  instrumental, 61, 67
  layer-line screen, 28, 57, 62, 64, 66
  of crystals, representative, 60
  zero-level, 59, 61
Shaded area, 114, 120, 127, 128, 129, 134, 136
  maximum radius of, 136
  minimum radius of, 136
  shape of, 136
  shift of, 116, 123
Shaded plane, 129
Shape,
  crystal, 89
  of recorded region, 142
  of shaded area, 136
Shellac, 47
Shift of shaded area, 116, 123
Shore, Violet C., 244
Shrinkage, film, 89, 90, 91
Single mounting of crystal, 177
Size, crystal, 89
Slits, layer-line screen, widths of, 67
Smith, H. G., 246
Smith, J. V., 244, 251, 252, 260
Solvent, 47
Space group, 1, 58, 69
  determination of, 69, 76
  enantiomorphic pair of, 76
Space-group determination, photographs desirable for, 58
Spacing, 75
  between rows of plane reciprocal lattice, 84
  of a stack of planes, 178
  reciprocal-lattice, 83
  row, measurement of, 82
Special layer-line screen, 56, 106, 115, 116
Specimen,
  with noncircular cross-section, absorption for, 229
  with uniform cross-section, absorption for, 229
Specimen mount, scattering by, 180
Sphalerite, 157
  cone-axis photograph of, 158, 159
Sphere,
  absorption by, 222
  of reflection, 6, 7

Spot,
　beta, use of, 101
　blind, 39, 96, 140
　doubled, 56, 92, 93, 103, 104
　focal, of the x-ray tube, 45
　Laue, 169
Stack of planes, spacing of, 178
Stoe, goniometers made by, 50
Stop, direct-beam, 38, 48
Streak, general-radiation, *see* General-
　　radiation streak
Strunz, Hugo, 1
Study preliminary to orienting, 49
Subgroups, 6
Sucrose, 164
Supper, Charles, Company, 188, 244
Supper, Charles E., 25, 36, 245
Supper goniometer head, 46, 47
Supper precession apparatus, 25, 89
Surface reflection, 233, 234
Surface-reflection field, 233, 241
　for crystal habits, 237
Suspension, 9, 16, 31
　gimbal, 31, 35
　Mark II, 219
　　Lorentz factor for, 198
　Mark III, 197, 204, 219
　precession, 10
Symbol, diffraction, 58, 59, 70, 73, 76
Symmetry, 3, 11
　crystal, 3, 6, 150
　4-fold, 5
　　photograph of crystals with, 6
　Friedel, 3, 14, 58, 70, 73, 76, 150, 177
　Laue, 71
　of a line, 72
　of cone-axis photograph, 162, 164
　of diffraction, 3
　of motion, 3, 6
　of the diffraction effect, 12
　of the reciprocal-lattice plane, 6
　of upper-level circle, 12
　of zero-level circle, 12
　of zero-level ring, 163
　precession, 71
　6-fold, 5
　　photograph of crystals with, 6
Symmetry axis, 58
　types of, 78
Symmetry element, 12, 73

Symmetry information, 6
Symmetry plane, 55
　types of, 77
Symmetry properties of crystals, 60
Synthesis, Fourier, 177
System,
　coordinate, 198, 199
　crystal, 70, 71, 83
　isometric, 83
　orthogonal crystal, 83
　orthorhombic, 83
　pinhole, 34, 37, 38, 46, 49
　tetragonal, 83
Systematic extinction, 73

Table, interfacial-angle, 55
Tabulations, reference, 50
Taconis, K. W., 260
Takéuchi, Yoshio, 233, 237, 238, 240,
　　245
Target, 223
Tavora, Elysiário, 66, 243
Techne, goniometers made by, 50
Technique,
　cooling, 247
　extrapolation, 90
　heating, 247
　low-temperature, 257, 260
　x-ray diffraction, 3
Temperature distribution in oxya-
　　cetylene flame, 256
Temperature range 1000°C to 2000°C,
　　heating device for, 256
Temperatures up to 300°C, furnace for,
　　248
Temperatures up to 1300°C, furnace for,
　　251
Tetragonal crystal, 61, 84, 177
Tetragonal crystal system, 70, 83
Tetragonal prism, 237
Theoretical limits of recording, 26
Theory,
　absorption, 221
　of common chord, 133
　of reciprocal cells, 69
　of reciprocal-lattice photography, 15
　x-ray diffraction, 3
Thermocouple, 255
Three-dimensional investigation,
　　intensity data for, 177

Three-dimensional parallelogram, 34
Tilden, S. G., 197, 198, 243
Trail, general-radiation, 169, 182
Transformation,
    from Cartesian coordinates to cylindrical coordinates, 202
    from one coordinate system to another, 198
Translation,
    determination of, 150
    measurement of, in reciprocal lattice, 82
Transmission factor, 222, 224, 228, 229
Transmitted reflection, 233, 234, 237
Triclinic crystal, 84, 87, 145
    adjustment of axis of, 125
    reciprocal cell of, 84, 87
Triclinic crystal system, 70
Trigonal prism, 237
Tube,
    pinhole, 38
    x-ray, 45
        appropriate, 44
        focal spot of, 45
Tunnel, Azároff beam, 45, 46, 49
Turquois, 88
Twinning, 49
Two-dimensional investigations, intensity data for, 177
Type,
    lattice, 72, 74, 76
    of symmetry axes, 78
    of symmetry planes, 77
    plane-lattice, 75
    reciprocal-lattice, determination of, 75

Unfiltered radiation, 101, 106
Unit,
    absolute, 76
    lambda, 76
Unit cell, 1, 3, 59, 69, 76
    dimensions of, 58
Unit-cell determination, photographs desirable for, 58
Unit-cell edge, probable error of, 89
Unoriented crystal fragment, 145
Unwanted scattering, 180
Upper base, 37, 38, 46

Upper level, 59, 92
    diffraction by a point in, 18
Upper-level circle, symmetry of, 12
Upper-level cone, 28
Upper-level precession photograph, 27, 28, 61, 67, 153
    example of, 20, 21
Upper-level recording, geometry of, 17
Use of autocollimator, 51
Use of beta spots, 101
Use of precession apparatus, 44
Use of general-radiation streaks, 100

Vertical axis, 6, 43
Vonnegut, B., 257, 258, 260
VYHH, 47

Warren, B. E., 257, 258, 260
Waser, Jürg, 198, 205, 217, 218, 244
Wavelength, intensity distribution with, 181
Wavelength error, 91
Weissenberg apparatus, 39, 172
Weissenberg method, 3, 8, 89, 161, 176
    back-reflection, 88
Weissenberg photograph, 150, 241
Weldon, Alice S., 245
Wells, A. F., 241
Wells effect, 241
Widths of layer-line screen slits, 67
Winchell, Alexander N., 50
Winchell, Horace, 50
Wolfe, R. C., goniometer designed by, 50
Wollastonite, 21, 102, 103, 109, 153, 174
Wood, Elizabeth A., 245
Wooster, W. A., 245
Wuensch, Bernhardt J., 233, 239, 240, 241, 242, 246, 248, 249, 251, 260

X-ray crystallography, 76, 89
X-ray diffraction techniques, 3
X-ray diffraction theory, 3
X-ray tube, 45
    appropriate, 44
    focal spot of, 45
    potential across, 167

Yuan-Lung, Chang, 245, 246

Zero level, 59, 78
    diffraction by a point in, 16
    recorded, radius of, 58
Zero-level cone-axis circle, 151, 153
    symmetry of, 12, 163
Zero-level cone-axis photograph, 72
Zero-level plane,
    adjusted, 128
    misoriented, 128

Zero-level precession photograph, 13,
    20, 21, 59, 61
Zero-level record, 59
Zero-level screen setting, 59, 61
Zero order, 14
Zero-order Laue cone, 11, 13
Zoltai, Tibor, 105, 245, 246
Zoltai device, 104